COMPANIONS ON THE TRAIL

By HAMLIN GARLAND

TRAIL MAKERS OF THE MIDDLE BORDER

A SON OF THE MIDDLE BORDER

A DAUGHTER OF THE MIDDLE BORDER

BACK TRAILERS FROM THE MIDDLE BORDER

ROADSIDE MEETINGS

COMPANIONS ON THE TRAIL

COMPANIONS ON THE TRAIL

A LITERARY CHRONICLE

BY HAMLIN GARLAND
MEMBER OF THE AMERICAN ACADEMY

Decorations by
CONSTANCE GARLAND

New York
THE MACMILLAN COMPANY
1931

Printed in the United States of America by
THE FERRIS PRINTING COMPANY, NEW YORK

CONTENTS

		PAGE
INTRODUCTORY		I
CHAPTER		
I.	LITERARY MOTHS	5
II.	CHEYENNE AND SIOUX CHIEFTAINS	20
III.	A SECOND SEASON IN NEW YORK	47
IV.	MIDLAND BOHEMIA	61
V.	COLORADO MEN AND MOUNTAINS	73
VI.	THE POET OF THE GREAT DIVIDE	87
VII.	MY FIRST LITERARY SUCCESS	102
VIII.	RENAMING THE RED PEOPLE	125
IX.	COLONEL LOWDEN'S CHALLENGE	142
X.	AISLES OF GOLD AND STREAMS OF SILVER	159
XI.	HOWELLS GIVES A LUNCHEON	172
XII.	MARK TWAIN, CARNEGIE, AND ROOSEVELT	192
XIII.	ANOTHER WINTER IN NEW YORK	208
XIV.	MEXICO AND ITS PRESIDENT	225
XV.	THE SILENT MISSISSIPPI	233
XVI.	AGING PIONEERS	239
XVII.	ST. GAUDENS AND HIS EAGLE	244
XVIII.	HENRY JAMES IN AMERICA	256
XIX.	THE TYRANNY OF THE DARK	265
XX.	JOYS OF THE TRAIL	274
XXI.	A ROMAN HOLIDAY	292
XXII.	MY OKLAHOMA NEIGHBOR	310
XXIII.	ASSEMBLING THE CLIFF DWELLERS	320

v

CHAPTER		PAGE
XXIV.	Tesla, Madame Modjeska, and Forbes-Robertson	339
XXV.	General Palmer and His Castle	353
XXVI.	Fuller and the Cliff Dwellers	368
XXVII.	Edward MacDowell	376
XXVIII.	The Voice from the Dark	382
XXIX.	The Russian Players	393
XXX.	Cliff Dwellers and Others	404
XXXI.	Wyoming and the Cliff Dwellers	418
XXXII.	A Ducal Ranch	429
XXXIII.	Alfred East and English Art	439
XXXIV.	Forest Rangers and Roosevelt	446
XXXV.	American Architects and Francis Hackett	454
XXXVI.	The Village Magazine	462
XXXVII.	Visiting Celebrities	476
XXXVIII.	Sons of the Middle Border	490
XXXIX.	Two Notable Dinners	503
XL.	Chicago Entertains the Arts	511
XLI.	Gray Days at Fifty-Three	522
	Concluding Word	538

COMPANIONS ON THE TRAIL

COMPANIONS ON THE TRAIL

INTRODUCTORY

In taking up and carrying forward the story of my meetings with men and women of distinctive character, I must assume that the reader is more or less familiar with "Roadside Meetings of a Literary Nomad," my first volume of comment on my fellow craftsmen, but a page of explanation may be useful even to those who have followed me thus far on the road.

"Roadside Meetings" deals with the years lying between 1884 (when I first went to Boston) and 1899, the year of my first visit to England. "Companions on the Trail" takes up the year 1900 when, as a married man of forty, I revisited New York from my home in Chicago. Up to this time I had not felt able to establish a residence such as a man of letters should have when he marries. After nearly sixteen years of writing and lecturing, I had acquired a plain old house in West Salem, Wisconsin, my native village, and a scantily furnished lodging in Chicago. Although still too poor to marry, I recalled a remark of Hawthorne (who married in middle life) in which he spoke of forty as the dead line over which no bachelor should cross, and so in November, 1899, I asked Miss Zulime Taft, a sister of Lorado Taft, to take chances with me. She did so, as I relate in another place, and the first chapter of this book deals with New York and New Year's Day more than thirty years ago.

In "Roadside Meetings" I based my narrative on dated records and published articles, but in "Companions on the Trail" I have had under my hand fourteen volumes of actual daily comment and characterization. I began these diaries in 1898, recording, either at night or early the next morning, the outline story of each day's happenings. Without these records I could not have written this manuscript, for only by reference to their pages can I be sure of the mood or the judgment of any date. With them I am able to give, faithfully, my contemporaneous concepts of men and books.

Although I have connected the comments by means of a slender narrative, this volume deals wholly with the literary side of my life, as my "Middle Border Chronicle" dealt with my family life. Whatever interest "Companions on the Trail" may have, it is intended to be a faithful record of literary and artistic conditions as I have known them and shared them. It characterizes, briefly of course, some of the enthusiasms, fashions, and developments of literature and art during the years lying between 1900 and 1914, the opening of the World War.

If the reader is moved to ask why this man or that book is not included in my narrative, I can only answer, "probably because I did not know the man or the book." I have followed no other rule than my own interest at the moment of writing. Many of the writers and artists mentioned were my friends. Some of them were only acquaintances, others still were passing strangers. I have not hesitated to include interesting personalities entirely outside the world of literature and art, as in the case of certain Western red men, forest rangers, and ranchers. In no case have I attempted to give a biography, but only my impression of the characters I have met or with whom I have been associated.

Whatever my publishers may say of this book, it assumes to be no more than a consideration of fourteen years of travel, contact, and reading by a writer intensely occupied with making a home and providing for his family, moving fast in order to keep at least three jumps ahead of the wolf. Rich in friends, honored above my deserving, I was forced during all the years covered by this chronicle to eke out—eke is a good old word for it—my royalties by lecturing, and whenever the reader is surprised by sudden leaps from Chicago to New York, or from Wisconsin to Denver, he should recall this explanation and say: "Oh, yes, another lecture tour"—and this will be correct except that "tour" is a little too opulent a word—"trip" would be more accurate. Many of these trips were meager in money returns, but they were rich in experiences, as these pages (I hope) will show.

I have one other confession to make. As the pages of my diaries were small, holding not more than two hundred words, I fell into the habit of "shorthanding" my comment. I crowded into a small page elliptical sentences and single descriptive words, trusting to my memory to fill in and expand. This I have done, but in the doing of it I have carefully retained the essential moods and judgments, and in most instances the exact lines or paragraphs.

With this information in mind, the reader will understand the sudden introduction of a city, a date, and a quotation mark. In fact the book might have been called "Red Letter Days From a Diary, with Later Comment by the Author," only that would have been trite and clumsy.

Finally, I must admit that there is nothing sensational in this book. It has no malice to work off, no enemy to score. It depicts an age without jazz, a period when wars seemed distant, and the screen drama was just beginning to be called an art. It is an old man's book, but then, why not? Old men for reminiscences and young men for jazz. It is, on the whole, a cheerful book, for, when all is said, the world has treated me well. I have had an exceptionally varied and fortunate experience, and I take this method of sharing it with my friends.

CHAPTER ONE

LITERARY MOTHS

I

ON my return to New York City in January, 1900, I found it in the midst of rebuilding, and I soon discovered that changes in the literary and artistic world were keeping pace with the swift transformations of the business world. New publishing houses were being established and new magazines designed with editors demanding a more sensational form of literature. The esthetic life of all America was centralizing, with appalling rapidity, on this small island. Boston, Chicago, Philadelphia, San Francisco, New Orleans, and other lesser centers were losing their best authors and their most talented artists in the all but universal rush to Broadway. The inland writer, like the inland publisher, was persuaded that in order to gain a national reputation he must speak from Manhattan. Like moths to a glowing flame these choice spirits of the South and West were fluttering at the windows of Madison Square.

Many were already at home on the island. As I went about I met Cass Gilbert and Albert Shaw from Minnesota, Augustus Thomas and Winston Churchill from Missouri, Hopkinson Smith from Maryland, Thomas Nelson Page from Virginia, John Fox from Kentucky,

George W. Cable from Louisiana, Charles Roberts and Bliss Carman from Canada—in association with scores of others almost equally successful and happy. They represented the growing concentration of American art, as James Barrie, Bernard Shaw, and Rudyard Kipling represented the exodus from Scotland, Ireland, and the provinces to London. As a national center our metropolis loomed ever higher, and its growing industries offered limitless opportunity to the youth of Toronto as well as to aspiring residents of the mid-West.

Many of these rising poets, painters, architects, and business men were sons and grandsons of New York or New England farmers or traders, and were merely taking the back trail of their pioneer fathers and mothers. My own case was typical of hundreds of others. From my father's farm in Iowa I had set out to retrace the family pilgrimage from New England to Ohio and Wisconsin, and in Boston had spent nine educational years before finding my way to Upper Broadway. Now I realized as never before that only in the continental metropolis could I find national recognition and support. "Here the worst and the best can be found. Here is the center of literary life."

One of the most recent of my fellow pilgrims from West to East was Edwin Markham of California, whose course of action, like my own, is typical of hundreds of others. Some years before, just after the World's Fair, he had called upon me in Chicago, a handsome man of forty odd—just showing gray hair, and while in the midst of telling me that he was one of the earliest native sons of Oregon and that this was his first trip to the East, I exclaimed: "What an opportunity! You must *discover* New England. Just as a Bostonian might visit and describe Oregon, you must write of Massachusetts. You must carry a notebook and set down at once all your impressions. I see an amusing and successful book in your hand."

He rose to the suggestion. His face brightened. At the moment a book of this character seemed not only logical, but inevitable. Here he was, a scholarly, genial, observant poet, a product of the Western Coast who by a singular combination of forces and events had grown to middle age without personal contact with the East. Confident that he could interpret what he saw with individual tang as well as with poetic insight, I urged him not to put it off. "Do it now. If you fail to write it now while your impressions are vivid you won't do it at all," I repeated in warning.

In imagination I saw him making a piquant, humorous book, but nothing came of my urging. He went away to the East and I heard no more of him or the book I had suggested to him. So far as I know, it has never been written.

With the exception of a few lines now and again in the magazines, I saw no more of his writing till in the spring of 1899 some one sent to me a page of the *San Francisco Examiner* in which his poem, "The Man with the Hoe," was made an outstanding feature of the Sunday literary supplement. This poem was set in large type and was accompanied by a glowing paragraph by the editor, Bailey Millard, who had discovered it, purchased it, and wished his readers to share his pride in it.

Much impressed by the verses, I mailed the clipping

to John Phillips of *McClure's Magazine*, with a notation on the margin, "Here is a great poem!" thinking that he might feel justified in reprinting it, or of ordering something else from the author.

The success of this poem was an amazement to Markham as well as to his friends. By setting it in large type, Millard had made it a sensational bit of news. Its author became known from coast to coast. Telegrams from magazines ordering other verse and publishers offering to print his book poured in upon the poet. Resigning his position as principal of a school in Oakland, he moved to New York in such haste that I, for one, was disposed to question the soundness of his judgment. "Can he, can any man, make a living in New York as a writer of verse?"

Whatever his doubts, here he was, an avowed resident of New York, whereas I, a Chicago citizen, could afford only an occasional visit to Broadway and as soon as I learned his address, I wrote him a note, giving the name of my hotel and expressing a wish to see him.

His reply fixes his address, at this time, at 545 Third Street, Brooklyn, and the date was November 24, 1900.

"So glad that you are back in our meridian and that we are to see you and yours again. I do not need to say that I feel very near to you—often think of you.

"I intended to call on you yesterday, but found that you were out. Can you and Mrs. Garland take dinner with us here next Tuesday evening at six-thirty? I hope so. Come as early as five o'clock if you can. I'll be home from Manhattan by that hour. If you can't come Tuesday, when can you come? Pray bring some of your poems to read to us—sure!"

A few days later my wife and I went over to see him.

We found him walled with books, his beloved books which he had brought all the way across the continent. Glancing at these laden shelves, I said, "This means that you have abandoned the coast?"

Handsome, confident, happy in his new home, he replied, "Yes, I've come to stay."

Neither he nor his wife exhibited the slightest sign of doubt as to the outcome, and I, concealing my conviction that he had made an illogical and dangerous trek, could only admire his courage. Here he was, a scholar no longer young, whose verse, up to this time, had paid him but a scanty income, rejoicing like a boy in the sudden blaze of glory which a single successful poem had flung upon him. His little book was selling and editors were eager for his verse—but would that demand last?

We talked of the famous writers of the coast, of Joaquin Miller, Charles Warren Stoddard, Bret Harte, Frank Norris, and many others, Californians who had in their turn come to New York. "We all come," he said with joyous chuckle. He was one of the happiest of all the back trailers and one of the wholesomest. His tastes were sober and his habits homely.

His mention of Norris aroused my interest. I had heard of him as the author of "McTeague," but I had not read a line of his writing. "He's a fine fellow. You should know him," said Markham.

In my diary I find this note: "January 16—Markham and his wife came to dinner with us and we had a good, noisy evening. He is in the spring flood of his belated success and is as happy as a lad at Christmas time. He was a good deal of a problem so long as we remained in our little suite at the hotel, for he is possessed of a resounding voice and his laugh is like that of a sea captain. Our walls were thin and the people in neighboring rooms could have heard every word he uttered if they had been so minded. My wife was somewhat stunned by Markham—but I assured her that his open-air quality of speech was only a survival of his youth in Oregon."

One day not long after this, as I was passing through the outer office of Doubleday & Page on Union Square, I saw a young man seated at a small desk. Doubleday who was with me touched the youth on the shoulder. "Frank Norris, you should know Hamlin Garland."

As Norris rose and faced me I thought him one of the most attractive young men I had ever met. Tall, slender, with prematurely graying hair and fine, candid, humorous glance, he looked the poet rather than the realistic novelist whom Markham had described to me.

We had only a few moments' talk, but I carried away such report of him to my wife that she expressed a wish to know him. A meeting was arranged by another California novelist, Juliet Wilbor Tompkins, and we at once ranked Norris with Edward MacDowell as one of the handsomest men of our acquaintance. He and his joyous young wife at once took place among our most valued friends.

"McTeague," his novel of San Francisco low life,

interested me keenly, although it was written somewhat in the manner of Zola. Howells spoke of it as the best study of San Francisco yet made and contrasted it with the work of Harte and Miller who were ungoverned romanticists—each in his way—poets and painters of the picturesque coast life. "But Norris," he said in effect, "is writing in the light of comparative criticism. He knows what he is doing. His art is thoughtful and restrained, though colored by his reading."

"January 20. At Juliet Wilbor Tompkins' home last night I met both Frank Norris and Ernest Seton-Thompson. We had a joyful evening up to the moment when my wife unthinkingly touched on the justice of the Boer war. Nearly all of us were pro-Boer, and Norris, who had been in Africa at the time of the Jameson Raid, questioned the justice of England's rule, and this stirred Seton-Thompson's British blood. Filled with English imperialism, he defended the war in Africa with fiery eloquence. His black eyes glowed with a menacing light, but Norris held his own with entire good humor. He knew what he was talking about."

On the day following this warlike discussion, we sat with Dan Beard, one of my long-time friends, in the Quaker Meetinghouse in Flushing, one of the most interesting Colonial churches I had ever entered. "The shiplike timbers of the room, the pine benches carved by mischievous boys of 1794, the curious old stoves with pans of water on their tops, the silent men and women, the children awed by the stillness broken only by an occasional cough or by the click of the ancient thumb latch in the door (as some late comer entered), gave me a vivid understanding of the services which this rude structure had witnessed for over two hundred years. It was all incredibly primitive.

"For nearly an hour we sat in profound silence. No one spoke. At last the leading elder rose, and we all filed out—the spirit had not moved any one to speech, but I was moved to write of it!"

In the intervals between our many social engagements, I contrived to work on several pieces of fiction and to market them—strange to say. In truth I had come to New York, hopefully but by no means confidently, with this particular business in mind.

Among the manuscripts was a novelette of Colorado life which I had written for my friend Edward Bok—who had printed several of my short stories. He could not see "The Hustler" in his columns, however, and so I took it to *The Century*. Gilder accepted the story at once but asked for certain changes in it. "Your material is very amusing and realistic," his associate editor, R. U. Johnson, wrote, "and all the American part seems to us attractive and well done; the English chapters do not strike us so favorably. We hope that you will put more movement into it and adapt it for serial use."

Gilder ultimately printed the story, paying me fifteen hundred dollars for it, but on condition that the Century Company should have the book rights under acceptable contract. These I gave, and I may add that it was highly successful—according to my scale of success.

It is my one humorous book—indeed I called it "an extravaganza," in order that its divergence from my more serious work might be explained. Its theme, that of contrasting Wagon Wheel Gap with London, was less trite in 1900 than it is now. Jim Mattison, a miner from the High Country in the Uncompahgre Mountains, whom his partners sent to England to sell stock in a mine, was its chief character; and my report of his comment, based upon my knowledge of such men in Ouray and Cripple Creek, gave the book its vogue. In justice to myself, I must record that this sketch—for it is hardly more than that—antedates by thirty years most of the somewhat similar studies of Western Americans in London.

The other manuscript, "The Eagle's Heart," I sold to the *Saturday Evening Post* for twenty-five hundred dollars, with which I was fairly content at the moment. But as I read to-day of serials bringing twenty-five thousand dollars—serials not so much better than mine—I am reminded of the small rewards for authorship which in 1900 made us all frugal and hesitant of outlay.

The business manager of the *Post* wrote me that this romance of mine raised the circulation of the *Post* more markedly than any other of their serials up to that time; and on this statement I built great hopes for the book, which Appleton was about to publish. Alas! it failed, miserably. Ripley Hitchcock couldn't see why—and neither could I. It was an adventure story based upon the lives of my playmates in Osage, Iowa (most of whom hoped at some time to run away and become scouts or cowboys), and was my attempt at delineating the homely genesis of a "bad man." Black Mose, a marvelous horseman and pistol shot, was its hero. Here again I must claim priority over Zane Grey and other authors of "Westerns," as they are called in motion-picture circles. Owen Wister and I were early in the field. Emerson Hough, Harry Leon Wilson, and Stewart Edward White came later. Priority is cold comfort, but that is all I can claim in this contest.

II

This winter in New York brought me into still closer contact with Ernest Thompson Seton (to use the later form of his name). I had known him since 1896, and although we had never been in the mountain West together, our talk was mainly on trails and trailing. Our aims were not precisely the same, but we had similar interests in the red people and the wilderness. He was (as I told him in 1897 when advising him as to contracts) three men in one—artist, fictionist, and zoölogist. With a prodigious capability for hard work, he wrote and drew and studied for sixteen hours of every day. "Until I visited him and saw him at his desk I thought myself a fairly industrious fellow, but in comparison with him I am a weakling. When he can no longer write to advantage he gets out his drawing board."

As he welcomed talk while making pictures, I spent many hours lolling in an easy-chair recalling the places we both knew and loved—mountain meadows in Montana and cliff pueblos in New Mexico. We both saw the red man as Catlin saw him, an animal adapted to a certain environment. Biologically he was guiltless as the panther or the eagle. We had no economic or religious prejudices concerning him. His sign language, his songs, his dances were of absorbing interest to us both; and while Ernest was picturing certain phases of savage life, I was meditating a novel which would present life on a Cheyenne reservation and some of its problems. We spent many hours inspiring each other in such designs.

Another of my friends with whom I shared enthusiasms for the West was Dr. Mitchell Prudden, who lived in baronial splendor on Fifty-ninth Street, but who spent his summers on the plains and knew Arizona and New Mexico like the back of his hand. He was the head of the Bacteriological Department of Columbia University, but he had spent many months wandering with a pack train of ponies from cliff dwelling to pueblo, and from cañon to cañon in the Southwest. His beautiful flat was filled with Hopi vases, Ute beadwork, Navajo blankets, and silver work, reminders of his camping places; and his library contained hundreds of books bearing upon primitive folk and their arts, books which he studied with care after his day's work amid his "bugs" was ended. He would not talk about his professional doings, but was always delighted to meet one who knew the plains and mountains of his beloved sun-land.

Our first meeting had been at the Hopi village of Walpi in 1895. I was there waiting for the Snake Dance; and one day, at sunset, as I was standing at the northern end of the great mesa, watching the return of the snake-hunting priests, I discovered a long train of canvas-covered ponies approaching from the northwest like a many-jointed worm. My curiosity was aroused, for no tourists were expected from that quarter, and I remained at the head of the trail to welcome the trailers, whoever they might be.

Upon reaching the foot of the mesa trail, the caravan halted and one of the horsemen came riding up the steep path. As his head rose above the flat rock on which I was standing, the rider, a tall, lean man of middle age, called out, "How are you? Is the dance over?"

"No, the priests have just completed gathering the snakes. The dance begins to-morrow."

He glanced about him. "Where are you camped?"

"We have a room in one of the pueblos."

"I wonder if I might make my bed down on this rock?"

"I see no objection," I replied hospitably.

He brought up his bed and slept that night on the ledge. Although a trailer of wide experience, it was evident that he was a man of wealth and cultivation. He told me that his name was Prudden. "I have come down from the cliff dwellings of Colorado to see the Snake Dance. I have been in the field for six weeks."

We saw the Snake Dance together, we visited Zuñi and the Grand Cañon together, and became so well acquainted in these expeditions that I promised to call upon him in New York. I never visited the city thereafter without calling upon him, spending many pleasant evenings in his company. I dined with him often, the two of us sitting at a small table in his immense dining room, sharing the most delicious food served by trained servants, talking meanwhile of camping in the desert or on the mountainside. "The great Southwest is my land of recreation," he said, "antidote to the germs which I study all the remainder of the year." There was something in him which reminded me of George

Bird Grinnell. Both were of similar stock, and both were lean and brown and quietly smiling.

Through Mrs. Seton-Thompson, my wife and I met Cecilia Beaux, who even at that time was considered one of the best of our painters—I will not say "women painters," for that would limit her. She was a tall, clear-sighted, and thoughtful woman of about my wife's age, a most interesting personality. "Her work, while not precisely masculine, is not feminine. She paints in masterly, forthright fashion, and her speech, like her brushwork, is clear, vigorous, and direct. Strength and clarity are her leading characteristics," was the judgment which I set down at the time. "I count her and Ida Tarbell among the most distinguished of my acquaintances. There is nothing pretty about Miss Tarbell. She is womanly without being what the word 'feminine' usually describes. Her historical work is careful and sustained."

My return to New York had quickened my interest in the plan for a National Institute of Arts and Letters; and in dining with Edward MacDowell, I seized the opportunity to present the project, and he, with a noble conception of American art, consented to come into the organization and to go on one of the committees. "We had a deal of talk last night about a new form of opera into which it would be possible to put our Indian life. He was critical—justly so—of all our composers. He did not mince words, when talking of our 'pedantic imitative art.' He was gay, swift, and humorous, but his talk demonstrated that he has a very high notion of what the music and poetry of this nation should be."

At this distance I cannot say how I came to know Edwina Booth Grossman, the daughter of Edwin Booth;

but we lunched at her home one day and naturally talked of her illustrious father, whose memory she adored. I told her of my first glimpse of her, in Boston, at the Boston Theater where she sat in a box to watch her father play Macbeth for the last time to an enormous audience. "He was called out again and again, and each time as he came before the curtain, he turned toward you and bowed!" I said. "You seemed very remote to me then—a radiant princess." Now here she sat, a pale, troubled little lady, who regarded me (apparently) as a distinguished literary man.

"I cannot relate my hostess of to-day with that radiant girl," I said to my wife as we came away.

"January 27. At McClure's 'plant' to-day I met Paul L. Ford, the historian, a quaint, dwarfish man with a reedy voice. He was not as deformed as I had imagined him to be, and his manner was jovial and debonair. He possesses a security of manner which betokens ample means and an assured social position. His head is small and shapely, not out of proportion to his body as is so often the case with dwarfs. He suggested a handsome young man seen through the wrong end of an opera glass. He chatted gayly with my wife about his books, professing an apprehension that he might not be able to live up to the renown of 'Janice Meredith.' On the whole he made a very pleasant impression on us both."

The first public meeting of the National Institute of Arts and Letters turned out to be an important event in American literature.

"Howells presided with charming tact, and Horatio

Parker of Yale spoke, a big, manly composer who voiced my idea of American art exactly. Henry van Dyke, a fluent, natural orator, presented a paper. Charles Dudley Warner was absent and Hamilton Mabie read an address from him which was pretty dry. Howells was fine, very restrained, very tactful, almost too modest. The meeting was a success."

Early in February a letter from my mother in Wisconsin announcing the serious illness of an aunt cut short our stay in New York and we left for the West with mixed feelings, as the following entry attests:

"Our stay in New York has been filled with pleasant experiences, but it has wearied me. I have met so many people and have had so many interruptions to my work on 'The Eagle's Heart' that I shall welcome the quiet of West Salem. Nevertheless we have enjoyed our stay and found it so profitable that I have prepared the way for a return. 'We will come every winter,' I said to my wife with a confidence which I did not precisely feel."

CHAPTER TWO

CHEYENNE AND SIOUX CHIEFTAINS

I

ALTHOUGH I spent a part of each year in Chicago and called my apartment in Elm Street my headquarters, I still made my home in my native village, West Salem, Wisconsin, about two hundred and fifty miles from Chicago, and in April, while I was there preparing two novels for serial publication, one for *The Century*, the other for the *Saturday Evening Post*, I received a long letter from Major George Stouch, an army officer who had acted as agent of the Cheyennes in Montana during my stay at Lame Deer in 1897. "I have been transferred to Darlington, Oklahoma," he wrote, "and as agent for the Southern Cheyenne and Arapahoes I am about to start on a tour of inspection of my reservation. I would like to have you come down and join us. Bring Mrs. Garland with you. Mrs. Stouch will go with us."

This letter was a most important event in my life, for I was eager to see Oklahoma, and had long wished to know more of the Southern Cheyennes. My summer at Standing Rock and Lame Deer had started me on a series of short stories dealing with the red people, a collection which was to be a companion volume to "Main-

20

Travelled Roads." With intent to present the Indian as a human being, I had in mind the title, "Our Red Neighbors." Some of these stories had been suggested by Stouch and I welcomed another chance to talk with him, for I was about to begin a novel which should be a description and an interpretation of the so-called "Cheyenne outbreak" of '97.

In addition to all these reasons for accepting his invitation, I was assured that I should see the prairies in all their springtime beauty, quite as my father and my uncles had seen them fifty years before in Iowa and Minnesota. From the study of these surviving pioneer conditions, I expected to derive inspiration for my books.

On April 23, my wife and I left Chicago for Oklahoma with keen anticipation of a delightful outing; and when we awoke, we found ourselves speeding through southern Kansas, a level, sunny, fruitful land, green with tender plants and grasses. Hour by hour, peach trees blossomed, and plowmen thickened in the fields. At Arkansas City we entered upon "Indian territory" across which prairie schooners were sailing their slow courses toward the West. The towns were hardly more than section shacks, and some of the railway depots were ancient box cars. Newly-arrived settlers were living in their canvas-covered wagons, the women cooking at campfires while the men with four-horse plows busily broke the sod. It was all a thrilling reminder of my boyhood in Wisconsin and Iowa. Oklahoma City was a town in a frenzy of building. Its streets were filled with muddy wagons and swarming with hairy farmers in faded garments—uncouth, earnest folk. The day was one of radiance, coolness, sudden showers, and bloom.

We reached El Reno at ten and spent the night there. While at breakfast in a pleasant dining room the following morning, we were told that a wagon was at the door. Mr. Hurley, the clerk of the agency, had come to take us out to Darlington some five miles away. The roads were muddy, but the country was exquisitely green and the sky full of brilliant clouds. The ride was enchanting. As we drove away over the swells to the north I recalled my first spring in Dakota, twenty years earlier, when in that walk across the primeval sod I experienced the exaltation of the pioneer land seeker.

Fort Reno, a cluster of frame buildings, crowned a high green swell of the velvet plain and, on the unplowed slopes, cattle lay scattered like bits of topaz. A little later the agency appeared, surrounded by trees, on the banks of a sluggish river. The sky had cleared, but the wind was singing a mystic, woeful song. The tepees of a Cheyenne village rose from a meadow starred with flowers. All things conspired to make the day unforgettable. It was a new-washed, green, illimitable world—the world of my youth. In less than an hour after my arrival, I was sitting in the major's office, surrounded by the red men I had come so far to see.

Later, the major took us over to the Cheyenne camp and presented me to some headmen. Smoking tepees denoted cooking, and men leading ponies to water suggested hunting. In such wise they had lived before the white man came. The women, cordial and smiling, greeted Stouch pleasantly as "Hay-gent." One old man said to me, "Hay-gent my father." All of the men were dignified and serious; and the camp made a powerful impression on me. It all appeared picturesquely primitive and happy, but impermanent, like a night camp on the trail.

In the evening, Cornelius, an Oneida youth, a giant in size and a man of ability, came to call on me, and his talk was not only interesting but historically valuable. Among other things, he said: "The white people who write of the red man do not give emphasis enough to the charm which was in our life in ancient days. It was really beautiful in many of its phases."

Cornelius had located here, after a most astonishing educational career in New York. "I intend to grow up with the law business of this country," he said. "Lawyers here will always be concerned largely with Indian lands, inheritance, and titles. The agency rolls do not show family relationships. Each man and woman has an individual name and there is certain to be much litigation."

"That is true," I replied. "Now that the Indians are landowners their names should show family connections, just as in the case of Italians or Greeks or any of our immigrant races. I shall bring this to the attention of President Roosevelt."

In the evening I told the story of my Klondike horse to the children of the Indian school, and made this note: "They are a bright-eyed lot—almost all pure bloods. Some of the Cheyenne girls are pretty, but all are essentially Mongolian. I was much impressed with them, but could not help thinking how arbitrary this scheme of education is: to make them conform—to cause them to act like white people—to cut them off from all that is deep-seated in them, is the purpose of their teachers. They sing our monotonous, worn-out hymns and they wear shoddy, agency clothing. In the end they will be merely imitations of poor whites."

On May 1, the major, accompanied by Mrs. Stouch, my wife and me, began his tour. The ride that day across a land opalescent in color, through glorious green meadows and over swells whereon patches of purple soil showed, was exalting. A crisp, fresh wind was blowing. The sward was resplendent with flowers and springing grass. The air, roads, sky—all perfect! We rode in a kind of youthful ecstasy free from care, leaving the business world behind us.

Late in the afternoon we came to the South Canadian River, and to a rude little tavern whose exterior was not promising. However, the landlord's wife was expecting us and we had a delicious dinner of fried chicken and hot biscuits. Afterward we visited the tepee of "Big Billy," an Arapahoe, and took some snapshots of his wife and daughters. The river, purple with loam, came out of a gorgeous sunset and the air was delicious. "Our day has been made perfect by that noble chicken dinner."

Stouch got us out early next morning and we drove across "the Caddo Land," a beautiful, rolling prairie broken by mesas and buttes of redstone. During the day we passed many land seekers in covered wagons, and at times we drove through wide cattle ranches; but no tepees and no cabins appeared on this superb stretch of primeval land until we came down into a shallow valley through which a slow and muddy creek meandered, shaded by black walnut trees. Over the tops of these trees, a clump of red brick buildings rose.

"This is Seger's Colony," said Stouch; "it combines a school, a subagency, and a missionary church—all those buildings," he explained, "are the work of Cheyennes under Seger's direction. He brought them out here, five hundred of the wildest warriors, and established this colony some twenty-five years ago. He is their teacher as well as their agent."

It was a surprising exhalation of civilized forms, this colony, and I was eager to know more of a man who could so instruct, so inspire, and so govern a savage people. The yards were clean and the barns and fields in good order. It was not beautiful, but it was substantial and well planned.

Seger came out to meet us, a stocky, middle-aged man, with pleasant blue eyes and a modest manner of speech. Although somewhat daunted by the strangers whom the major had brought, his words were hospitable. His clothing was commonplace—nothing but a huge white hat indicated his many years of life among the reds.

As I walked with him toward his office, a tall red man stopped him and with graceful motions of his hands asked him a question. Seger replied in the same silent way, with amazing skill and fluency. When I spoke of it he said, "Yes, I transact all my business in the sign talk. You see, my colony is about equally divided between Cheyennes and Arapahoes—and while I spoke Arapahoe when I came out here, I had to drop it. It wouldn't do to slight the Cheyennes. As I couldn't talk both languages, I compromised by using signs which they all understood."

I began to perceive in this low-voiced, untidy little man a character of singular endowment, and Major Stouch was almost as interested in him as I, for he had never seen the colony before and had only talked with Seger for a few minutes at Darlington. As they discussed their problems, I listened, realizing my good fortune.

Seger, like Stouch, was a native of Pennsylvania and of German derivation. Like Stouch, he had been a captain in the Civil War, and on being mustered out had turned his face toward Kansas. From Kansas he had drifted down into Oklahoma, earning his living as a stone mason. For several years he had been employed about the agency at Darlington as a builder, but soon developed such friendship and control of his red neighbors that he was put in charge of the school. Later still, when the warlike Cheyennes were making trouble for the agent, he suggested that a camp be established for them in the unsettled country. "Make me their subagent and I'll take them out on the Washitay and teach them the white man's road," he had said.

He told me these things with a lurking smile in his eyes, modestly yet frankly, and my interest deepened. The more I learned, the more amazing his career became. He had not only lived alone among these five hundred warriors; he had brought his wife and children to live among them. For years they had no other neighbors; but he had won the love and confidence of both tribes and they obeyed him like children. He had shown them how to sow, how to reap, and how to lay bricks.

He had taught their children to read and to wear white men's clothing. "I not only understood them—I became one of them. One summer I asked to be instructed in their tribal customs. 'I want to go entirely Indian for several months,' I said to Wolf Chief. 'It is only fair— I am asking you to walk the white man's road, and I should travel the Indian's road for a time. Then I can lay them side by side.' This pleased them hugely and for several months I studied their legends and customs."

All that evening while he and Major Stouch discussed agency affairs, I had ears only for him. Like Louis Primeau at Standing Rock and Carignan at Sitting Bull's camp, he instructed me. He knew the red man from the heart out. He had joined in their games, listened to their stories. To him they were not "treacherous fiends" or "wily devils"; they were "folks"—men and women of the Stone Age.

What tales he told! In his awkward, elliptical way he related experiences in which humor and pathos mingled. Tears came into his eyes as he recalled a day when the women, learning that his flour was all gone, shared their meager store with his wife in order that her children should be fed. He described his situation one night when his little daughter was so near the point of death that he dared not leave her to go for the doctor—sixty miles away. As he sat in despair, one of the laziest, most intractable of all his wards, a handsome young Cheyenne, came into his cabin and casually remarked, "Miokany, give me a paper to the white doctor at the agency —and I will fetch medicine."

"I was almost distracted with anxiety," said Seger. "I couldn't go to the agency for fear my little girl would die while I was away, and while I didn't trust that young Cheyenne I gave him a letter to the doctor and asked for medicine. Hawk tucked the paper into his belt and went out. Soon after daylight the next morning he sauntered in smoking a cigarette, his quirt on his wrist, and handed me the doctor's prescription. He had ridden over one hundred miles in the dark in less than twelve hours."

As he ended this story his voice broke and tears filled his eyes, disclosing a relationship between himself and his wards which I had never known before.

He related many other incidents to prove the essential humanity of his charges, and also brought out the humor in which they faced the complications of their new life.

One of these stories ran about like this: "Old Big Owl used to drop around by my door just at noontime and I always asked him to share our meal. One day we had pork chops, and the old man was delighted with them. 'They are good meat,' he said, 'almost as good as buffalo. I wish I had some pig meat!' 'You can have if you'll raise 'em,' I said. He replied, 'But I have no mother pig.' 'I'll give you a mother pig if you'll build a corral for her and take good care of her,' I said.

"He went away excited as a boy, and a few days later he came in to say that the corral was ready. I gave him a little pig, tying its hind legs together. He hung it over the pommel of his saddle and rode away. The very next day he came galloping over the hill, the pig flapping and squealing from his saddle. 'I have brought back the pig,' he said; 'it is too small. It slips through the holes in the corral. I will leave it with you till it grows bigger than the holes.' His point of view tickled me so that I took back the pig and kept it for a month.

"He raised quite a drove of hogs, but got into trouble the following spring when Black Wolf, who was raising potatoes, brought him in to complain that Owl's hogs were rooting up the potatoes he had planted.

" 'That is true,' Owl admitted. 'My pigs have dug up those potatoes, but it is the nature of pigs to root in the ground and eat what they find. If Black Wolf does not want his potatoes dug up and eaten, he should hide them in a tree and not in the ground!' "

Stouch treated Seger as a valuable subordinate, but to me he was a welling source of information concerning the red men. "Have you ever written these stories down?" I asked.

"No, I can't write 'em, but I often tell 'em to newspaper men."

"You must make a record of them, no matter how crude—they are history," I urged. "You know these people as no one else knows them."

Stouch said to me privately, "Seger's letters are filled with the weirdest sort of spelling and punctuation. He never spells a word twice alike, and the Department is threatening to drop him because of it. He is woefully illiterate, but I shall report in his favor. He is invaluable just where he is."

Early next morning the chiefs began to assemble under a great tree in the park before the school, many of them in full tribal costume, eager to see the new agent who, as a "white soldier chief," had won their interest. Seger was their marshal. With swift and sweeping gestures he described Major Stouch and explained that I was a "paper-talking chief," and a friend of all red men. "He will tell the Great Father at Washington what he hears to-day."

My seat beside Stouch enabled me to watch every face and to hear each speech. I had never before attended a formal council, and with pencil and pad in hand, I let nothing essential escape me. The center of the half circle of headmen was Wolf Chief in native dress with the eagle feather of authority worn at the back of his smoothly brushed head. To him this was a most important moment. As a red warrior, a chieftain, he was about to address his "Little Father," who was also a soldier and an officer.

The Arapahoes, distinctly less noble in bearing, were in the background. The Cheyennes, while friendly with them, considered them an inferior race. The speeches were all given with formal dignity and a rhythmic grace which would have distinguished a United States senator. Seger was not the official interpreter, but as he sat beside me he muttered a comment on each oration.

At the close of the council I kept my eyes on him— for everywhere he went the red men questioned him with gestures; and as he answered them he muttered their meaning in order that I might follow the talk, thus giving me glimpses into the red man's mind as well as a knowledge of his own character. When we took our departure for the next subagency, I said to Stouch, "I hope we are to see Seger again. He interests me deeply."

"Yes, we shall come back this way," he assured me.

On the following night we lodged at the subagent's home at Arapahoe and visited a near-by village on a bank of the river, a beautiful camping place. The group of tepees was charming; but a big drum was beating, and as we approached, this sound became menacing in character. The singing was equally sinister and savage.

Entering one of the tepees, we found a game called the "dance of the hands," a very graceful and interesting game, in progress. The players were seated in a half circle and two singers were at the drums. "The singing was Oriental in character—Turkish or Persian —in which, at intervals, the women shouted with startling shrillness. One beautiful little girl especially attracted us. Outside, an old woman chanting some impassioned words alone in the moonlight added a line of minstrelsy. What was she saying? It was all wildly primitive and idyllic. Gracefully light of hands, the players tossed the polished bones which were their playthings, unmindful of the singer outside the door."

A council having been called for the early morning, Arapahoes to the number of thirty-eight assembled and took seats on the grass below the porch of the agency. "While Major Stouch and I faced them, Prairie Chief, Walks Good, and Mad Wolf spoke. Bob Tail Bear, a handsome, decisive fellow in citizen's dress, showed himself to be a modern, progressive Cheyenne. His face, though pitted with smallpox, was attractive and his voice musical. Richard Davis, a sturdy, serious fellow, a graduate of Carlisle and a successful farmer, was interpreter. One or two of the speeches were works of art with measured intervals and short refrains. They were, in effect, prose poems."

"May 6. Red Moon. As I awoke this morning I heard again the wind of the plain singing its familiar, desolate song, but the sky was bright and the landscape beautiful. This opposition of melancholy wind and shining sky is characteristic of the prairie world. Just before nine o'clock several little Cheyenne girls came in laden with prairie flowers which they shyly gave to my wife, who was touched by their courtesy."

Stouch introduced me to White Eagle, a typical Cheyenne—handsome, reserved, and proud—a man of power who had refused to call upon the agent. We visited several camps, finding them all neat and attractive. The people are much like the Northern Cheyennes —a strong, cleanly, attractive race.

All day the wind blew strongly from the south— hot and dry, but the tepees in the shade were cool and comfortable. At Happy Woman's home we tasted her bread which pleased her greatly. She was cooking beneath the shade of a bower and doing it handily and with very little effort. Housekeeping was a simple matter with her.

May 7 was another day of council with the Indians. "Climbing into a big army wagon, we were driven down to the bank of the creek, where under the trees the Cheyenne chiefs were sitting, waiting for their warriors to assemble.

"An old man, the village crier, went forth calling on them to hasten. 'The agent is coming. Everybody must come to council!'—and soon the people came rolling in, mostly in wagons. The women had erected a windbreak around the council ring and in this the speaking began. All was ceremonious and dignified and some of the arguments were very cogent indeed. White Shield made an especially strong speech which I took down in longhand. In the evening we returned to the camp to take some pictures by flashlight. It was all so interesting that I came away with regret. The primroses, white in the moonlight, yearned from the grass. The stars blazed. The tepees, lighted from within, glowed like lilies— white, with golden hearts."

"May 8. Major Stouch and I spent the entire fore-noon in talk with White Shield in his tepee. He was very grave and very impressive as he put his case to the agent. Again I acted as secretary.

"The other Indians listened with great respect to all that he said. White Eagle, his brother, sat next to me. His superb profile, his smile, half humorous and half disdainful, and his shining blue-black hair united to make him one of the handsomest red men I had ever seen. He looked the aristocrat."

Here are some of the sentences I caught from the interpreter's version of his chief's speech: "It seems to me that every time we try to help ourselves by doing right we involve ourselves in trouble. I feel at times as if I could not go on. My heart is too weary. I don't know what I am to do. I turn and turn and lose my way. I am expecting—I am hoping for some great man—a savior to show us the way. To my thinking we were not quite ready to take our allotments—we were not quite able to take care of ourselves. It is a bad policy to start on a long journey with a poor pony. We were poor and ignorant, not ready for the white man's way. We did not know how hard the road would be. We were hunters, but we knew that the white men fed and clothed themselves by labor on the earth and we were ready to do the same. Bad white men surround us.

They rob us, they shoot at us. They wounded one of my sons in the furrow behind his plow. And now I am tired —I am weary of this place. I look around and I see no place to go.

"We are red men. When we make friends we are loyal. We help one another. We stand by one another. We confide in one another. Each of us knows the other's thoughts. If we find we are wrong, we lay our bad thoughts aside. The Great Spirit made us. He gave the red man one way, the white man another way. Our way has come to an end. We are walking your road. We are eating the food that grows on the plowed land. We are ready to listen to what you say—but you must not hurry us. All our old troubles are buried—they are deep under the ground. The Great Spirit will lead us in the new way."

II

On our return to the colony I again discussed red men with Seger till late into the night. "He is a very valuable man to know," I made note. "He is able to give me the humorous and human side of Cheyenne life. He *knows* these people. He has lived with them for thirty years. He uses the sign language with astonishing readiness and precision and is able to enter into the actual moods of both Cheyennes and Arapahoe. He conducts all his business with the older people in this silent method of communication. I have never known a white sign talker of like skill."

On May 10 we drove back to Bridgeport, arriving at one in the afternoon. "In the evening we all went up to the Arapahoe camp to attend a dance in honor of the agent. It was a beautiful evening and the moon shining upon the tepees caused them to gleam like pearls. The children, squaws, and many of the old men danced. One very grave chief, looking like a drawing by De Forest Brush, sat smoking. A band of drunken whites came down the road shooting and shouting. The major feared trouble; but it soon appeared that these 'jokers' were off the reservation. The Arapahoes struck us as being less fine, less manly, than the Cheyennes. They were more docile—more like the negro. The Cheyennes are Algonquin and unconquerably free. They will break but they will not bend."

At Darlington, where we arrived next day in time for lunch, I made this note: "In retrospect our trip grows more valuable as well as delightful. It has awakened in me the settler's land hunger and I am already planning the investment of my savings in those glorious prairies."

"May 12. I spent much time last night talking with a young Cheyenne called Robert Burns, who is agency clerk, an able fellow who speaks English fluently. For several hours we discussed his people. Although able and interesting and well educated, his red psychology came out in his talk. As the night deepened, he admitted that he could not rid himself of a belief in certain superstitions of his tribe. 'After all, I am Cheyenne,' he said. 'One of the beliefs of our medicine men is that a magic arrow or a magic bullet can be sent by force of the will to pierce the heart of an enemy; and in spite of my education I have a kind of half belief in it.'

"I reminded him that this belief was similar to that of witchcraft in New England, in which a wax figure of the enemy could be pierced, to the torture of the living person. This talk with him was especially valuable, for I am now fully resolved to do a book of Indian stories."

On May 13 we took the train for Anadarko, where I reported to Colonel Randlett, the agent. He was absent, but the clerk, Mr. Carroll, took us for a drive to see one of the domed grass houses in which some of the Wichitas still lived. It was raining in torrents as we entered the huge wigwam, but the roof was impervious to it. This structure interested me enormously. It was as primitive as a Kafir hut—a huge, thatched hive—as aboriginal as those in which the Indians of Virginia dwelt in the days of Pocahontas.

"I should feel repaid for my trip to Anadarko, had I seen nothing but this prehistoric dwelling," I said to Carroll.

The following morning was so hot and the roads so muddy that we decided to put off our visit to Fort Sill; and during the day I met Quannah Parker, a celebrated chief, a man of dignity and intelligence, who told me much of the Comanches and Kiowas. He was tall, smiling, boyish. I took him for an educated Comanche preacher. He spoke English very well, wore a gold watch, and his shoes were a bright tan. His coat was a Prince Albert frock.

Carroll, the clerk, informed us that Father Isadore of the Catholic Mission school would like to have us dine with him that night; and as we had no other engagement, we accepted. Carroll drove us out in a rude sort of hack with a canvas cover which only partly sheltered us from the rain which was falling heavily. But when Father Isadore, a jolly Alsatian with a laugh like a bugle, met us at the door and ushered us into a room lit by a fire, we were well repaid for our bleak ride.

"It was like a chapter out of a novel. At dinner we ate roast turkey and drank wine, waited upon by one of the teachers of the school, a sister of austere character, who stood, between courses, with folded arms and scowling brow. That she did not approve of us was plain, and that she considered the father's bottles of wine an extravagance, if not a sin, was still more evident. She resented his jesting and his boisterous laughter. He had stepped out of his religious office and was entertaining company which she held in suspicion.

"Happy in his guests, he talked of literature and art, displaying an acquaintance with magazines and newspapers quite surprising in one living so remote. He was indeed a most amazing character—a combination of peasant, scholar, and heroic evangelist. In telling us of his early experiences in Oklahoma, when a raw, inexperienced boy he came as missionary to the frontier, he roared with retrospective amusement, confessing his blunders and his sufferings. 'I couldn't speak English, I couldn't speak Kiowa or Comanche, and I had no way of earning a dollar—but I had something to do, and by God's grace I did it.'

"He has won out. His school shelters and instructs some eighty Indian children, and serves also as a center of religious training and medical advice. He has something which I have not. His heroic devotion to a cause is magnificent. I like him because he enjoys good food and knows the qualities of French wine."

He had never met a woman like my wife, an artist

trained in Paris, and he glowed with appreciation of her knowledge of French art and French people. He overflowed with questions concerning me and my work, but I held him to his own astounding experiences, a history which the stern sister endeavored to curtail by abruptly passing a dish. I imagined that she considered him inebriated—and so he was, but it was an intellectual intoxication, a glow of delightful intercourse. "I let you go with reluctance," he said, "not only because I have enjoyed your news of the outside world, but also because the lightning is flashing and the rain falling in torrents."

We insisted on setting out, however, leaving him in the open door waving us adieu.

What a night! The level prairie was a lake of water which the lightning vividly illumined now and again for miles around, through which the horses splashed with eager haste to reach their stalls. How Carroll kept the road I cannot say. It was like sailing a boat; and when we drew up alongside the platform of our hotel, it was like landing at a wharf.

It had been a perilous and uncomfortable trip, but our dinner and Father Isadore were worth the journey. We thanked Carroll for his share in it, and left next morning for the North, eager to set our feet on the floor of a Pullman car.

My mind was filled with new characters and new concepts of the red people. Major Stouch, John Seger, White Shield, White Eagle, Quannah Parker, Robert Burns, Father Isadore, and his sisters—all suggested themes for my book of stories in which red men were to be treated as neighbors.

III

Having in mind a plan to write some sort of story of Sitting Bull, the famous Sioux chieftain, I applied to General Miles, at that time the head of the army, for a letter of introduction to the officers in the field. To this request he most graciously acceded, and the note which he signed opened to me the doors of every "fort" or barracks in the West. With this in hand I planned a visit to Standing Rock, the agency near which the Sitting Bull had lived for many years.

On the 1st of July, accompanied by my wife, I left the Northern Pacific Railway at Bismarck and drove to a point on the Missouri River opposite the agency, where a rude boat was operating as a ferry. The presentation of my letter to the commander of the fort provided for us a rough cabin and a share in the officers' mess. It also opened to me the records of the agency as well as of the fort, so that I could study them with reference to the Sitting Bull and his band.

Again as in '97, I found the Sioux assembled for the Fourth of July celebration, encamped in a vast circle of tents, some five thousand of them waiting to share "The White Man's Big Sunday." Again I wandered about among these primitive people, seeing much and remembering little. My artist wife was especially delighted with the picturesque groupings of plumed warriors and wild young horsemen, but I sought out the aged story-tellers whose reminiscences were interpreted to me by Louis Primeau, a half-breed trader from Rock Creek.

Primeau, a handsome man of about my own age, was

the son of a French fur trader in St. Louis. Although educated in English, he spoke the Sioux language perfectly, and impressed me as a quiet, thoughtful man who weighed his words carefully before uttering them. I liked him at once and confided to him my purpose. "Tell your friends among the Sioux that I have come to write of Sitting Bull as a friend. Tell them I wish to know the truth concerning their great chieftain." This he promised to do.

Through him I gained the confidence of the local trader, John Carignan (a native of Canada) who was of almost equal value to me in writing my story of "The Silent Eaters."

"The Sitting Bull was an Indian and believed in *remaining* an Indian," said Carignan. "He was a chieftain and had the welfare of his people at heart. He was my neighbor; I knew him well and I respected him." (He and Primeau both spoke of him as "the Sitting Bull" as a Scot might name "the MacGregor.")

Primeau not only comprehended my purpose in a literary sense; he gave up his day to the task of introducing me to his people, and of interpreting me to them, as well as conveying their thought to me. It was deeply gratifying to see their stern faces soften as he said, "This man is a 'writing chief' and friendly to the red men."

One of the great games of the Fourth of July celebration was a mimic battle, or rather a series of scouting expeditions, which a group of warriors realistically staged in the great field enclosed by the tepees. In these open-air plays it was necessary to have an "enemy." Some one must enact the rôle of hostile scout, to be trailed and captured and bound. No one wanted to act in this despised character, and I observed that the victim, repeatedly bound, shot, and scalped, was always the same man, and when I spoke of this to Primeau, he said, "Yes, it is true. No one else wants to be the enemy."

"He deserves reward," I said. "When he comes near enough, hand this dollar to him and say that I think he is the bravest warrior of them all."

Shortly afterward, covered with dust and panting with fatigue, the weary "goat" of the game came near enough for Primeau to address him. With wondering gaze fixed on me, the old fellow took the coin from Primeau, and then, being called back into the game, trotted to his position at the stake.

Some days later, as I was visiting one of the camps in the Rock Creek Valley with Primeau, he lifted the door of a handsome tepee and silently entered. As I followed him I met the glances of two elderly Sioux, the owner of the lodge and a guest. One, the host, was shaving tobacco on a piece of wood, and the other, his guest, sitting at his right hand, was eating from a shallow dish.

Primeau spoke to the chief, who returned his greeting politely but coldly. I perceived that Primeau as a half-breed was not considered an equal by either of the warriors. On closer view, I was amazed to find in this dignified and well-dressed owner of the tepee the man who had so loyally served as "enemy scout" in the games at Standing Rock. He had not really observed me at the moment when Primeau handed him my dollar, but now as he learned that I was the giver, his face lighted with a smile. "Ho, ho! My friend. Sit down. I am glad to see you. My heart is warm toward you." He then explained to his companion what I had done, and he, too, smiled and called out, "Ho, ho!"

For an hour or more I was in another world, the world of the bison, a world that had passed away. I had already begun to plan a life of the Sitting Bull, written from the standpoint of an educated Sioux, in which the red men should be heroic patriots, and this afternoon, in the tepee, was spent in discussing the Black Hills treaty, the battle with Custer, and the capture of the great chieftain. These warriors filled me with a higher notion of my task. No people is wrong unto itself. Every race, being a product of environment, bases its moral laws on its need of survival. Nature cares nothing for the individual. Whether a man scalps his enemies or eats them is all one to nature, provided such action insures the continuance of his kind. If it imperils birth, it is wrong and the race dies out.

The Sioux, born of his environment and fairly in harmony with it, asked for no change. He complained of no weather and no hardship. He changed only when his environment changed. He knew no "massacres"; to him they were battles. He was not a "horse thief"; he was only a skirmisher despoiling an enemy. Why bring into his interpretation of life the notions of an utterly alien and infinitely older state of organized society? An Italian naturally glorifies Garibaldi; a Scotchman, William Wallace. Would not an educated Sioux—if free to open his heart—make a special pleading for his chief, the Sitting Bull?

In the midst of this talk, came a mention of the secret society called "The Silent Eaters," a group which contained the most trusted of the Sitting Bull's friends, warriors who acted as a kind of bodyguard during the most active years of his chieftainship; and I seized upon it as the title of my proposed history. "The Silent Eaters"—what a world that phrase suggested!

"They were so called because they did not sing at their feast," said Primeau. "And because they smoked and quietly talked—meditating on many things. Slohan, the historian of the band, is still living up the valley. I'll take you to see him to-morrow if you'd like to talk with him."

Of course I wished to see him, and the next day Louis drove me up the valley toward the aged man's home. At every turn in the road, I asked questions of this or that red man we met—always coming back to the Sitting Bull and his last days as host to the prophet of the Ghost Dance religion.

"He tried to believe it," said Primeau. "He wanted to go into trances as the others did. He sang the song, he danced; but he could not believe. He was too much the thinker. The historians are all wrong about him. All wrong about the dance—it wasn't a war dance. It was a 'medicine dance.' They believed that if they put away all weapons, everything which they had gained from the white man, the Great Spirit would turn his face upon them again and that he would bring back the old world of the buffalo—'as one hand slides above the other.' 'We are weak,' they said. 'We can't stop the white man's coming. You must help us, Great Father!' . . . That was the substance of all their songs and prayers. It was pitiful! I used to hear them singing their plaintive songs all night long. I saw them in trance lying rigid on the ground. I watched their shining faces when they came out of the trance and told of having visited the beautiful old-time prairie covered with buffaloes.

"The agent and the newspaper reporters filled the country with lies about the chief. I knew him. He came often to eat at my table. He talked with me about the Ghost Dance and told me that he was giving his cattle to feed those who came. All the dance meant was that the red people had given up all hope of holding back the white invasion and had turned to the Great Spirit for help. They hoped by this magic to remove the white invader and bring back the world they knew when they were young."

Here again I am giving the substance of many, many hours of talk with this man whose mingled French and Sioux blood gave him a singularly clear understanding of the situation. He liked me, he trusted me; and with him as guide I explored the secret places of the red man's thought.

We came at last to a pleasant level bank overlooking a small stream. On the right stood a combined cabin and lodge—such as most red men built—a union of the old life and the new, and, while we waited before the camp, Primeau looked to the left and said, "There is Slohan."

Looking where he pointed, I saw a solitary Sioux— an old man kneeling, his head bowed, motionless as a bronze statue.

Following Primeau's lead, I approached this silent,

rigid figure, feeling something strange, something inexplicable in the pose, for he did not move as we approached nor when my guide spoke a greeting. He half sat, half knelt, a coiled rope in one hand, his hair falling over his face and the sun beating down upon his fine head.

Softly, almost timidly, Primeau asked a question, then repeated it in a loud tone. Slowly Slohan lifted his head and turned a glance upon him, then whispered a husky reply.

Primeau recoiled. "Let us go!" he said. "Slohan is mourning his little grandson. He has been crying three days. His voice is gone."

We withdrew a few paces and for several minutes Primeau silently considered whether to go away or to break into the old man's mourning. Savage that he was, his grief was entitled to respect.

Remaining at some distance, I watched Primeau as he again approached the mourner. Again his bent head lifted. He brushed back his straying gray hair. Turning painfully he fixed his dim eyes on me. I could not hear his hoarse whisper, but I could read in his face a lightening mood.

Primeau was saying, "This white man is a friend of the red man. He is, like you, the story-teller of his people. He admires the Sitting Bull and he wishes to know the truth about his life. He wishes to speak with you."

At last the mourner raised his hand and made a sign of consent with his finger and said, "To-morrow my heart will be lighter. I will come down to see you and talk with the white man. I cannot talk now!"

He was still kneeling there as we drove away, but I believed—as Primeau said—that we had lifted the shadow of his grief by turning his thoughts back to the days of his young manhood.

True to his promise he came to see me the next afternoon, riding an aged pony, a handsome and dignified man of seventy. His hair was brushed, his clothing in order, but his face was still sad and his voice husky.

All that afternoon—a witheringly hot day—we sat in the shade of the cabin and talked of "The Silent Eaters," of the Sitting Bull, of the Ghost Dances, of the ancient history of the Sioux, and as we talked, Slohan grew in stature. He was essentially the poet, the dramatist. His gestures, in accompaniment to his speech, were magnificently picturesque and graphic. He forgot his grief as he forgot his present. He was no longer the poor, ragged, lonely old prisoner in the wan land of the white man; he was a councilor of his great chief, the chosen leader of the tribe, the Sioux of the plains.

When I shook hands with him in parting, I said to Primeau: "Tell him that I am his friend, and that I will faithfully report all that he has said. He shall live in my book along with his chief, the Sitting Bull."

After he had ridden away I said, "To most white men, he would appear a wretched mendicant. To me, he is both historian and philosopher."

CHAPTER THREE

A SECOND SEASON IN NEW YORK

I

ON returning to New York in October, I brought with me the material which I had gathered from the Sioux and Cheyenne reservations, and a group of sketches each dealing with a distinct phase of primitive character—stories which I had planned to bring out later under the general title, "Red Pioneers."

Having sold several of these studies to *McClure's,* I felt confident of selling them all. Some of them had been suggested to me by Major Stouch, some by Louis Primeau, and others by John Seger, who knew the changing heart of the red man—which, by the way, I had considered as a possible title for the book.

Such a volume was inevitable. As the red hunter had always been the antagonist of my westward-marching people, he had come to be an essential part of the picture which I was helping to paint, of the plains and prairie life. He was not (with me) a subject of religious controversy—I had only an ethnological interest in his songs and supplications. I was concerned with him solely as a human being, more or less in harmony with his environment like the panther or the eagle. I had no desire to change his faith. Whatever the literary quality of my interpretation, my purpose was to get

47

his point of view just as some of my fellow craftsmen were attempting to interpret the life of our later European immigrants.

"It doesn't matter to me what other writers have set down concerning the lives of the red people," I said to my editorial friends, "I am an impressionist and these tales spring from my personal impressions of red life and red character. To me a Cheyenne village is like any other collection of people, a mixture of good and bad. I found poets and philosophers as well as hoodlums among them. I have seen 'savage' fathers tending their babies in the glow of sunset; and I have heard red mothers wailing heartbrokenly over their dead. My stories take the cruelty and dirt and sloth of camp life for granted—such facts have been sufficiently dwelt upon. I have drawn the tender and humorous side of their lives as well as the patiently heroic side. If you don't want such interpretations, it is your privilege to return them."

In spite of my attitude, I sold a series of these pictures, each one the characterization of a type. "Rising Wolf, the Ghost Dancer," was a picture of a Cheyenne mystic. "Hippy, the Dare-Devil," "White Eagle, the Red Pioneer," "White Weasel, the Dandy," were among the descriptive titles. One of the most significant of these stories, "The Spartan Mother," which was based on Seger's experience as a teacher in Darlington, was bought by the *Ladies' Home Journal. Harper's Weekly* took several others. I had no cause for complaint. Most of these editors were too far away to be influenced by frontier judgment; they rested upon my statement.

Meanwhile, as an exact opposite to all this work, my

humorous novelette was scheduled for publication by the Century Company, and Gilder, who was not much interested in my study of primitives, spoke of his liking for "Her Mountain Lover." "You got beauty into that book and it will live," he assured me gravely.

"I had fun writing it," I replied. "I've packed into it memories of several glorious summers in Colorado. It *is* Colorado, scenically, whatever it may lack as a novel."

With all my manuscripts before me and surrounded by Navajo blankets and other reminders of the West, I set to work on them in my little hotel parlor which fortunately was at the back of the house and singularly quiet. The presidential campaign was raging just around the corner in Union Square, but I heard little of it. McKinley and Bryan were the candidates and nominally chief antagonists, but as a matter of fact Roosevelt, candidate for vice president, was doing most of the Republican campaigning. He and Bryan were going up and down the state in the customary final flurry. If one took their words at their full meaning, each believed that the success of the other man's party would be ruinous to the nation.

Notwithstanding his tempestuous campaign, Roosevelt, for some reason, set apart an hour for lunching with me at the Century Club. In accepting his invitation, I ventured to hope that we could avoid politics, and before we had unfolded our napkins he said with accustomed humor, "I accept your wise suggestion. We'll talk Injuns, Montana trails, and other safe subjects."

He was in the final days of a most dramatic campaign, with the whoop and halloo of the press pursuing him, and yet here he sat, neat, compact, lithe, and muscular, as quietly at home as any other member in the dining room. We occupied one of the small tables near a window and his presence was not exploited. Now and then an acquaintance came up to shake hands—or some one called from the long table in the center, but mainly he bent to me, dwelling with reminiscent joy on our mutual memories of "The High Country." No one could have been a more delightful, unassuming host, and for a time we kept entirely clear of politics. He knew that I was opposed to McKinley, and when at last we touched on the campaign—it was impossible not to do this—I said, "If *you* were the presidential candidate, I would support you with all my heart—but I think I shall vote for Bryan."

He looked grave. "He's a good man, an almost typical Western man, but he'd make a bad President. He doesn't think—he can't think. His free-silver theories, most of his theories, are wrong."

I can only give the substance of his judgment, but he was dispassionate in his statement of it, and to the free-silver part of it I was forced to agree.

My interest in the National Institute of Arts and Letters was keen, and as an officer of it, I had been in constant touch with Charles Dudley Warner. As chairman of the first meeting he had called upon me for service and his sudden death on October 20 was sadly shocking. Although I had never known him intimately, he was a kindly and dignified figure in my world. His going gave me my first chilling sense of the changes which were swiftly coming to me. "Stedman is soon to go," I wrote to Henry Fuller, "and Howells is an old man. When he and Gilder pass, our generation will be the dominant force in letters. We cannot be called 'our younger writers' any longer."

As I looked around me, I found my fellow authors in the midst of unexampled prosperity. Ernest Seton-Thompson (as he signed his name at this time) was in high demand, both as lecturer and writer. Winston Churchill's books, like those of George Barr Mc-Cutcheon, were selling in hundreds of thousands. Young Stewart Edward White was enjoying a boom, along with Frank Norris, Ellen Glasgow, and Booth Tarkington. They all had something to sell which the larger public wanted. Only a few cared to read my books.

Warner's death, as Howells said, was a warning and a prophecy to the older men. "We old fellows feel a pang when one of our number drops away," he said somberly, and I realized that he, too, was nearing the end of his day.

Each morning I worked a little on "The Silent Eaters," which grew in interest as I wrought. "I'd like to make it a prose epic," I confessed to Fuller who had encouraged me in its original draft. One evening I went out to witness the closing phase of the campaign. The Roosevelt demonstration was a superb display of fire-works, but the crowd was singularly lethargic, as if made up merely of onlookers, and I came home with the feeling that McKinley needed all the votes he could get. That night I made the record: "It would be making strange history—a great turning point in our national course—if Bryan should win. The importance of it all comes over me with great power now and again. To reëlect McKinley is merely to do the expected thing. To reverse his policy and to elect Bryan would mean a mighty stirring of stagnant waters."

"As I was coming away from Mrs. Seton-Thompson's tea, this afternoon, I met Mark Twain on the walk searching for the entrance with the action of a stray rooster, his head turned sidewise and upward. I greeted him and he asked, 'Can you show me the Seton-Thompson trail?' 'That I can,' I replied, and sent him up the elevator, smiling. He appeared shockingly old, a small, hesitant, white-haired gentleman. All his Western qualities have been planed away or softened by quiet city life.'"

As week-end guests of Mr. and Mrs. Samuel Untermyer, my wife and I enjoyed the grandeur of "Greystone," their castle on the Hudson. "It was the palatial home of Samuel Tilden, but Untermyer has made it still more palatial. It is gorgeous beyond any I have ever known. It is overpowering, but our hosts are entirely human. I was especially reassured to find on the walls canvases by Winslow Homer, Homer Martin, and other of our American painters, and in discussing these and other artists, whose work we agreed was sincerely indigenous, I ventured to commend my old friend, John J. Enneking of Boston, whose work in my judgment was notably faithful to New England.

" 'I know his work,' Untermyer said, 'and I like it, but I have seen only a few of his canvases.'

" 'His studio is filled with portraits of New England hills and woods and valleys,' I replied. 'I am always urging him to exhibit in New York, but he is afraid of the critics—or of the expense. New York has never seen his work—as I see it.'

" 'I'll take the matter up with the Lotos Club and see if an exhibition cannot be financed there. Meanwhile see Enneking and help him select a group of his pictures,' said Untermyer."

The result of this week end at "Greystone" was a handsome exhibition of Enneking's paintings at the Lotos Club. I take pleasure in recording this generous act of a busy attorney. I never afterward thought of him as entirely the savage lawyer he was considered to be.

One afternoon, we drove to Irvington to call on a friend, and on the way passed through Sleepy Hollow, which I was surprised to find a wild glen—scarcely changed from Irving's time. "It was late when we reached the northern end of the valley, and the sky was gray and wild over it. An old house, such as might have stood there in Revolutionary times, added to the remoteness of the place. From this we returned to the splendor of the Untermyer place which is the finest residence I have ever visited. On Monday morning I returned to my shabby little apartment in the Jefferson!"

II

The failure of the ancient firm of Harper & Bros. had given me some anxiety about Howells' position, but during one of our walks in the park he said, "I am to go on with the new firm. I am to get a large salary, as salaries go—and all my writings are to be taken, so that I shall end my days in comfort if not affluence," he added with a smile which took away any effect of boasting. I sincerely rejoiced in this provision.

"November 3. As guest of honor at the Campfire Club, I ate a bad dinner and listened to some bad speeches—my own the worst of them all. Charles G. D. Roberts, Canadian poet and novelist, made a short talk in which he said that he no longer found it necessary to go to the forests for a taste of wild life; he found the wild life of New York quite sufficient—for him. Nevertheless, he is ranked with Seton-Thompson as a writer of wild animal stories."

On Election Day, my wife and I dined with the MacDowells. Edward was in high spirits and very droll. He and Marian cooked the spaghetti and told stories (antiphonally) of their hardships in Germany and their early life in Boston—"We hadn't a cent and nothing to wear," said Marian—which was all very amusing in the light of their handsome flat which overlooked Central Park. "Edward was like a fine boy glowing and shy and sensitive, and we spent the entire evening in lively jesting and story-telling. He refused to talk music for a moment. Astonishingly apt of phrase, his humorous sallies had the quality of literature. We came away filled with admiration of them—so joyous and so keenly intellectual were they both."

On the day of the election I made a trip out to Lawrence Park to see Stedman and to enjoy a few hours' respite from the city, but the poet's mood was so bitter that it depressed me. He was a sick, restless, and unhappy old man. "His beautiful home (he declares) is intolerable to him. He talks of giving it up for a winter in town. He longs for the city and Wall

Street. His wife, a good, plain little woman, was giving a tea, but he refused to show himself in the reception room. 'I never go to Mrs. Stedman's teas,' he said bluntly. 'Stay here with me. There is no reason why you should go in among all those women and be bored.' "

His anthology, on which he had been working for so many years, was off his hands, and yet he was not at ease. His books no longer comforted him, and his correspondence appalled him. "How can I answer all these letters?" he demanded irritably. "Why do people write to me without excuse?"

At the close of the reception, he walked with me to the foot of the hill, complaining all the time of the pain in his head, dilating in monologue upon his loneliness and his poor heart. He was old—his work was done; but he refused to admit it.

The Lotos Club dinner to Clemens which took place on the 10th was one of the most brilliant affairs of my experience, and my presence there was due to Untermyer. "The dining rooms were crowded with men, most of them leaders in professional or business life. Howells was there and so was T. B. Aldrich, Irving Bacheller, and many other writers. Roosevelt was at the speaker's table, and so were Chauncey Depew and John Hay. All around me sat scores of brilliant and successful citizens, but when named by my host they meant little to me. A Mr. Lawrence presided in the usual way—verbose and self-satisfied.

"Mr. Howells read an exquisitely tasteful and very brief address and St. Clair McKelway followed with a prepared oration full of misplaced adjectives; and then at last Mark Twain was called upon. As he slowly rose and stood waiting, with half-shut eyes, for the applause to die down, I thought: 'The old man has eaten too much and drunk too much. His brain is sluggish, I fear he will fail'—but I was unduly alarmed. When he began to speak it was with slow precision as if feeling his way. I had not heard him give a public address in many years, and I detected in him a mellowness, an air of quiet authority which none of the speakers, eminent as they were, possessed. He appeared to be talking to us as friends with nothing of the orator in his voice.

"He told of his business failure, of his lecture tour in the effort to pay off his debt; and when he said, 'I have paid it, every dollar of it,' we all applauded with genuine admiration. He was witty, and at times comic, provoking laughter; but the general effect of his speech was somber. He was no longer young and his wife was a hopeless invalid. It was an enthralling address, and all that came after it was anticlimax, so far as I am concerned. No one should have spoken after he had resumed his seat."

As guests of honor, at the Grossmans' one afternoon, we met Emma Thursby, once the radiant singer, now an old woman, and Bertha Runkle, the authoress of "The Helmet of Navarre."

"Miss Runkle is a tall, rather plain girl—shy and self-conscious. We also met Edwin Elwell, the sculptor, a big, blunt fellow, who vigorously attacked the realists, counting me among them.

"He was a curious mixture of gross egotism and Swedenborgian mysticism and talked of 'possessing the divine afflatus' as a message from God, while looking, as he himself confessed, 'like a butcher.' He began life as a blacksmith and his crusade against what he calls the 'materialistic art' of to-day has the vigor and tactless directness of his forging. Despite all that, he is a good fellow and a fine sculptor."

On November 16, we dined with Mr. and Mrs. Frederick Meyers, and went to see "Henry Fifth" as presented by Richard Mansfield. "It was a superb scenic production, but as a drama it had only the value of a colorful pageant. Mansfield's mannerisms in reading obscured the lines so that they seemed bombastic and empty. It is one of the least satisfactory of all Shakespeare's dramas, containing the frankest appeal to race prejudice," was my feeling as I came away.

At a dinner at Walter Page's, talk fell upon Theodore Roosevelt, vice president elect, and many interesting stories were told of him. Page said, "When informed of his election as vice president, Theodore remarked, with meditative curtness, 'Isn't that nice!'— and not a word more! He has what few of our public men possess, precision of phrase and a sense of humor."

As guest at the annual dinner of the Dramatists' Club on the 18th, I enjoyed a very interesting conference. "J. I. C. Clark presided with grace, Augustus Thomas made a very adroit speech on a high plane, and Joseph Jefferson responded with a delightful talk with Yankee accent. Hopkinson Smith spoke optimistically of our art exhibit at the Paris Exposition, referring with especial enthusiasm to Winslow Homer's painting which won a gold medal. Sidney Rosenfeld, Paul L. Ford, and I were the last of the speakers.

"In general, the men impressed me as a very alert, humorous, and surprisingly abstemious group. One or two ate and drank themselves into torpor, but most of them remained intellectually alert to the end. I came away with increased respect for their attitude toward life and the stage."

As a result of this meeting, J. I. C. Clark called upon me a few days later and talked about a possible dramatization of "The Eagle's Heart." We got to the point of preparing a scenario—but that is as far as it ever went.

That evening, Howells and I were guests at the Book-Builders, a club of eighty or ninety young printers, binders, and artists. Dan Beard, who presided in a quaint, slow way, presented Howells as a typesetter turned novelist, and so won their sympathetic understanding.

It was a pleasant coming together of young men who work for a living. None of them had achieved fame or fortune and all were overwhelmed by the presence of Howells who was quite as intimidated by their respect. He spoke with delightful humor but very briefly. "I am in torture when on my feet before an audience," he confessed.

One day shortly after election I received a characteristic letter from Henry B. Fuller, who pretended to an alarm over the social career of the Garlands. He began by reference to one of his books which I had read but could not praise.

"You have done noble. You have read it—and read it right away! (On the principle of getting a bad job well over with?) But anyway—of course I knew you wouldn't like it. Didn't I tole you so, far in advance? And I didn't *want* you to like it. If you had written to me, 'Such a theme treated in such a way interests

me,' I should have trembled for you; I should have felt
myself witnessing the impairment, the possible disinte-
gration of one of the really significant and valuable
figures in our literature.

"Now let me give you, for your own private use, the
combination to the singular phenomenon known to the
literary push as H—— B. F——.

"H. B. F. has not enough interest in the people of
actual life to care to write about them. He only puts
in people of un-actual life because a novel or romance
or whatnot must have figures, personages, and because
the novel form is the only literary form to-day that
secures any attention. The only thing H. B. F. really
enjoys (after inventing) is to 'take his pen in hand,' to
write (strictly and simply)—to string words together.
He gets enough of the crudities, vulgarities, and asperi-
ties right where he is; he wants to bust forth, and break
away and scoot through the blue air of heaven.

"Chicago is hearing strange things of the once more-
or-less primitive Garlands; they seem to be consorting
with the children of Mammon and to be thicker than
thieves with the Rich of the Earth. Where do you think
all this is going to lead you? *I* see you, five years from
now, turning out Chatfield-Taylor stuff for the dwellers in $900,000 palaces. Well, you know best. When
you shall have settled down upon the gold-plated meads
of Millionairia, why I will just move along and take
your place in the humble Western field you spurn. Poor
Wisconsin! Poor human nature! Poor *homme sauvage,*
snared in a golden trap!

"I have just bought a new suit of clothes, and had
my old coat dyed.

"How does New York like Mrs. Garland's blue tailor-made suit? (are they 'on to,' yet, the evening gown I helped her make over?)

"Let's hear from you again, with lots of lit'ry news. Roswell Field, asst. editor *Youth's Companion*, after Dec. 1st.

Yours,
(Signed) Fuller
(20th century psychologist).

In reply to this gay letter I described our little apartment in the Jefferson and asked him to assure all my Chicago friends that of the gold I brushed against none remained on my coat sleeve. "Nevertheless it has been a prosperous and pleasant season and gives me confidence in the future."

CHAPTER FOUR

MIDLAND BOHEMIA

I

THE New Year of 1901 found me back in my old lodgings on Elm Street, Chicago, deeply engaged on a new story of Indian reservation life which I called "The Captain of the Gray Horse Troop." I had held this theme in my mind ever since my visit to the Cheyennes in 1897. I had filled a notebook with information and impressions at the time, and I was now prepared to write a novel embodying some part of the three-cornered struggle which had taken place between the cattlemen, the red men, and the federal soldiers who had acted as peace officers. My plan was a large one, worthy my best efforts, and I was in the midst of it when the Century Company called upon me for a revise of my serial novelette, "Her Mountain Lover," a demand which I resented at the time as an interruption to the larger work upon which I was at work. However, I liked the Colorado comedy and was resolved to make as much of the theme as I could.

My life in Chicago was much quieter—socially—and I found it a good place to work. "Coming back to it from New York is like returning to a country town, at least so far as I am personally concerned. My companions are mainly artists and writers of narrow routine, who make no serious demands upon my time. New York has the growing complexity of a continental capital, while Chicago, like all other American cities, remains definitely local and circumscribed. Our literary and artistic groups are small and struggling. Everybody knows everybody else. Mostly we cling in one small cluster to the Fine Arts Building, but other obscure groups exist elsewhere. We are all on the esthetic border and swamped with the commonplaces of trade and politics. We have the candid air of pioneers. Most of us are young and just from the farm or the village. Speech is uncultivated and art instruction rudimentary—and yet there is earnest aspiration among us."

Early in January, Fuller confided to me that he was making a fictional study of these artistic and literary strugglers, especially of the group in the Fine Arts Building with which he was associated. With a chuckle, he said: "You are there and so is Lorado, and several other of our friends."

His statement was borne out a little later when at a dinner given by Taft he read "Dr. Gowdy and the Squash," a perfectly delightful story in which a well-known Chicago patron of the arts and a down-state realistic painter of barn doors and pumpkins were chief characters. It was a capital satire and we all shouted over it. Fuller smiled when I declared "Dr. Gowdy" to be a certain very eloquent local preacher who considered himself an art critic, and we had all met the painter whose portraits of baskets of corn and squashes were so skillful that one could not tell the pictured grain and vegetables from the real articles when placed beside them.

While on the subject I here record the fact that
Fuller went ahead with his plan and in the end produced a book which is as fine and as authentic as any
similar study of art life in Paris or London; a book of
high cosmopolitan quality, cultural, keenly satirical, but
kindly. That he had written with chuckles of delight
while describing our literary and artistic Bohemia was
evident, for as he read it to us he joined in our laughter.

That I appreciated the value of his work at the time
is evident by this note: "January 1, 1901. Fuller is distinctly the ablest and the most interesting of all our
writers, but his health is not good. He is looking worn
and haggard. He takes no care of himself, especially as
to his eating. He dines wherever he happens to be, I
suspect on cheap food, alone and morose. He remains
as remote as ever, so far as his actual home life is concerned. No one of us dares call upon him at his residence for the reason that we are not sure of a welcome.
He lives somewhere on the South Side in one small
room, totally without the dignity which should be his.
I do not even know where it is—no one knows his tele-
phone. He read for us to-day 'O'Grady and the Grindstone,' a long short story on which he is at work; and
we chortled over its good-natured satire of Chicago. I
had just received a letter from Henry James in appreciation of my 'Eagle's Heart,' and Fuller read and
reread this letter with keen interest. It amused him to
puzzle out its crisscrossing lines and parentheses. I had
been surprised and gratified by James' interest, for
nothing could be farther from his own experience than
my book.

"At the Tafts', Fuller read the final chapters of

'O'Grady and the Grindstone,' which we all know is based on actual happenings in the Chicago art colony. He read it well and crowed and chuckled when we applauded the hits of it. His delight in it was as keen as ours."

One of the literary meeting places on the North Side which Fuller and I both frequented was the home of Mrs. Coonley Ward, a widow of bookish tastes and considerable wealth. It was her custom to give dinners of twelve or fourteen plates and to receive less honored guests afterward. Her parties were a notable mixture of people. Some very nice writers and a few fashionables mingled with sharp-angled, forceful reformers of one kind or another. She was a tolerant soul. When I first went to Chicago, I thought her house and its doings very fine. Spacious and hospitable, her home lacked harmony and design. Like its owner, it made no claim to being artistic or fashionable; but it was cordially open to all "earnest souls" of her acquaintance.

Another critic of Chicago almost as merciless as Fuller was Robert Herrick, an Eastern man bitterly impatient of Western rawness and bombast. His novels were not as fine as Fuller's, but they were fine. In lunching with Miss Wallace in Beecher Hall at Chicago University, I had my first talk with him and with Miss Reynolds, another teacher. "Herrick said very little," I wrote, "but that little was well arranged. Cold and repellent in expression, his ability is so apparent that I excused his chilly greeting. With me he has always been fairly cordial, but I have seen him freeze others into silence, even those who approached him trustingly. His impassive face and curt speech make him an austere guest; but Robert Lovett and Vaughn Moody both assure me that this is only a manner. At this little party he was almost gay."

"February 22. A letter from Mrs. Frank Doubleday concerning the recent order of the Indian Department instructing its teachers to foster aboriginal art, led me to spend the forenoon writing letters to her and to the commissioner, endorsing and commending the order. We seem to be making progress. In the afternoon I sat on the platform while Frederic Harrison of London gave an address on Washington. Later at 'the Little Room' I met Childe Hassam whose name sounds Turkish, but who is, I am told, New England to the bone. He is a very able painter of the impressionistic school."

"West Salem, March 17. A message from my father has brought me back to my native village in Wisconsin. I am in the old homestead and busy on my novel. Spring at last! This day could not have been finer even if made to order by the wisest of snow-bound creatures. The sun is coming down in floods of golden flame—the ground literally streams with melting snow. Every gully is a river. The children are paddling and digging ditches just as I once did. The cocks crow and the hens *caw-caw*. Everybody is out to walk as far as the planks extend while a feeling of delight, of deliverance (which only the North enjoys) fills every heart. The snow, receding, uncovers the earth which gives off a familiar odor—the smell of rich mold which prophesies the springing plants. The smoke of burning leaves would make this a perfect day."

"March 27. This day I conceived an ending to my

novel, 'The Captain,' and worked it out with enthusiasm. I also sent away my 'Silent Eaters' to the Century. Howells' article on 'The History of American Literature' by Barrett Wendell is a beautiful roast of a critic who assumes too much. Fuller, who was delighted with this review, has a column concerning it in to-day's paper."

"On April 9 I gave my lecture (at the Chicago Art Institute) on 'The Commercial Value of Beauty' to a mixed and meager audience. Had it not been for Brown, Taft, and Fuller, I would have been completely disheartened. I went away vowing to deliver no more free lectures. My criticism of the city reached the press, however, and a reporter called to ask for an expression of opinion regarding the *Tribune's* plan of inciting citizens to garden and clean up vacant lots. Some of the papers resented my criticism, but I do not regret my words. 'It is a disgraceful thing that this great city should be so forlorn, so neglected, and so utterly drab,' I said.

"April 13. At Clarkson's studio to-day Harriet Monroe read a paper on 'The Passing West,' a fine piece of analysis, an essay of poetic significance. It widened the horizon of all who heard it. In the evening I ran across to tell her how much I liked it."

II

Early in April I received a letter from Vice President Roosevelt which touched upon a point of difference between us and pleased me on several other accounts. In my trailing I carried neither rod nor gun, and while I enjoyed Roosevelt's descriptions of the mountains and marveled at the accuracy of his notes, I had little sympathy with his "song of the bullet." He wrote from the vice president's chamber.

"Your letter of April 1st gives me genuine pleasure and I shall greatly prize the book. I never read serial stories in the magazines and I have been waiting until it shall come out in book form. That I read everything you write is of course needless to say.

"I shall not be in Washington in April, but when you come to New York I hope you will be able to take time to bring Mrs. Garland out here to lunch some day. I should like to show you some of my trophies. Let me know before you arrive—without fail.

"Your account of the Alaskan trail appealed to me very strongly. I suppose I am utterly illogical, but it always gives me a pang to think of the fate that befalls the pack horses under such conditions. I am very glad you brought your pony home and ride it. I find it just as you say—that is, about three days restores me to my ease in the saddle, though I am sorry to say I have grown both fat and stiff, so I should now hate most bitterly to try to manage what we used to call on the range a 'mean horse.'

"As I grow older I find myself uncomfortable in killing things without a complete justification, and it was a real relief this year to kill only 'varmints,' and to be able to enjoy myself in looking at the deer of which I saw scores or hundreds every day and never molested them."

III

On May 1st, feeling the need of further study of the Cheyennes and being in the grasp of a spring land hunger, I went to Oklahoma and purchased a farm near Seger's Colony.

"May 6. Here I am among the Cheyennes again. It is another world—green, radiant! The birds are singing—red men are jogging by—tepees are clustered on the hills. I met George Stouch on the train at Oklahoma City and we rode to El Reno together. At Weatherford Seger met me, looking rusty, dim-eyed, and wholly commonplace; but as he drove me down to the colony, I felt again the wealth of his experience. To the banker at the corner he was almost negligible; to me he was a surviving crag of a sunken world."

On the streets of Chicago he would have been noticeable only by reason of his limp, wide-brimmed hat. Naturally short, he was beginning to stoop and his coat was a bad fit. His trousers bagged at the knees, his collar was soiled, and his hands dark with dust and tan; but when he began to talk in his quiet, soft-spoken fashion, he loomed large. He recalled the days when this whole vast plain was the hunting ground of the red men now virtually imprisoned on their allotments.

Each day, and at every opportunity, for two weeks, I accompanied Seger on his rounds among his wards, carefully observing him as he interchanged signs with them, and at night we talked endlessly of his experiences.

My notes of these conversations were hasty and fragmentary at best, and I again urged him to write down all that he could remember. "Your life is a most essential part of Oklahoma history," I argued. "Can't you talk it to a stenographer? Get it recorded, no matter how roughly."

He told of the days when White Shield and his band had helped him carry mail across the wilderness, swimming the streams, breasting blizzards, and confronting midnight thunderstorms. He told me a pathetic story of old Yellow Horse who had heroically led the way into the white man's country. "One night the old man sent for me—and when I reached him it was early dawn. He was lying on his death-bed watching the rising sun. On his breast he had the schoolbooks which his little dead grandson had studied—and outside his tepee, placed where he could see them, were his plow and his mowing machine. They represented the superior magic of the white race, and now that he was going into the western sand hills, he wanted them where his eyes could rest on them. 'My friend,' he said, 'I am going the dark trail, but I want you to know that I have tried to follow your teaching. I have finished.'" Tears were in Seger's eyes as he ended his story.

"Darlington, May 20. Seger drove me back to the train yesterday morning, but it was long after sunset when I arrived at Fort Reno station. No one was at the depot to meet me and I struck out across the prairie afoot and alone. It was a very dark night and I walked warily for fear of skunks and Indian dogs. It was a stirring experience—that walk through a red camp, assailed by wolfish curs. It enabled me to understand Parkman and Catlin, and provided me with deeper color for my novel!"

I had long desired a tepee, one that I could use for a study on my lawn, and the next day after my return to Darlington, I made search for one. None that I liked were for sale, and when Antelope's mother said "we will make one if the white chief will buy the canvas," I seized upon the suggestion. "How much cloth do you need?" I asked. "Many yards," she replied. "We wish to make for you a chief's lodge—a heap big one."

Immediately upon receiving the canvas she assembled a group of her friends and set to work. They were all highly interested and their chatter was like a pioneer quilting party.

Stouch said, "They never had such a commission before. They say, 'We are going to make a noble house for the "white paper-chief."'"

Two days later, Robert, my Cheyenne interpreter, called on me to say that my lodge was ready for the raising. "They intend to make a ceremonial of this and wish you to be present."

As the old women drew the canvas over the poles they chanted a song of good magic. They said, "May this prove a brave shelter against the wind and the rain. We wish the white paper-chief much happiness in it."

There was something profoundly moving in their chant and in their smiling faces. They convinced me of the sincerity of their benediction. As I paid them for their work I told Robert to say to them: "The white man is proud of his new lodge, and his friends far away in the North will admire it when he sets it up. I shall keep it for many years. Whenever I enter it I will think of you, my friends." This made them all happy, and I went away with a feeling that they were, in truth, my well-wishers. They were not savages—they were my red neighbors.

"West Salem, Wisconsin, June 3. This morning brings news of the death of James A. Herne—and my mind is filled with thoughts of the many plans we once shared and the many enthusiasms and controversies we once owned. I should have been at his bedside yesterday, and I cannot be at his funeral to-morrow. He filled a large place in my life for many years. He was a mixture of greatness and littleness—as we all are. Although one of the most humorous men of my acquaintance, he was a sad man. I did not consider him a great writer, but he was a deeply stimulating friend. Some day I shall write of him more fully than I can do at this time!"

"Each day I grind away at my novel, finding a third revision of it a good deal of a grind. A great many offers for stories are coming in, but I stick close to my tale. 'In a constructive way, I think it the largest thing I have done,' I wrote to Fuller; 'but it does not entirely satisfy me even in its third draft.' My attitude toward it is utterly different from that which I assumed in writing my first stories. I am in the position of a man with a good market for his product and little time to produce. The demand for my short sketches and novelettes is strong, but my power for imagining them is diminishing. My romance absorbs all my energies. In casting up what I have done during the last year, I find that I have written 225,000 words, notwithstanding two trips to Oklahoma, one to the Pacific Coast, and another to the Atlantic. Evidently marriage has not interfered with my work to any noticeable degree."

In writing this novel of Montana—which had taken on the color of a more heroic life than my earlier stories depicted—I had the advantage of a close-hand study of the Northern Cheyenne reservation at a time when its warriors had been goaded into resistance by the insolent aggression of the cattlemen. "I spent many days with the agent. I messed with the officers and I met and talked with the headmen of the tribe. I saw them against their background. My story sprang out of my observation and is true to the scene. After all, it is intended to entertain rather than instruct."

The placing of an artist in the midst of the outbreak was natural, for at this time almost every fort and Indian agency had its visiting painter or passing illustrator. I had myself taken a painter and a sculptor among the Utes and Navajos. Several men of my acquaintance were painting portraits of typical individuals among the Northwest tribes, and to imagine a young woman established in a studio at Lame Deer was not in the slightest degree fantastic—and added to the interest of my story.

However, I am willing to admit that my chief concern was with the outlook and action of the Cheyennes. I perceived in some degree the tragic significance of their last stand here in this dry, bleak land, a fragment of the bright world they had once possessed—people of the polished Stone Age confronting an age of electricity and the machine gun. Like Slohan and Looking Stag, Two Moon and American Horse, they were going down to defeat in uncomplaining dignity—despairing yet without rancor.

CHAPTER FIVE

COLORADO MEN AND MOUNTAINS

I

THE summer of 1901 was appallingly dry in the Middle West, and the Garland homestead in Wisconsin, though fairly spacious and shaded with green trees, was almost intolerably hot as July drew on. The ground was parched and the gardens sad and drooping, and yet at night the air appeared to be wringing wet. Sleep was almost impossible, and as I watched my wife—who had been sick for several weeks—lying wan and inert on her couch, I thought with longing of the high peaks and ice-cold, rushing streams of Colorado, and made plans for taking her there as soon as she could safely travel. I mention this because it is significant of the change which had taken place in me. Rightly or wrongly my mind had turned away from the scenes of my youth. I was more and more concerned with the red people of the plains and the men and women of the High Country. I regarded my "Main-Travelled Roads" as a picture painted.

We left West Salem on a burning day and for twenty-four hours sweltered in our car, especially while passing through Iowa and Kansas, and then late at night we met the blessed breath of the Rampart

Range! On the second morning we were at Colorado
Springs, in the home of our good friends, Louis and
Henrietta Ehrich. Our room—the same room we had
occupied two years before—faced the great peaks, delicately tinted with purple, over which a snowy wall of
clouds was majestically rising. It was like looking up at
the bastions of a celestial city; a region of cool air,
swift streams, and alpine flowers. Even as we ate our
breakfast on a spacious porch, thunder began to crash
and roll amid the upper cañons, and the wind took on
a delicious icy edge. Summer had no further terrors
for us!

On the second afternoon, our host and hostess took
us with them to "Glen Eyrie," the home of General
Palmer, the most distinguished and in some ways the
most powerful citizen of Colorado. He had been a
brigadier general during the Civil War, and his regiment of Pennsylvania cavalry was famous in the history of the Army of the Potomac. He was also known
as a railway engineer and the head of the Rio Grande
Railway, but I had never met him and had never seen
his beautiful home in a cañon at the foot of Pike's
Peak. I was a little concerned, therefore, when the
Ehrichs proposed taking us to a "Glen Eyrie" garden
party, although they assured me that General Palmer
knew of us and would welcome us.

Our scruples grew less disturbing as we saw the
streams of carriages converging upon his gates. The
entire country seemed on the way. The garden which
filled the lower cañon was a most delightful assemblage
of the wild flowers of the region. At the upper end of
this park stood a gray, towered, stone mansion whose

roofs overtopped the pine and piñon trees with suggestion of England.

On the lawn in front of his castle, the general, a tall,
blond man, clothed in white flannels and standing on
a Persian rug, was welcoming his guests. Beside him
stood his three young daughters—all very English in
voice and manner. As Ehrich introduced us, the general heartily said, " I know about you, and I am glad
to see you here."

Naturally we had not much opportunity to talk to
him during the afternoon, but the following day he
invited us to join a party of his friends whom he was
taking to Cripple Creek in his private car. On the way
up the mountain he told me that Colorado Springs was
about to hold a celebration in honor of the explorer
Zebulon Pike who discovered (one hundred years before) the great peak which bore his name. "I am to
make an address at the unveiling of a statue on August
1st, and I need your help," he said.

I assured him that I was deeply interested in the ceremony and that I knew something of Pike's exploit. "I
shall be glad to aid." Thereupon he referred several obscure historical problems to me. As a result I found
myself deeply engaged in this ceremony, and also in the
sesquicentennial which the town had arranged in connection with the Pike celebration. Everything conspired
to bring me into closer contact with the men of Colorado as well as with its history; for as we were leaving
the car at the end of our trip, the general said: "Immediately after the festival, my daughters and I are
going into camp at the foot of Sierra Blanca, and
I should like to have you join us. Your friend Ehrich

has agreed to come, and so has his other guest, ex-Governor Sterling Morton." Although I had only a vague notion of Sierra Blanca, I promptly accepted this invitation.

That night at dinner I met Henry Russell Wray, a young Philadelphian, an artist and writer who had come to Colorado as a "one-lunger" (as the invalids who flocked to Colorado in those days were called) and was enormously taken with him. He was one of the gayest, most amusing, and at the same time one of the best-informed men in the Springs. Short of stature, ruddily handsome of face, gray-eyed and mirthful, he kept me laughing almost continuously. He knew everybody and had an endless string of comical stories at his command. He bore no malice, and his jests were never coarse. He saw the funny side of everything, even the Pike statue which he described as "a large, pale grasshopper with the colic."

My attention was drawn to him by reason of the picturesque quality of his phrases and his knowledge of mountain men and mining life, but another side of his character appeared when he told the story of a visit to James McNeill Whistler at his studio in Paris. "I was something of an artist myself," he said, "and when one afternoon a friend asked me to go with him to Jimmy's studio, I snapped at the chance. Whistler met us at the door—a thin little man with a ratty mustache and a stony glare. He was not a bit friendly—in fact he was as sour as a lemon—although my companion was an intending purchaser. I was disgusted with him. He had been my little tin-god-on-wheels for years, and I didn't expect him to act like a moth-eaten rabbit with dyspepsia. He wore a single eyeglass—which irritated me, and his British accent made me venomous.

"In the midst of an explanation of why he couldn't do this or wouldn't do that, I looked him in the eye and broke loose: 'Mr. Whistler, where were you born?' My question and the tone of my voice staggered him, and before he caught himself he said, 'Troy, New York.' 'Then for God Almighty's sake, talk like it!' My friend was scared. He thought Whistler would shut the door in our faces but he didn't. He looked at me a moment, then said: 'Wait till I put away my brushes and we'll go out and have a New York cocktail. I know an American bar near by.'

"He put away his brushes and we went to his American bar. We had a drink, several of them, and Whistler warmed up. He abandoned his eyeglass and his English accent. At last he invited us both to go home with him and meet his wife, so we set forth, three abreast, Whistler in the middle—he got along better there—and as a procession we were pretty close to a public disturbance. Whistler was in high good humor and spoke French persuasively to the policeman who stopped us, and so we reached his house in fair condition! As he swung the door open he made an expansive gesture—'Enter, gentlemen, the place is yours.'

"But it wasn't—it wasn't even his—not at that hour! As we entered the long dim drawing-room, I saw (about two miles away) three coldly silent, portentous female figures—one in black, all standing waiting. A war cloud hung over that part of the room, I could see that, and poor little pappa lost his cocksure attitude. He was comical. In the tone of a small boy who has played truant and hopes to placate his mother with three measly shiners James McNeill said, 'My dear, let me introduce two American friends from Philadelphia.'

"It didn't work. The women responded with a freezing politeness which said 'Get out,' and without ceremony we got. Whistler was a god in certain circles of art, but he was only a subaltern in *that* company."

I can only give the substance of this tale with some hint here and there of its wording, which had, of course, that element of exaggeration which is the essence of American humor. Later, Wray wrote it out; but he never quite caught in ink the joyous audacity of his spoken description—in fact, he never again in my hearing told this story so well. It was the kind of tale which biographers of Whistler never give; something which Wray's boyish irreverence—not to say impudence—drew forth. All Whistler's English pretensions were laid aside. He was Jim Whistler, of Troy, New York, shaking cocktails and talking of the States and old friends in human, neighborly fashion.

My wife and I discussed the Wrays that night with lively interest. We quite took them to our hearts, for Mrs. Wray, a demure little Pennsylvania Quaker, aided and abetted her roguish husband in all his drolleries. They belonged to the same province of artistic Bohemia in which my wife and I dwelt. With them we were at home.

From the Ehrichs I learned that Wray was acting as secretary to the Chamber of Commerce and editing the local paper for which he did a good many special articles. "Both these positions," said Ehrich, "bring him into contact with men of all classes. He can tell you more about conditions out here than any other man."

This I found to be true. He not only knew men and affairs, but had a swift understanding of the literary value of the material. Unable to use it himself, he could talk it, and did talk it, endlessly, to me. It is impossible to say how much he suggested to me, for in addition to this comment he introduced me to several men who represented "the red-necks" in "The Miners' War" at Cripple Creek, and to certain "Little Londoners" who commanded the forces opposed to the union. To him, to Ehrich, and to General Palmer I owe much of the material which forms the background of "Hesper," my second Colorado novel.

On August 1st I witnessed the unveiling of the plaster cast of the monument to Lieutenant Pike, and at the sesquicentennial Wild West rodeo which followed, I was given a seat in the box set aside for Vice President Roosevelt, who had come to Colorado Springs especially to review this parade. With me sat Sterling Morton, ex-Governor of Nebraska, who was also a guest of Louis Ehrich.

When Roosevelt came into the box he greeted me cordially and asked after my wife. "Is she with you? I want to know her."

"She is staying at the Ehrichs'—old friends of mine," I replied.

"Give me the address. I shall call on her this afternoon," he said.

"Oh, no!" I replied. "She and I will call upon you. You are royalty now."

"Nonsense!" he replied. "I shall call at four."

He was in his proper element at this rodeo. He loved the West with its daring horsemen, its skilled hunters, and its gunmen. He admired the men who were willing to take chances, men to whom mountain storms and streams were a part of the game—and this admiration I shared. Many trailers of this type, some of them his subordinates in the Spanish American War, had assembled to meet him, and all the actors in the pageant which presented red men, cowboys, Mexican pioneers, pueblo people, Modern Woodmen, and Coronado Conquistadores (mingling to express the development of Colorado) were fully aware that his eyes were fixed upon them. To me he represented the finest mingling of the East and the West, the hunter and the historian, the rancher and the soldier.

Among the few who remained critical of him were General Palmer and Sterling Morton, who were not only opposed to him politically, but disliked him personally—admitting at the same time his great ability—a prejudice which did not affect me, for I had acquired not only an unbounded confidence in his future as a leader but an affection for him as a man.

As soon as the parade was ended I hurried back to Ehrich's to prepare my wife and her hostess for the great honor of the vice president's call. "What shall I say to him?" asked my wife.

"Say whatever you have in mind. He knows many of your artist friends and writers—besides, he'll do the talking."

He came promptly in a carriage—this was before the automobile—and for half an hour chatted pleasantly with us all. He was full of delightfully humorous anec-

dotes of his Rough Riders, and quite won my wife's
heart by his friendly, unofficial attitude.

As he rose to go I accompanied him down the
walk to the gate. "Where do you go from here?" I
asked.

"Down into the wolf and mountain lion country.
Some of the boys have arranged a hunting trip for
me." Then, referring back to some of our talks on
game shooting, he said, with entirely serious intonation,
"You'll be interested to know that I've come round to
your position. I kill only 'varmints' now. By the way,
I am giving a breakfast to some of my soldier boys
and guides to-morrow morning at the hotel. I want you
to come. Bring Morton and Ehrich if they care to sit in
with a bunch of Rough Riders and hunters."

This invitation was of great value to me, but Morton
and Ehrich were curious rather than eager guests. "The
table held fourteen plates. John Goff, a small, rather
abashed cowboy and hunter who had been Roosevelt's
guide in northern Colorado, was given the place of
honor. On the host's left sat a tall Rough Rider named
Daniels. I came next to Daniels and on my left was
another of 'the old Guard,' Lieutenant Llewellyn. Ehrich and Morton, coldly silent, were at the opposite
side of the table. It amused me to watch their critical
glances as the speakers under Roosevelt's prompting
told stories of hunting, of San Juan Hill, of camping,
cow-punching, and the like."

To me, this was all deeply interesting, and I was sorry
when Roosevelt rose and the breakfast ended—but as
we walked out into the street Morton exclaimed, "Did
you ever hear such a bloodthirsty powwow? It was

like the talk of Sioux or Comanches boasting around a campfire."

Ehrich was almost equally contemptuous, but to me it was a delightful exhibition of Roosevelt's genius for friendship and his essential democracy. He was hunter, soldier, and cowboy with the others, but he was also the writer to whom this was delightful "stuff." I could not share Morton's disgust.

II

Two days later, Ehrich, Morton, and I took the train for Fort Garland with intent to join General Palmer's camp party. We reached our station late at night, a mysterious little town, set in the midst of a dim plain, silent and sweet, with vast domes of mountains rising like prodigious clouds against the western sky. General Palmer's men met us and took us to a near-by boarding house with orders to spend the night.

Early the next morning a team came for us and drove us away across the level valley directly toward the mountains whose summits were gray with clouds. Sierra Blanca, nearly fifteen thousand feet above sea level, is one of the highest of Colorado mountains, and forms the southern bastion of the Sangre de Cristo Range. All along the way we passed Mexican farms with adobe houses, their dark-skinned owners at work in their small fields. It was difficult to make myself believe that I was in Colorado, so alien was the scene.

At the foot of Mount Baldy, on the bank of a glorious mountain stream, we came upon General Palmer and his daughters occupying a small village of tents and attended by a platoon of trained servants. In a grove near by, a herd of horses all saddled and bridled awaited their riders.

For luncheon we had a steak from Denver (ordered by telegraph) with mushrooms and sweet potatoes, and that night our four-course dinner included three kinds of wine, which we drank from tin cups. "This is the kind of roughing it I like," said Morton with a laugh in his eyes.

After dinner, at the request of Elsie, the eldest of the girls, I read a chapter from my Colorado novel, and as I did so I had the feeling of adding something literary to the landscape. In my small, crude way I had put this region into words—I will not say literature—and now here I was voicing my lines in the presence of the very pines and people I had so greatly admired.

In my small way but in a grander scene I was playing the minstrel as Whittier had done in reading "Bear Camp Water" or "The Tent on the Beach."

Ehrich was literary enough to derive a definite satisfaction from this. He loved Colorado and whatever tended to make it better known. For him its scene could not be over-praised. He took a deeper interest in me thereafter, urging me (as Wray did) to continue my study of the mountains. To them my "Main-Travelled Roads" belonged to the sad, drab low country. "It is time to come up higher," they said.

The general who had expressed disappointment at the failure of my wife to come with me, now sent his special car back to Colorado Springs to get her, and two days later she joined us and for two weeks we continued in camp there in such luxury that I feared its moral effect upon us both. We had nothing to do but ride and feast and sleep. Hot water was brought to our tent door, our horses were saddled for us, and our mail brought by courier.

Our host was always the regimental commander. Everything about the camp proceeded by military routine, prearranged and exact. The general issued orders as if we were a troop of cavalry on special exploring detail. Rain or shine we set forth each day on a certain prescribed tour of observation with guides, camp wagons, and servants—till all the roundabout country had been covered, and then one night our commander said, "On Monday we move to Wagon Wheel Gap by rail. Our cooks and orderlies will bring the horses and camp equipment overland."

On Saturday Ehrich and Morton left us; and in my diary I find this note: "Morton made a most agreeable impression on us all. He is a big, patriotic American, Sterling by name and sterling by nature. He is essentially the farmer, the pioneer. He loves the work of subduing the wild lands. He is a powerful influence in Nebraska—a builder. He is neither hunter, trailer, nor man of letters. His interests are few and his prejudices deep and strong."

One of the primitive characters who swarmed about the general was a grizzled prospector who claimed to have a mine high on the western slope of Sierra Blanca. He lived on a small ranch somewhere near our camp and drove a pair of bronchos hitched to a light wagon. In talk with him I conceived a plan to climb the great peak. "I must not neglect the opportunity," I told the general. "I'll hire this prospector to drive me round to an old mining camp on the western side. We'll stay all night there and go to the top the next morning."

"I'll send one of my men with you," said the general.

This I would not have. I wanted to go alone guided by this relic of the days when mining was a vital industry of the region—I wanted to listen to his outpouring chronicle. He was an almost perfect embodiment of the gold-seeker, the man who carries in his pocket pieces of rich ore from a hidden lode. He was small and faded and wistful—essentially the poet even in his garrulity.

I carried out my plan. We drove round the broad, hot, treeless base of the great peak and climbed a neglected road to a forgotten camp halfway to the timber line. Here we lodged, sleeping on the floor of an old cabin. "I've seen the time," said my guide as we stood looking down at the far-away lights of the valley, "when this whole mountain was alive with miners. We all thought we owned the world in those days."

As this was the end of the wagon road, we took to the saddle next morning and climbed steadily all the forenoon, passing other melancholy huts which my companion remembered when they were filled with hopeful youth. He recalled the miners who had owned this or that claim, and the names of the saloons and dance halls, standing now amid thickets of berry bushes laden with fruit. The trails were overgrown by the forest and washed away on the cliffs.

"I went to the top of the mountain," I reported to my wife, "but that is unimportant when weighed against the harvest of impressions I have gained."

Out of that venture came a long short story, "The

Steadfast Widow Delaney," but its indirect effects were far more valuable. Thereafter I was able to understand and sympathize with those who were not only miners but poets, whose joy was in the search, lovers of the high trails.

My record reads: "August 16. Every hand was busy at packing this morning, and at noon our beloved camping place was a desolate spot. The glorious stream called for delay, but its call went unheeded. The vagrant dog who had made friends with us wandered disconsolately around the grove sensing the sad change.

"As we rode away, Sierra Blanca, a vague, tremendous blue mass, loomed behind us, an ever enlarging giant on whose head rested a turban of gray cloud. Slowly hooding itself in vapor, it withdrew into that solitude which mountains of such magnitude often seek."

That night, we dined long and sumptuously in the general's private car while the purple domes of the Sangre de Cristo Range faded into the mist of things remembered. I acknowledged a feeling of sadness on leaving this beautiful valley. It was like abandoning a beloved home. As I write, I recall the exact courses of the streams and the precise shapes of the peaks. This spot remains in my memory as the most luxurious and carefree camping place of all my mountaineering.

CHAPTER SIX

THE POET OF THE GREAT DIVIDE

I

ON the edge of a circular valley locally known as Wagon Wheel Gap, a group of hot springs had become known to health-seekers and a small wooden hotel had been built there. It all belonged to General Palmer, and it was in this rather commonplace resort that we came to rest the second night after leaving Sierra Blanca. The view was superb. To the north and east lay the Gap, and to the west the wooded heights of the Continental Divide invited an exploration. Some six or eight miles up the river lay Creede, once a renowned gold camp.

While we were at this place I was greatly surprised by a letter from William Vaughn Moody, who wrote from Denver: "I am on your trail. When can I meet you and where?"

This was in accordance with a previous agreement. I had said to him, "I'd like to show you the Rocky Mountains," and he had said, "Wire me instructions and I will meet you at any time." Now here he was in Colorado waiting upon my promise, and here was I under command of General Palmer. There was only one thing to do—explain to the general that I must meet a friend who knew nothing of the mountain West, and take charge of him. This I did.

87

"Nonsense," said the general. "Wire Moody to come here. We'll be glad to know him."

Although I had met Moody frequently I hardly felt acquainted with him, so singularly withholding and saturnine was his manner. His impassive, bearded face and his large, observant eyes had something sad and remote in their expression. He was slow in responding to question and when he spoke it was with reluctant, almost sour, brevity. His best friends, however, assured me that this was only a mask and that he was in reality highly sensitive and warm-hearted. With high admiration of his work, I had acted upon this statement, but we were, by no interpretation, intimate.

Like Edwin Markham he had achieved sudden success with a poem—or to be exact—with two, one "An Ode In Time of Hesitation," and the other, a very moving one, on a portrait of his mother. But he had written many others and was considered, rightfully, the chief American poet of the moment; and yet I was not at all sure that the Palmers would enjoy him as a guest. However, I wired him and set about making plans to take him on the trail. He knew nothing of camping and had confided to me that he could scarcely sit a horse; but I resolved, nevertheless, to lead him into the wildest part of the range to the west of us, in order that he might know something of Colorado's scenic glory.

He arrived in a most unwonted state of good humor, his eyes alight with amusement, and at once explained that he had shared his seat on the train from Alamosa with an old rancher who was returning to his home in Creede. "He confided to me," said Moody with a quizzical smile, "that he was on his way home from Denver where he had gone to make some purchases of household furniture for his wife. 'But,' said he, 'I fell among the Galatians and lost all my money—and I am about to be called upon to face my family and explain my loss.' " The old reprobate's expression, "I fell among the Galatians," tickled Moody beyond measure. "My rancher friend was a biblical scholar—he had St. Paul in mind. His statement was precise. He fell among a pleasure-loving, frivolous people who led him into spending money in pursuit of a good time."

There was nothing saturnine or laconic about Moody that day. He bubbled with talk, and glowed with delight of this mountain world. He was indeed a charming guest and General Palmer cordially urged him to join the party, but he replied: "You are very kind, but I came out for a camping trip into the mountains with Garland. I am in his hands."

While waiting for our camp outfit we both joined the party in a gallop up the valley to Creede—the mining town which Cy Warman had made famous by a poem with this refrain:

> "It is day all day in the daytime,
> And there is no night in Creede."

The valley was glorious with pink and green slopes and purple-green firs and majestic borders of rocks; but Creede was a filthy, one-street village of shacks built along a grandly picturesque cañon. Great horns of purple and green and yellow rock rose above the river which had been turned into a sewer—a shameful pollution of a noble stream. Mills and ramshackle homes filled the narrow, tortuous valley for miles, enabling us to understand the "gulches" of Bret Harte's time. My gorge rose as I noted the obscene desecrations of this glorious region; but it was all marvelous to Moody. He hardly spoke, but his big, reflective eyes caught every detail.

On the following day I took him for another practice ride up the Goose Creek trail till we came in sight of the snowy Continental Divide. He was wearing a soft black hat when we left the Gap, but he soon took it off, rolled it and tied it to his saddle, riding thereafter with bared head, his face lifted toward the soaring eagles and the snow peaks, awed, transported, exultant.

"At last we turned and started back down the trail, confronting a scene of unearthly beauty. In the foreground lay the pine-clad hills over which our trail ran, and beyond, wall upon wall, citadel beyond citadel, rose the Cochetopa Range glorified by the setting sun and made grandly mysterious by the drift of clouds. Again and again Moody stopped to gaze as if to fix forever in his memory this overwhelming picture of peak and cloud, whilst I, believing that I was assisting in the education of a great poet, refrained from comment, confidently expecting that something magnificently inspirational would issue from this hour."

The following morning with tent and cooking tools on a pack horse, I again led the way upward. Moody, though somewhat lame, was eager for the ride, and we pushed steadily up the glorious valley till late afternoon. We camped that night on the bank of a rushing stream with a portentous wooded cliff behind us, and the poet, tired though he was, sat till nearly midnight beside the fire, listening to the birds and watching the light fade from the lofty summits of "the Big Divide."

He was admittedly a tenderfoot, helpless as a child. "I know nothing of camping, or the care of horses, or trailing," he quite frankly confessed. "I can't even cook, but I can wash dishes and carry wood"—and I could not complain of one so humble in manner and so grateful. I made him as comfortable as I could, acknowledging my responsibility. He was like a peasant in a king's palace, awed but happy. He listened with tense interest to the noises of the darkening forest. "What is that?" he would ask when a bird or beast uttered a cry. Several times in the night he woke me to ask an explanation of some new and startling sound. I was glad to have him do this. He was not alarmed; he was only curious. He was, for the time, my pupil.

On the second morning he rose with difficulty. Our camp was at snow line, nearly twelve thousand feet above the sea, and he had suffered for lack of blankets. He hobbled about, chilled and lame, so lame that he was unable to stand erect. I was alarmed about him, but the sun and the fire and my hot coffee straightened him up, and by eight o'clock he had forgotten his pain in the splendor of the morning.

At two o'clock we topped the Great Divide and stood face to face with an assemblage of peaks hardly to be surpassed in all America. On every side colossal ridges tumbled against the sky, many of them fourteen thousand feet above sea level, shining with fields of snow. Turning our horses loose on the short, sweet grass, we ate our lunch in a sheltering, sunny hollow, at an altitude of thirteen thousand feet. Silent with emotion, Moody faced this world in the spirit of the explorer as well as that of the poet. But as he was still suffering from lumbago and I was afraid that another night in camp might disable him, I therefore decided to cut our trip short and return to Wagon Wheel Gap —a decision which he welcomed, although he was loath to leave the High Country. "I didn't know such beauty existed in America," he said as we saddled up and reluctantly set out on the downward-curving trail.

After a long, hard ride, part of the time in the rain, we reached the hotel. General Palmer and his party, we were told, had gone to Ouray; and so after a few days' stay with me, Moody went on to Colorado Springs and soon after returned to Chicago. Unquestionably his stay in Wagon Wheel enriched and inspired him, and in his play, "The Great Divide," as well as in later poems, I was able to trace the effect of his intense and passionate study of the mountains while with me. I confidently predicted a still more definite use of this material.

While on this subject, let me add that I was in the audience when Margaret Anglin gave (in Chicago) the first performance of "The Great Divide." Many of Moody's associates on the university faculty and most of his literary friends were in the audience; and when the curtain fell on the first act, we all applauded thunderously. It was a noble beginning; and while we waited for the second act, the house buzzed with excited comment. "Here is a great play." Twenty minutes went by, thirty minutes, and the buzz grew into a murmur. "Why don't they go on?" we demanded. "They are losing the effect of the first act."

Fifty minutes passed. Rumors of ill fortune began

to spread. "Miss Anglin is ill," said one. "One of the men has been injured," said another. At last authentic news reached me. "Moody and the star are wrangling over the terms of a contract. Moody has called for a lawyer to go in behind and secure his rights."

After more than an hour's wait, the curtain finally rose on the second act; and that the play survived this disrupting delay was proof of its power. When the final curtain fell, Moody was acclaimed a fine new dramatist by all the critics, and this, the greatest of our native plays. It had a long run and released Moody from the drudgery of teaching. He left the university and went to New York. Henry Miller played the leading part in this drama for two years, and I took pleasure in thinking, perhaps without reason, that our expedition in the Rocky Mountains had helped the poet shape and color his scenes. I had shown him a sunset from the Great Divide.

The inside story of this production as given to me by Henry Miller was highly dramatic. He said, "Miss Anglin, who was playing in Chicago, read the play and was so impressed with it that she called me on the long-distance phone and said: 'I've found a great play and a great part. I want to produce it at once.' I was her manager, you know. I knew nothing of Moody as a playwright, but over that thousand miles of wire I detected something of Margaret's intensity of interest and instantly replied, 'Very well, go ahead.' She went ahead as you know."

Miller who put the play on in New York naturally took the part of the hero—although Moody's friends felt that he was too old for it. He made a success of it on Broadway, and Moody, like every other successful dramatist, abandoned Chicago. We met thereafter at the Players or in the Century Club; but I never quite recovered the glow of friendship which I enjoyed that week in Wagon Wheel Gap. He grew more taciturn, more introspective each year. At luncheons, even when guest of honor, he sat in silence, almost Oriental in his abstracted calm, his bearded face a mask, his eyes, roving from face to face, with no more expression of interest than the lens of a camera. He was neither unfriendly nor contemptuous, he merely withdrew—a ruminating Buddha, concerned with space outside of time.

He never repeated the success of "The Great Divide." He never rose to the heights which I had confidently prophesied; but he grew in fame and fortune up to the hour of his premature passing, and his friends believe that he was only in the middle stages of a great career when Death cut him down. I am not so sure of this, for his verses are not as vital to me now. Can any poet survive in this day of change?

On September 5th I returned to Ehrich's home in Colorado Springs. That night at dinner, Professor Brewer of Yale sat opposite me. "He is the old-fashioned professor," I confided to my diary; "one who lectures continually in season and out, vastly learned, very noble, but tiresome. He told, however, one deeply moving story, the story of his ship which struck a rock somewhere off the coast of Greenland. 'The exploring party of which I was a member,' he said, 'was forced to abandon her, and to lessen her danger to other vessels it was decided to leave her with all her lights on and her engines going. As we took to the small boats and rowed away, we watched her move ahead, her windows glowing, her machinery throbbing. She was like a wounded, deserted, living thing; and when at last she sank, we all uttered a groan. What a theme for Kipling!' "

Late the following afternoon came the news of President McKinley's assassination and I set down these words: "His death will change the world, for Theodore Roosevelt is now President, and will break the combination which Mark Hanna and his group have formed."

Ehrich's house was always open to the traveler who was worth while, and I was not surprised to find Snyman, visiting representative of the Boers, a guest. "We all liked him. He is a big, sincere fellow. His manners are admirable, his mind quick and clear, and his judgments liberal. He made us feel the bigness of his cause and the grandeur of the struggle his people are making. He seemed like a fine Pennsylvania German—not in the least alien. His attitude is one of manly courage and liberal outlook. Nothing small or bitter came out in his report. He admires an open enemy. Such a man with such a cause is calculated to stir men," was my final judgment of him.

II

On leaving Colorado my wife and I went to Santa Fé and to the Grand Cañon, where we fell in with Lucy and Harriet Monroe. On our way back along the Santa Fé Railway we rode for half a day with Charles F. Lummis of Los Angeles, who was on his way to Isleta, the pueblo in which he had begun his study of the pueblo peoples some twenty years before. "We found him interesting and picturesque—unconventional in most of his ideas and sturdy in his opposition to any so-called progress which does not add to the happiness of humankind. He wore a crumpled brown corduroy suit with a Mexican scarf for a belt, and his hat was a wide, soiled, white sombrero. He amused me at the same time that he won my respect."

In showing us pictures of the house he was building in Los Angeles, he said, "I am laying the stone with my own hands," and pointed out the huge tree round which he was constructing his walls. My penciled comment on this ends thus: "A really epic performance."

Like several other Western authors, Lummis was greater as a character than as a writer, although his books on the Southwest (in which he specialized) are interesting and valuable. He was a native of Massachusetts, but affected a bluff, rough-and-ready manner as to the border born. As a thinker with violent prejudices, he had made as many enemies as friends. He knew the brown people of Arizona and New Mexico intimately and defended their rights; and his sense of historic values made him one of the founders of the Southwestern Museum in Los Angeles. Last year at a luncheon one of his friends told the pathetic story of his death. "Charley knew that he was dying, but he hoped to live long enough to read the proof on his last book. This he did. The completed volume came to him—the day before he died."

Vital, impulsive, stormy, and often unreasonable,

Lummis talked and wrote and fought—building for himself a secure place in Southwestern history.

"September 20. We are homeward-bound across the dry plains of Kansas. Our vacation is over. Its pleasures are in retrospect. It has brought me several new and valuable friendships. Among these I count joyous Russell Wray, Sterling Morton, and General Palmer. And I have gained new admiration for William Vaughn Moody and Theodore Roosevelt. In my odds and ends of time I have revised 'The Captain of the Gray Horse Troop' which is now on its way to George Horace Lorimer of the *Post*. I am certain that my day on Sierra Blanca has given me a theme for a long short story. I shall call it 'The Steadfast Widow Delaney.' "

"Oregon, Ill., November 2d. To-day at the camp at Oregon 'Lord' Heckman, in his brake drawn by three powerful horses, took us all for a drive down to Colonel Frank Lowden's gorgeous farm. Wallace permitted me to drive part of the way, a joyous experience. The party was merry and the day superb. Lowden, a handsome and genial host, is an ideal landed proprietor, and Mrs. Lowden has all the grace, the beauty, and the dignity which duchesses are supposed to have—and often lack. Their farm here on the banks of the Rock River is significant of the turn toward country life now setting in."

On our return to Chicago, Fuller came in to spend the evening and confided to us with a gay chuckle that he had been having more fun with us in his new book, "Under the Sky-Lights." "It is a kind of Chicago 'Latin Quarter' chronicle," he said.

A few days later I took a plunge into an almost forgotten world by way of a visit to my old friend Dr. Bashford, who had become president of the Ohio Wesleyan University. I had not seen Mrs. Bashford for many years, and I found her a serious, almost grim, elderly woman; but the doctor, although equally devout, was quite the same genial, humorous, helpful soul he had been when he visited me in Ordway in 1884. I liked him, but his religious outlook and his cant phrases irritated me. "The rooms of his house are spacious, but without a particle of grace. His library is dreadful. It is made up for the most part of sermons, theological essays, and Scripture exegeses. A week with him would drive me to revolt—and yet I cannot forget that he, in a sense, is responsible for my career. He was instrumental in setting my face toward Boston—and literature. It is not for me to turn my back upon the man who rescued me from a drab Dakota town. What would I have done had he not knocked at my door that summer day?"

On my return I said something like this to Fuller, who spent the evening with me in unusually frank talk of which, fortunately, I made record. "I was glad to welcome Fuller after a long, hard day of writing. He is the ablest literary man in the Middle West and never fails to interest me. This night he was particularly alert and very candid. He opened his life to me. He confessed the poor sale of his books—'it amounts to being privately printed,' he said with a chuckle which concealed his chagrin. He was interested in our summer in Colorado and the personalities we had met, and wanted to know all my plans. His life, like his books, falls into

two divisions: his youth, remote, shadowy, coldly intellectual, interested in artistic movements and principles rather than persons; his present, wherein he hates
his surroundings, despises many people, and loves a
few. Painfully aware of my shortcomings, he is not
lacking in sympathy. He is growing wiser and sweeter
all the time. Soon he will write his best book."

Hearing that Ernest Seton was at one of the
hotels, I went down to call upon him. He was in the
midst of a strenuous lecture season, weary but triumphant. "He has made two hundred thousand dollars in
the last four years, and his vogue as writer and lecturer
still holds. His success is deserved. He has something to
give and the world is buying it. He is at once story-
writer, naturalist, and illustrator—and this triple activity has won a multiple success. No one can logically
begrudge him his just rewards."

Charles F. Lummis turned up at Taft's studio, dressed
in the same rumpled suit of corduroy I had noted in
New Mexico. "Although without an overcoat, he was
reeking with sweat and his hair was tousled into wig-
like tufts. He looked like some half-Mexican rancher,
but stated with pride that he was on his way to Washington to discuss Indian affairs with President Roosevelt. He cursed the Chicago climate, noise, and dirt.
'All cities are monstrous, destructive, and futile—Chicago the worst of them,' he argued with savage intensity, smoking cigarettes with nervous speed. 'I can't
sleep in Chicago,' he complained. 'I am going on to-
night.' And away he went, carrying a bandbox which
he declared was all the baggage he possessed, leaving a
rather unpleasant impression upon me as well as upon

Taft and his group. Without in any degree defending his manner of dress and his outlook on life, I valued his knowledge of the Southwest and of Southern California which made him helpful to the President. Once I would have admired his truculent nonconformity; but I am beginning to wonder if it pays to be picturesquely crumpled and dirty. Couldn't a man think just as well in a presentable suit and clean collar?"

This changing viewpoint was emphasized by the shift of the entire artist colony which Fuller described as "The Rabbit Warren" to the handsome tenth floor of the new Fine Arts Building. "Art in Chicago is becoming respectable, and, to Lummis' way of thinking, enfeebled; but I do not feel that way about it," I said to Taft.

The very next day I left for Cleveland to call upon Tom L. Johnson, whose advocacy of the single tax and a warm friendship for Henry George had made him a notable figure in the economic world. He was at this time the mayor, a rotund, smiling, clear-eyed man, whose business ability had won respect even from those who had no sympathy with his radical notions concerning city government.

"On learning that my wife and I were in the city, he invited us to lunch with him at his home. This we accepted, finding his house almost palatial and his wife delightfully hospitable. Tom—as everybody called him —quite won us both by his frank smile and candid speech. 'When some one is pointed out to me as one of my enemies,' he said, 'I pay him special attention—if he is worth while—by asking his advice. I do my best to bring about an amicable understanding. I don't believe in fighting people behind a wall of prejudice.' And as he said this, I understood how winning he could be. We left him with a deepened regard for his loyalty and devoted citizenship."

CHAPTER SEVEN

MY FIRST LITERARY SUCCESS

I

As my novel "The Captain of the Gray Horse Troop" had been accepted by Lorimer for the Philadelphia *Saturday Evening Post*, I stopped off on my way to New York City to conclude some of the details of its publication. The Curtis Publishing Company was swiftly expanding with prosperity and the *Post* had become one of the most widely circulated magazines of the day. Lorimer said, "I am not editing this periodical for New York City but for the nation," and his editorials, country-wide in their appeal, had little regard for polyglot Manhattan. The era of high prices for manuscripts had not yet set in—at least I did not share them. In offering me twenty-five hundred dollars for my novel, Lorimer said: "I can have my choice of a dozen serials for that price"—and I, a recently married man, desirous of establishing a home, was in no position to decline his offer, although I believed it to be worth a great deal more.

My wife and I went back to the same three-room apartment in the hotel on East Sixteenth Street wherein we had lived for several months the previous year. In an hour after the arrival of our trunks we were at home and in contact with several of our friends.

The greatest change in our circle was the death of James A. Herne, but Katharine met us with a brave show of confidence in the future of her children. At the office of *McClure's* I found William Allen White and Ray Stannard Baker in conference with John Phillips, and my comment on this meeting reads: "This magazine is now a big caravansary, but I haven't much confidence in it. I do not understand why White of Kansas should be doing studies of New York politics, but Phillips believes in him almost as firmly as he trusts Ida Tarbell. As the editor and proprietor of a paper in Emporia, Kansas, he is reported a success. I cannot believe that he intends to settle in the East. He is one of our literary vedettes and I should be sorry to have him desert his post."

McClure was away, and there were signs of the split-off which soon took place and resulted in Phillips becoming the editor of *The American Magazine*. Like Lorimer, he was a Mid-Western man and believed in editing his new magazine on a national basis. Just what the points of difference between himself and McClure were I did not specifically learn; but I knew that McClure was a difficult man to work with. Phillips carried with him Baker, White, and Miss Tarbell, and as they were all loyal friends, I naturally played along with them in their new venture.

One of the first plays I saw was "Colorado" by Augustus Thomas—a skillful and interesting play, but not up to the author's great reputation. It lacked spontaneity. At Mrs. Herne's we met Frank Norris again. My record describes him as "a stunning fellow—an author who does not personally disappoint his admirers.

He is perilously handsome, tall and straight, with keen brown eyes and beautifully modeled features. His face is as smooth as that of a boy of twenty, but his hair is almost white. I have never known a more engaging writer. He is a poet in appearance, but a close observer and a realist in his fiction. We had a lively evening together, really got at each other's prejudices as well as enthusiasms. He seems confident of his future, as well he may be, for his work is in demand and his mind in a glow of creative energy. I know of no one for whom I can more unhesitatingly predict a noble career.

"He told me of his grand scheme for 'a trilogy on wheat.' 'My first novel,' he said, 'deals with a California grain farm; the second will take up Chicago and the Wheat Pit.' He spoke of his first volume, 'The Octopus,' as 'The Squid,' and when I criticized it for its reminiscences of 'Germinal' and 'La Terre,' he admitted smilingly that Zola's work had been his highest admiration. I then reminded him of a wise admonition which Howells once gave me when I had laid before him a program for future work. 'Can you be sure of your continuing interest?' he had asked. 'In my experience I have repeatedly found that my grand schemes for the future grew cold before I attained to the writing of them; something more vital intervened.'

" 'As a matter of fact,' I said to Norris, 'I never got to the writing of that particular novel. As Howells foretold, it grew cold in my desk.' Norris was not much concerned. 'I have a third volume outlined,' he said."

Among my friends who (like Ernest Seton) represented wild lands and wild creatures, I valued George Bird Grinnell, editor and part owner of *Forest and*

Stream, whose many years' experience among the plains Indians had made him an authority on their history and customs, and when he asked me to visit him at his house on West 156th Street, I was glad of the opportunity. I especially wished to see him in the light of his own fire.

"His house is a joy," I wrote next day. "Just the sort of homestead for a family reunion—the kind of mansion to date from. Its dusky, wide, mysterious rooms are such as a child would remember with shuddering delight. Savage weapons are on the walls, wolf and bear skins on the floor, and in the corner bookshelves stand volumes filled with pictures of red men and animals."

Although a member of an old New York family, Grinnell's thought and his writing were almost wholly of the Far West, and as "the White Chief" of several red tribes, beloved and honored as their counselor, he often entertained delegations of them. With a gleam of amusement in his eyes, he said, "These chiefs, in coming to see the President, make a point of stopping to smoke the pipe of meditation with me. I have never been disturbed by the manners of my red visitors. 'They are instinctively dignified and courteous.' If they don't know exactly how to proceed they watch their host. My city friends are continually surprised by the essential dignity of my redskin friends."

Grinnell was held in high respect by Roosevelt, who several times alluded to him and to me as "my Indian sharps." Once he called us both to Washington to discuss with him some phase of the reservation problem; for while I had no such knowledge of Indian character and history as that which Grinnell owned, I did know a good deal about the conditions on ten or more of the reservations, and was able to suggest answers to some of the questions which the President was called upon to answer.

Grinnell was a lean, brown man of middle height, not a noticeable man in a crowd, but his history was distinguished. He had been on the warpath with the Pawnees in the sixties and by his later studies of the Cheyennes, Crows, and Piegans, had acquired more knowledge of these tribes than any writer of his day. His interpretations of Blackfoot legends were among the most sympathetic and authoritative of "Indian" tales; but beyond that he was the scholarly historian in his presentation of the origin and distribution of the red people. He spent a part of each summer among them, welcomed as "the little father" and a "paper chief." Quiet as he was, modest as he appeared, he could not be deceived nor intimidated. Cautious in taking a position, he was tenacious of it when attacked.

We met infrequently, but kept in touch by letter— and as my new novel dealt with life on the Northern Cheyenne Indian reservation, I was glad of his criticism. Careful to claim no deeper knowledge than an *impression*, I only said, "So and so they seemed to me." In this way I retained his coöperation and support. Whether he saw them precisely as I saw them was not important, for I made no pretensions to historical accuracy.

I never met him at a banquet or in some reception room that I did not feel the vivid contrast between his urban manner and the magnificent vista of his Rocky Mountain adventures. In the bronze impassivity of his countenance I was reminded of my red friends. He appeared to be dreaming of the captive people who, in their tiny huts and tepees, were not only suffering from hunger and cold, but mourning for the good days of the buffalo. As a matter of exact truth, his mind *was* engaged with these themes, for he was always writing on some phase of Amerind history. He praised my Indian stories, not for their exact truth, but for their sympathetic point of view; and applauded my contention that a village of Sioux or Cheyennes was like a village of white men—a mixture of good and evil. "It has its hoodlums, its bad men, but it has also its poets and philosophers."

"Garland's intentions are right," he said to an editorial friend of mine, "and in the main he hits off the red man's character pretty well."

II

On Christmas Day my wife and I were rescued from a hotel dinner by Irving Bacheller and his wife, who were spending the winter in an apartment in Harlem. Up to this time I had thought of Bacheller as more editor than writer; but his latest novel, "Eben Holden," had caught the fancy of Christmas buyers, and as we sat at meat that night he told us that his publishers were overwhelmed with orders. "The .presses cannot supply the demand," he said with a note of astonishment in his voice. "I can't understand it. All at once—after a slow start—the book begins to sell in thousands."

He told me that he had begun this tale as a boys' book, but that it had developed under his hand. "It is a picture of life in the North woods much as you have pictured the life of Wisconsin and Iowa," he said. "It is based on my own boy life. I've joined your local-color school. 'Eben Holden' is full of the thoughts and deeds of my own people who came over the mountains from Vermont two generations ago."

My wife considered Bacheller, Norris, and Edward MacDowell the handsomest of all my friends; and certainly Irving was a colorful figure that night. "He is large of frame and ruddy of face, with smiling blue eyes and blond hair just beginning to show gray. His voice is gentle, and his glance absent-minded yet humorous. He tells stories with quaint and precise art, and is a delightful host. We have known each other for ten years." This night made us brothers in a common inheritance and interest. Our wives drew together also, and from that time forward the Bachellers and the Garlands were in constant communication.

While Grinnell and I held a common interest in trailing, plains' life, and primitive lore I knew little of his family, but Bacheller and I owned a common stock of family life and New England tradition. We sang the same ballads and knew the same pioneer customs and legends. Our people sprang from the same Massachusetts root and we held similar ideals of citizenship and conduct. We often amused our friends by recounting incidents in our early lives, or by striving to excel in the singing of songs. He had a melodious tenor voice and when he lifted it in one of the ballads which his people had brought over the mountains from "Vaermount," I listened with respect. My art was on a homelier level.

Out of the royalties from "Eben Holden" he built, a

year later, a handsome home at Sound Beach, Connecticut, and there in the light of his noble fireplace, we held many a contest in song and story. His best ballad was one in which he imitated a shoemaker, a performance of such merit that I was forced to match it with "The Rolling Stone," my choicest possession. Sometimes we had senators and judges for listeners, but often we sang for each other with no desire for other auditors.

I have called Bacheller an absent-minded man, and he was. His wife declared that he would forget his head if it wasn't fastened to his shoulders. He admitted that he had scattered umbrellas, galoshes, canes, shoes, and toothbrushes from Maine to Oregon. When his mind was engaged on a problem, his material world vanished. Once as we were waiting at the station for the city-ward train, he fell into deep conversation with a friend, and his wife, calling my attention to the bag which he had put down on the walk, said, "He'll go off and leave it. Slip up and get it."

This I did, and as the train came along, Irving, still in talk with his friend, climbed aboard the car. "What did I tell you!" said Ann. "He won't think of it till we come into the station."

Suddenly he started up. "Ann! Do you know what I've done? I've left my bag on the platform!"

With all his gentleness and absent-minded dreaming he was a man of shrewd judgment, with a marvelous faculty for making profitable investments. He made money in stocks and in land—especially in land—and soon had one of the handsomest estates in Riverside, whilst I was pinching along on three thousand dollars per year. He had many friends among the money-makers, men like Barton Hepburn and Owen Young. He joined the most exclusive golf club and was on genial terms with all his wealthy neighbors. Nothing, however, interfered with his writing. He had his hours of privacy, and his capacity for closing his mind to outside impressions enabled him to compose regularly every morning.

As the time came to put my "Captain of the Gray Horse Troop" into book form, I was in doubt about a publisher. Doubleday & Page wanted it but would not meet my terms, and while I was looking about for a more enthusiastic house, Howells suggested Harper's. "They are entirely reorganized down there," he said, "and I believe they will make a success of it. You will find two fine young men in the book department, Major Leigh and Fred Duneka. I am sure they would welcome any manuscript of yours."

This suggestion led me to call on Frederick Duneka, editor-in-chief of the firm. He was a Southerner, a Kentuckian, I believe, a newspaper man who had been taken into the house along with Colonel George Harvey to represent "the Morgan interests." Major Leigh, who was at the head of the sales department, came in at the same time. Neither of them was in any sense a man of letters; but they were approachable and alert, ambitious to bring the firm back to the high position which it had so long maintained.

They not only met my terms on the book, they volunteered to feature it, and one morning, as I rode downtown on the elevated road, I was astounded to find my portrait, almost life size, posted on all the sta-

tion billboards as the author of "The Captain of the
Gray Horse Troop," Later, articles appearing in the
literary columns of the papers almost persuaded me
that my book might win a place for itself. However, I
had suffered so many disappointments in other cases
that I remained calm. The young men at Harper's
were disposed to treat me as a personality (almost as a
celebrity) of the home-grown variety, and while realizing that this acclaim was for a season only, I permitted
myself the pleasure of being dined, especially as my
wife was included in most of my invitations.

Among my many letters of commendation of this
novel came one from Roosevelt, who found it a fairly
accurate picture of Montana reservation life. He was
particularly pleased with my treatment of the army
officers involved. His approval meant much to me. To
Brander Matthews it was "a rattling good story," but
to Grinnell it was a fictional study of no great importance. The book went into several editions at once and
ultimately sold nearly one hundred thousand copies—
the largest sale I have ever had. It did more. It gave
me confidence in the future and I began to listen
to Bacheller when he urged me to buy a home in
Riverside.

In this he was reënforced by the Setons, who invited
us to one of the pleasantest of our New Year parties,
a housewarming given at "Wyndygoul," their new
home in Cos Cob. Ernest had bought a large tract of
alternating wooded ridges and swamps, and had built
a quaint cottage on a rock overlooking a pond which he
had enlarged by damming a stream. On this pond he
had put wild geese, ducks, and other birds, and on his

estate, protected by a high fence, he had assembled various small animals. It was precisely the kind of "rancho" a man of his interests would create and enjoy, but the company that night was not all of his kind. Lloyd Osbourne, Richard Le Gallienne, and Emery Pottle were more at home on upper Broadway than in a forest, but Carl Lumholz, Mary Fanton, and I were a little nearer to an understanding of Seton's Western enthusiasm. I recall working with him at the job of making a tepee out of a sun-smit Sibley tent and after we had it up in the front yard, he made a fire by twirling two sticks, in primitive fashion, and so dedicated its fireplace to the red god of hospitality.

He was like a boy in his zest for every symbol of wilderness life and would have enjoyed eating his dinner in the tent, but all his guests, including myself, were disposed to hug the chimney indoors. We preferred to sit at a pretty table laden with the best of things to eat, and as I look back upon this scene, at those heads untouched by gray, and hear again the laughter— But there! I will not dwell upon that, and to offset this moment of sadness, I will set down something which our young hostess never knew.

My wife and I left the party at midnight (the piano and the tom-tom were still sounding) and as we climbed the stairs at the northeast corner of the house, a keen wind was blowing and the air of our chamber was already near to frost. No doubt the bedding had been carefully apportioned among the guests, but that we needed more covering was plain. In the hall just outside our door lay a lovely white fur rug, and this, in spite of my wife's protest, I planned to appropriate. As soon as the house had quieted down I opened the door, caught this rug by the tail, and snatched it in.

It proved a grateful addition to our covering, but I slept uneasily. "I will awake early and restore it before the maids are astir," I promised my wife, and at the first hint of dawn I arose and carefully relaid the rug in the icy hall. So far as I know, our hostess remained ignorant of our sufferings and my heinous social crime.

Lloyd Osbourne's boyish delight in New York, so typical of Western visitors, amused me greatly. He had but recently arrived from California and was frankly rejoicing in his good fortune. "The city is so big, so complicated, and so surprising," he explained. "One can discover new worlds every day. I never open my mail without a feeling of excitement. Something happens to me every hour. There is always an invitation, a bit of news, or a story in my box."

In this statement, which was far more graceful and adroit than I could record it, there was a most significant distinction. New York was our only great city— the others were towns, just as Birmingham, Manchester, and Edinburgh are towns, small and limited in comparison with London. Each time I returned to Chicago I felt the smallness of the literary colony, and the paucity of its social and esthetic enterprises. Its lack of surprise, of complication, led to a dull routine compared with life in New York with its hundreds of concerts, lectures, plays, exhibitions, dinners, receptions, and innumerable publications recording them. Any other city was a town. Day by day this complexity, this implication of literary and esthetic life, intensified. Whitman's Manhattan had become the national center of our arts and letters. I looked upon my career in Boston and Chicago as a day of small things. Later with Macmillan's and Harper's both working to advance the sale of my books, I assumed an air of success—except when in the presence of Seton, Bacheller, and others of my really successful friends.

One night my wife and I dined with a magazine editor, Miss Duncan, a dinner which deserves mention, for it had far-reaching consequences. I went rather reluctantly, for I was tired. "They are all strangers to me," I said, "and I shall have a poor time of it."

Ellery Sedgwick was one of the guests, and in some way the talk fell upon spiritualism; and when he learned that I had enjoyed much experience as an investigator, he and one or two other guests plied me with questions (as I argued afterward), and when we came away just after eleven, I said to my wife, "Well! It was a very pleasant evening, after all. I quite enjoyed myself."

"You ought to be pleased," she responded with ironical intonation. "You talked every minute of the time."

A delightful dinner with Marian and Edward MacDowell came to us a few days later. It was to have been an Italian dinner of which Edward MacDowell was the cook; but for some reason the spaghetti refused to soften, and to eat the slippery tubes was beyond our most heroic efforts. However, our host was so comical in his comment upon his failure that we were rather glad of it. It led him to talk of his life in Switzerland and of his return to Boston. "I made my first appearance in Music Hall in a purple ten-dollar suit," he confessed.

"I saw you," I replied. "I heard you play that afternoon, and it seemed to me you stood on the highest pinnacle of earthly fame."

He chuckled. "I hadn't a dollar—and no other engagements in prospect."

"I had only a half-dollar, and I used that to buy a standee ticket to your concert."

That evening with the MacDowells was a small tempest of laughing comment and droll debate, for they were both widely informed on books and plays, and their judgments were swift and searching. There was something cosmopolitan in Edward's attitude toward American music, although his compositions were more and more of the New World and his desire to express it more and more definite. He never lingered on any topic, but his brief remarks had in them something which struck fire. His music was increasingly American and yet retained the quality of the Celt. He was Scotch-Irish in subconscious inheritance.

Another of the homes to which we went with perfect understanding was that of Albert Shaw, whose editorship of the *Review of Reviews* had made him one of the most valuable of our citizens. He, too, was a Middle Westerner, remotely from Iowa, a tall, handsome, genial man of forty. His house was at Hastings-on-Hudson, a spacious mansion in pleasant grounds, a place of books and generous hospitality. He had already reached a high place in American journalism. Beginning as an assistant editor to William Stead of the English *Review of Reviews,* he had risen to the point of taking over the American edition, of which he had made a great and powerful national organ.

He was a great talker—not because of any egotism but out of the fullness of his knowledge. His mind was encyclopedic in its scope, especially on political and economic subjects, and as he talked he twisted his watch chain unceasingly, looking down upon his hearer with watchful, appraising glance. He was one of the happiest of our friends. With a loyal wife, a beautiful little son, a lovely home, a prosperous business, and a large circle of admirers, he seemed ideally successful. "He has made his own way by tact, courage, and keen intelligence. His influence is on the side of every good work," was my tribute.

On our return to the city, the following day, Sunday, we called upon the poet Stedman in his queer little apartment at the Westminster Hotel. We found him in high spirits—quite frisky in truth—and surrounded by a miscellaneous throng of admirers, mostly elderly women, to whom he was talking in a rambling, disjointed fashion, moving restlessly about and touching briefly on all sorts of literary subjects. My comment is revealing: "He has never been careful of his invitations and I was rather bored and depressed by his guests. He spoke most feelingly of Howells, calling him 'the best American since Lincoln': a judgment which surprised me—coming from him. There was an element of pathos in his confinement in this mean little hired apartment. After having seen him in the space and comfort of his house in Lawrence Park, I wondered at his choice."

He was always the editor of a poetic anthology and loved to quote from classic verse. Howells, on the contrary, never quoted the words of an author either in prose or verse, although he often recalled some writer's thought. I realized that Stedman was the exponent of a passed fashion in scholarship. The younger men could not quote even if they had been minded to do so. Stedman did not quote to display scholarship, but for the reason that by doing so he retasted the joy he had once taken in delectable lines.

In dining with Mr. and Mrs. August Lewis, I renewed acquaintance with William Lloyd Garrison, a distinguished gray-haired man with one crippled hand and a face scarred in a railway accident. He had just returned from Philadelphia, where he had made a public address protesting against the exclusion of the Chinese —quite in the temper of his renowned abolitionist father, and I could not avoid the thought that he was consciously and laboriously living up to his inheritance. There was something admirable in this devotion; but as he went on I found it irritating as well as pathetic. He was very Boston in manner, gentle but "sot"—very firmly so, and always the reformer.

"January 17. Frank Norris looking very handsome— but not as strong and ruddy as he should be—lunched with me at the club, and as we walked away up the street together, I found myself quite overshadowed by his graceful figure and pale, clear-cut features. He was wearing a wide hat and his wonderful eyes glowed beneath its rim with dusky fire. He is the most impressive of all our young writers. There is something fine and sweet and boyish about him. He is in the full tide of his powers and all his friends predict a swift success.

"At dinner with Harry George a few days later, a

certain Mr. Meeker with a frontal development somewhat like Arthur Brisbane's, told us a great deal about
Tesla, the inventor. 'He is a gloomy man, subject to fits
of despondency. He believes that messages from a very
great distance came to him while experimenting on
Pike's Peak. He thinks they may have come from as far
away as Mars.' How good a basis Meeker has for this
characterization of Tesla I do not know; but he deepened the mystery which surrounds all of Tesla's work.
Some people consider him a great genius, others think
him mad."

One day George W. Cable, Gilbert Parker, James
Creelman, George Riggs, and I made up a luncheon
party at the Players and a most interesting hour resulted. Gilbert Parker was the guest of honor and the
talk was notably good. At one time, for some unexplained reason, the discussion turned upon the life and
character of "Boss" Croker, and Creelman and Parker
both related most amusing stories of the famous Tammany chief. Parker told of a conversation in which the
Boss described the beginning of his career. "He said:
'I'd been to a parley in a neighborhood saloon, and
when I got home I found the door locked, but my
father had left a window open. As I crawled in and
crept upstairs, I heard dad say, "Dick wants to be a
policeman; but with such habits as he's got he never'll
get as far as *see*lectman." As I sat on the edge of my
bed pulling off my socks, I said, "By Got! I'll be *see*lectman and I'll be alderman 'fore I die"—and by Got I
done it—and the first thing I done I give the old man
a job!' "

Creelman, whose work as writer on the *World* gave

him wide knowledge of journalism, discussed W. R. Hearst and his effect on American journalism. "When he first came to New York, he went for a walk on the East Side, and as he mingled with the Jewish, Italian, and Irish throngs he said, 'I cast my lot with these people. They have no representative—I'll print a paper for them. I'll be their advocate'—a resolution which proved a good business policy afterward."

Creelman and Parker were the star performers during the meal. Riggs, Cable, and I were the audience. Cable said less than I, but greatly enjoyed the stories. "He is such a gentle little man—he couldn't interrupt any one."

Howells, who was loath to appear on any platform in any capacity, and especially poor as a presiding officer, was president of the National Institute and reluctantly took the chair at our annual dinner on the 24th of January. He looked old and sad that night, tragically sad it seemed to me, so instant in humor he had been during all the years of our acquaintance. Stedman also looked his age. In truth nearly every man present was gray-haired. Hopkinson Smith was almost white—so was Cable; only Brander Matthews remained much the same as when I first saw him. Edward MacDowell and I were the youngest men in the room and we were not so very young, even by contrast. "I cannot claim to be one of the younger writers any longer," I said to him, and with a chuckle he replied, "Nor I to being a promising young composer."

Bliss Carman was there, silent as an owl, but his wide smile showed enjoyment in every good joke. "He is a queer old chap. He wears his hair sawed off square just above his ears, and his big scows of shoes have no heels. He affects a tie which resembles a black stock and reminds me of Emerson and Bronson Alcott. I believe in being independent in dress—when it is becoming— but Carman is a bit freakish. He is a fine character, nevertheless, and a real poet. I am willing to accept his peculiar dress as a part of his personality."

"January 30. Lunching at the club to-day I met two of our leading sculptors, Augustus St. Gaudens and Frederick MacMonnies, who have recently returned from Paris. MacMonnies said, 'I've been abroad seventeen years,' and added, 'I've come back to stay.' His attitude, like that of St. Gaudens, marks a significant shift of center in our artistic world. Their return indicates that our esthetic dependence upon France is nearly over, but how absolute it has been for nearly half a century—especially in painting."

St. Gaudens spoke of Lorado Taft's work in Chicago with appreciation; but MacMonnies bitterly opposed schools of art. "They foster mediocrity," he argued. "To cultivate taste in citizens is admirable, but to turn loose on the public a horde of young persons who imagine they are artists is bad. I don't believe in artistic philanthropy such as Taft practices."

There was something cogent in his reasoning, but I had to confess that I sometimes encouraged young writers. "Once in a while I find my efforts rewarded."

"About once in a thousand cases," he rejoined savagely.

One of the thousand who turned up that very day— a slender, graceful, gray-eyed young fellow from Michigan—was Stewart Edward White, whose novel, "The Blazed Trail," had aroused my enthusiasm. He approached me modestly, a hesitant look on his face, and after speaking of my stories most pleasingly, said, "I look up to you as a veteran."

"I don't quite like that," I replied. "As a man of forty-two, I still count myself among 'the younger writers.'"

As we talked, I found that it was my skill as a trailer which had first aroused his interest and thereafter we discussed pack trains and Alaskan outfits. He told me that his father had been a Michigan lumberman. "I gained my knowledge of lumbering from firsthand observation," he said.

I liked him, and set him alongside Frank Norris as one of the most promising of our hinterland authors. He spent but little time in New York City, however.

"To-day at Stedman's I met Emily Dickinson, a tall, slender, graceful creature in a very smart gown. She turned out to be a long-time acquaintance of Richard Burton, and on the basis of this mutual friendship we reached an almost instant understanding. She professed to like some of my writing and I could honestly reciprocate. I admire her singularly concise verse. Her work is related to Emerson, but must not be counted a poor relation."

One night at a dinner in the studio of William Ordway Partridge, who was sometimes called "the literary sculptor," the question, "Can a democratic art arise?" was debated. The Rev. Thomas Slicer presided genially, while such diverse personalities as John Dewitt Warner, Frederick Dielman, Recorder Goff, and Edwin Markham spoke. The accusation that America as a great democratic nation had made art a fad, an aristocratic plaything rather than a necessity of common life, was sustained; also that we were about to enter upon a new and very vital period of painting, sculpture, and authorship.

My record reads: "To my way of thinking, however, all this is a weak echo of Tolstoy, and I do not agree with it. As a believer in an aristocracy of mind, of character, and of will, I have no faith in the taste of the working man; there is nothing sacred in his judgment on art and literature. To me some of the speakers confused the esthetic with the economic. Democratic art is poor art—the dime novel, for example, or the comic sections of the daily press. Some of the arguments produced in me a feeling of sadness as well as of irritation. They were so well meaning and so futile! 'What we need is more attention to the masters and less regard for the mob,' was my own contention. 'The Hearst newspapers are addressing the mob; our duty as artists is to raise the level of craftsmanship instead of lowering it. We should be democratic in our sympathies, but aristocratic in our art.'

"Partridge is held to be too much the writer, the advocate, to be a great sculptor, and in this he is the antithesis of MacMonnies, who has no vital interest outside his art. Perhaps this idea of austere artistic devotion is a convention. Men like Lorado Taft and Daniel French carry forward civic interest without losing caste as sculptors, although in Taft's case there is undoubtedly a loss in concentration of effort. However, what he loses on one side he gains on the other."

III

This studio discussion came back to me the next day as I was on my way to Chicago, for I read—or rather reread (after many years) Howells' "Undiscovered Country," finding it a book of power notwithstanding its quiet conversational method. "He has gained in artistry, in finish, and in breadth of outlook since this story was written, but it remains, notwithstanding, a masterly book. The principal characters are beautifully and subtly presented. No man is more of the democrat in his economic theories than Howells, but his art is finely, exquisitely aristocratic. He sympathizes with the mob, but he never writes for it. A man's wealth or poverty does not define his taste. Many of his readers are so poor that they cannot buy his books, but they are intellectual aristocrats nevertheless."

Lorado Taft was democratically wielding a hammer as I came into his studio, and as he went on mending some packing cases, I spoke of Partridge and the meeting in his studio. As an intellectual aristocrat he agreed with me, but wanted art to "serve the people." Here again I argued that serving the people was the business of economics and that we should not mix our art with our political economy.

From this discussion we went over to the Art Institute Café and there ate a very democratic (and very bad) lunch, surrounded by artists of slender incomes and equally slender talents. It was all homely and familiar, but not inspirational. I thought of MacMonnies' blunt charge that such schools fostered the mediocre in art. "But then," I argued, "Chicago is on the border of the art world and its teachers, in cultivating a taste for the beautiful, whatever the proportion of creative artists in their classes, are doing missionary work. No doubt Paris similarly looks upon New York schools and artists as provincial. To the artists of France, New York is on the borderland and Chicago a lodge in the wilderness."

CHAPTER EIGHT

RENAMING THE RED PEOPLE

I

I⊤ chanced that on my return to New York I arrived about nightfall, and as I rode across the river on the bow of the ferryboat the looming masses of mist-hid buildings on the island and the golden lights sparkling high in the air created the impression of a town on a mountainside. "How beautiful the city is!" I exclaimed. "And it must grow more and more beautiful as our builders come to a sense of its marvelous position here on a great ridge looking out over a majestic bay." I forgot, at the moment, the rows of shabby, sordid shops and crowded tenements. The mantle of dusk and distance covered them.

There was no escaping the question of democracy in art, for almost immediately, at a dinner given by Howard Mansfield in honor of Frederick MacMonnies, I sat with E. C. Stedman, Russell Sturgis, Edward MacDowell, and John La Farge—all aristocrats in their way, as young William H. Vanderbilt and Robert de Forest were in their way—conferring on the plan for establishing an American Academy in Rome. "There was nothing democratic about this. If yellow newspapers represent 'the pee-pul,' none of the men at that dinner were democrats. How I came to be included

in the group I never knew, for I was not an advocate of
the project. I suspect my invitation came through
MacDowell, who is a prime mover in the enterprise, a
director, I believe. Just what he expects to accomplish
I did not discover. Surely it would not tend to make
our composers more American."

My first talk with Augustus St. Gaudens came next
day, and I was deeply impressed with his austere yet
sincere character. It was hard to associate him with
either shoe-making or cameo-carving—for he, whatever his beginnings, had become an esthetic aristocrat.
My comment reads: "Less youthful in all ways than
MacMonnies, he is a reflective, self-centered, big man—
a man capable of patriotism in art and large enough to
meet his fellow sculptors without jealousy. He is one
of a circle meeting often at the Players—Twachtman,
Simmons, Reid Metcalfe, and Remington, a noisy
crowd—but he seldom laughs and never argues. So far
as my observation goes, he sits among them tolerantly,
drinking but sparingly, his strange, long, rough-hewn
face gray and immobile as a granite mask. Now and
again he smiles at some remark or when the controversy rises into clamor; but is always on the edge of
the group. European in the breadth of his knowledge,
he is essentially American in his sympathies. . . . I am
starting to rewrite 'The Spirit of Sweet-Water,' restoring the first part of the story which Bok left out when
printing it in the *Ladies' Home Journal*. I am also restoring the original title, 'Witches' Gold.' It will make
a small novel and Doubleday will bring it out with
illustrations. . . .

"My wife and I had much pleasure to-day, February

26th, in helping Jeanette Norris celebrate her husband's birthday. Three weeks ago she gave birth to a little Jeanette—yet here she was, sitting at the head of her table, gay and blooming. Such maternity seems a rational part of life. She had bought a beautiful new desk for Frank and had photographed him seated proudly before it. We claimed (and obtained) a copy of this picture as a souvenir of the dinner. 'Life is coming to harvest with Norris,' I said to my wife as we came away. 'He deserves all that has come or may come to enrich him.'"

One of my wife's most admired friends was Mrs. John P. Jones, and through her I came to know her husband, ex-Senator Jones of Nevada, who knew and loved General Grant. The Jones family lived in a huge but rather old-fashioned apartment in Fifty-seventh Street, and there we occasionally dined. The senator had been a miner in his youth, and still retained many of the miner's prejudices. In the midst of his beautifully ordered household he held to a diet of beans and bacon, and this rude dish was brought to his end of the table by the butler. He was a most entertaining host and told me many interesting stories of Grant whose memory he revered. "He used to come to my house in Washington almost every Sunday and play 'Boston,'" he said, "the most unassuming man in the capital."

Jones' life had been a series of adventures and in his opinion coincidence had ruled it. His rise to wealth was an incredible "happening," but then he belonged to an incredible group in an incredible age—a group which included Fair, Crocker, Huntington, and Hearst—pioneers, miners, and city builders. Some called them "rob-bers," others "exploiting capitalists"; but no one called them small. To Jones they were all grand figures, giants in brain and brawn, and perhaps he was right. It is not easy to imagine California without them.

One afternoon a tall, gray-haired man of sixty or more came into my hotel and said, "I am Will Carleton."

Will Carleton! I was astounded. He had been a renowned figure in my school days in Iowa. His poems, "Over the Hill to the Poorhouse" and "Betsy and I Are Out," were known to every household. I used to recite them to my father and mother, who felt in them something very true and very moving; but I had not seen the author's name in print for so long that I thought of him in the past. I believed him dead, yet here he stood, heavy and old and gray, a faded, diminished literary figure of whom no one took account. He told me that he was living in Brooklyn; and though he appeared a man of small income he was not shabby, and his tone, while sad, was not bitter. He soon won my regard.

"He is a noble nature, sincere and hearty and wholesome. After all, his verse was a pioneer product, right in feeling, however crude in expression. As he talked, his books came back to me, bringing memories of 'Petroleum V. Nasby,' 'Mrs. Partington,' and 'Josh Billings,'—all very appealing to me at that time. How far we have come from the days when such men were great figures, and the *Toledo Blade* a literary messenger!"

Another somewhat later phase of my life was brought back to me at a dinner given in my honor by the Manhattan Single-Tax Club in the Marlborough Hotel. I appreciated the compliment conveyed, but found my-self quite out of key with most of the speaking, which was rather poor and peppered with all the well-worn phrases of anti-poverty propaganda. Any cause, no matter how noble in its beginning, comes inevitably to a stage where its catchwords and worn phrases are wearisome, and our tax crusade had entered that phase. Believing quite as firmly as ever in the principle of taxation so eloquently advanced by Henry George, I had lost my proselyting zeal. The dinner was a pleas-ant but rather futile affair. I felt like a man receiving compliments for something he had never accomplished.

Irving Bacheller, handsome, genial, and eloquent, was there and helped make the dinner notable. Harry George represented his father and made humorous allu-sions to my soap-box experiences on Boston Common and elsewhere. But these experiences were all receding swiftly and I found little in common with these strenu-ous comrades to whom my writing is equally unimpor-tant and remote. "Every step I have taken into the realm of literature was a step away from the world in which they lived and wrought."

On March 17th I received the advance copy of "The Captain of the Gray Horse Troop," and as the reviews came in found myself in greater favor with the critics than I had ever hoped to be. "Although this novel is somewhat controversial (dealing as it does with the Cheyennes in their 'outbreak' in 1897), it is meeting with almost universal praise even by those who have been most bitter in condemning all my earlier books. Photographers, reporters, and magazine editors unite in assuring me that I am no longer an obscure and struggling author—and yet these expressions are only partial in their effect. I have grown accustomed to dispraise—and this sunshine troubles me by its warmth. It is like the kind of day my father used to call a 'weather breeder,' by which he meant a precursor of storms." However, as a husband and householder, I persuaded myself to credit and to enjoy this welcome on the part of those who had been my most caustic critics.

One of the first to receive an autographed copy of this book was Howells. As I had shared my troubles with him, so now I hastened to let him see my "Captain"; and as Lorado Taft chanced to be in town, I took him with me, for he had long admired the great novelist. "We found him in his library just returned from a trip down the Ohio River to his boyhood home. He liked Taft and talked to him with unusual copious flow. I had never seen him so animated. His return to early scenes had moved him and stimulated him. He was fairly jocund, and Lorado, who has his own piquancy of phrase, stimulated him to more than usual comedy of action. He laughed heartily at some of the sculptor's sallies, causing me to regret my own lumbering gravity. 'I wish I could make him laugh like that,' I thought as I listened to his chuckles."

To Roosevelt went one of the first six copies of the book and his comment upon it was highly favorable. He knew my country, he knew the red people and was broad-minded enough to grant my contention that these men of the Stone Age had their rights and that they were not to be exterminated by greedy cattlemen.

One night soon after this my wife and I again dined with the MacDowells—and as we were ushered into the big music room which overlooked Central Park, we found Edward leaning far out of the window, brooding in black despair (as we afterward learned) upon the city. Upon seeing us, his smile broke out like sunshine and we had a merry evening. Nevertheless all through our merriment I retained a feeling that he was contemplating something desperate as he hung over the windowsill.

II

As the time came to leave New York for Chicago, I bought tickets by way of Philadelphia, with an overnight stop to visit Edward and Mary Bok whose interest in us remained keen. They were like members of our family, fortunate and happy relatives. We talked much of Kipling with whom Bok had once crossed the ocean. Edward said, "One day as I was lying in my steamer chair reading 'The Brushwood Boy,' Rudyard came up behind me with a roll of wet newspaper and gave me a fearful swat. 'Put that book down,' he said. I was hurt and disgusted. 'That was a bad boy's trick,' I remarked. I was hot, and when he saw that I meant it, he sat down beside me and tried to make me forget it. He apologized and then explained the genesis of the book. 'I was seven years writing that story,' he said, 'and it represents my own life—in a way.' He offered to read it aloud to me as compensation for his cruel swat, and in the end I forgave him. I loved him. But I was always careful when touching on English politics. He was savage in his defense of the British Empire. He is a stern youth, but streaked with gentleness all through; a big boy in some ways and a prodigious genius in others.

Think of his giving an old friend a nasty swat like that! It was a mean trick—utterly inexcusable—as he realized a moment later."

Bok was another singularly successful and happy man—in a class with Albert Shaw. He had a lovely wife, a beautiful home, a great and growing magazine, and a host of friends—all of which was indisputably his due. He had won his position by his industry and on his merit. He was a mere underling at *Scribner's* when Curtis took him on; now he was a chieftain in his own right. No one could be more American than he, and yet he retained a tender spot in his heart for Holland, his mother country. Of this I had curious proof. In one of my stories, a character, speaking of a German neighbor, called him "that Dutchman." Bok on reading this said, "Change that. I won't have you call a German a Dutchman."

I tried to explain that the phrase was spoken by one of my characters. "No matter, I won't print it," he retorted, and I gave way. He was jealous of the honor of his native land and I respected him for it, even when his jealousy seemed unjustified.

"March 29. On reaching Washington I called at once on the President, who received me for a few moments and asked me to come back at nine in the evening. This I did. Senator Hanna was in the anteroom as I came in and we waited together for a few minutes. At last the President sent for me to come in, and with a humorous twist of his lips, remarked, 'A senator is supposed to rank a Western novelist and so I shall see Hanna first. Be good enough to wait—and come in after he goes.' He then said something which I cannot precisely recall, but his meaning was perfectly clear. He does not take Senator Hanna at the current valuation, and is in no danger of being dominated by him—a reflection which pleases me."

After Hanna left, I went in and we had a half-hour talk on trailing, fiction, and other nonpolitical subjects. I think he enjoyed my calling for the reason that I never asked him for anything and never talked politics.

He spoke in praise of my "Captain of the Gray Horse Troop," and particularly commended my treatment of the army officers in their attitude toward the Cheyennes. "But you've changed your attitude toward the pioneer," he said with a chuckle. "You now see that these advance men of our civilization were a grim lot— necessarily. I tried to make that clear in my 'Winning of the West.' Poets and artists are not much good fighting mosquitoes, snakes, and savages. It took men almost as remorseless as the Algonquin to win their way across the continent."

"That's true," I replied, "but the pioneers of Wisconsin and Iowa were men of different character. They were essentially fine—like my father and my uncles."

He smiled again. "I fear you idealized them, as a boy, and you carried the concept into all your earlier stories. Now when you have become the advocate of the Sioux, your eyes are opened to the greed of the white cattleman to whom the Indian is a cumberer of the earth and should be destroyed. Your pioneers in similar case would be similarly minded."

Forced to admit the truth of his contention, I fell back upon the plea that my book was, after all, a novel and that its plot was based upon Captain Curtis' defense of the Cheyennes.

To this he agreed. "It's a good story," he said. "I am reading it with Mrs. Roosevelt."

"I don't see how you find time to read the books of your friends."

"I take time," he sharply retorted.

March 30th was a glorious spring day, and my wife and I spent most of it wandering about the capital with Senator Beveridge for a guide. "He is a boyish fellow," I wrote, "pleasantly full of his own importance and frankly rejoicing in his political power. He is only thirty-nine years of age and is naïvely confident of his future. He amused us by his insistence upon all his prerogatives as senator. Wearing a silk hat and a noble frock suit, he made the attendants 'stand around'! 'I am Senator Beveridge,' he announced to a doorman who didn't recognize him, and towered, loftily inflated, while the henchman cringed, a play which amused my wife almost to open laughter. He claimed to be 'working night and day' at his official duties, but he had oceans of time for us. With all his vanities he is a real man."

He took us to luncheon in the Senate café, and introduced us to Senators Hanna, Lodge, Hale, and others of the most renowned of his fellow lawgivers. Some of them knew me—notably Lodge of Massachusetts and Allison of Iowa—but the others looked at me quizzically as who should say, "Oh! More of Beveridge's Indiana constituents." Nevertheless they liked him and we were grateful for the courtesy intended.

(One morning long afterward, when his superb "Life

of John Marshall" had made him a member of the American Academy, President Nicholas Murray Butler called his attention to me by saying, "Beveridge, you know Garland?"

"Oh, yes," replied Beveridge with a laughing light in his eyes, "Garland and I knew each other when I was a colt with my tail over the dashboard"—an expression which indicated his country bringing-up as well as his sense of humor.)

On April 1st I again called at the White House to leave with Roosevelt a specially bound copy of "The Captain of the Gray Horse Troop." My wife accompanied me, and the President, after greeting her most cordially, asked where we were staying and how long we were to be in the city. We told him. Thereupon he said to us, "You will receive to-night an invitation to our musicale on Wednesday." Then turning to me he added, "You are interested in conservation. Come to my cabinet meeting to-morrow morning. Gifford Pinchot will be there."

Of course I seized upon this opportunity to see him in executive action; and for more than an hour I sat in the cabinet room listening to a discussion of certain land and water disputes. Pinchot's attitude delighted me. He was the gentleman and the man of independent means giving his best services to the country, somewhat as titled Englishmen do. "He is the finest type of office-holder I have ever met. As chief forester he holds one of the most advanced positions in the government—so advanced that he has the exploiters of our public lands all against him."

(This meeting turned out to be a most important

event in my literary career, for it led to ten years' study of the forest ranger and the mountain West.)

Theodore Roosevelt was to me a natural leader, an intellectual ruler, and to have won his interest and his friendship was an achievement of which I was frankly proud; and when on the morning preceding the musicale he asked me to come to his office and discuss the Indian problem with him, I responded with a feeling of surprise and some doubt of my value as a councilor. Dr. Hart Merriam was included in this conference, and for an hour we debated the red man's claim. "We must not forget, Mr. President, that these people of the Stone Age——"

"Polished Stone Age," he corrected. (What other President could have done that?)

I went on, "These people of the polished Stone Age require time to pass from their age to the age of electricity. It is a mistake to imagine that a single generation or even three can bridge the chasm. They are gregarious. To make solitary homesteaders of them is to destroy them. Their lands should be allotted in such wise that they can live as the French peasants do, in villages, and farm their outlying lands. Others of them, like the Navajo, are natural herders and should be allowed to continue as such. They must have time for adjustment."

In all this Merriam supported me. I then passed to the question of renaming them. "As you well know, Mr. President, the names by which these people are known to the whites are, for the most part, bungling translations made by ignorant interpreters or by contemptuous whites. Some of the finest and most dignified chieftains I know are burdened with names like 'Tail Feather's Coming,' or 'Scabby Horse'! My suggestion is that we ask each group to choose a family name of their own—just as if they were Russians, Italians, or any other foreign people; and then give each member of the family a distinctive name. Instead of calling them 'Grover Cleveland' and 'Robert Burns,' as the missionary school-teachers now do, we should define their relationships. Furthermore, it is necessary for legal reasons that these relationships be shown, for many of these people now own valuable lands and other property."

Roosevelt listened to me in silence as I outlined my plan. At the close of my address, he took a small card from his desk and penciled a few words upon it. "See the Secretary of the Interior," he said, handing me the card, "and lay your plan before him." And as we rose to go he added, "I know the Indian service is cursed with bad agents and inefficient department heads, but I intend to see that the red man gets substantial justice. You may depend on my coöperation."

With his card in my pocket I went at once to call upon the Secretary of the Interior. He received me in silence and without rising, and his tone was that of a tired, worried business man. I was a little irritated by his attitude. "Here is a card from the President," I said and handed it to him. The change worked by that slip of pasteboard was amazing! It was a very small card with only a few words penciled upon it, but it brought that official to his feet with its magic. In the simplicity of my unofficial thinking, I had considered it merely an introduction to the secretary, but he considered it an order. I was for the moment the personal representative of President Roosevelt. I owned the office from that time forward.

After I had outlined my plan for restoring the tribal names of the red allottees, the secretary took me to the Commissioner of Indian Affairs and said, "Mr. Garland comes with a mandate from President Roosevelt. Coöperate with him in every way possible."

The commissioner listened to me while for the third time I outlined my complaint and my plan. "These red people have the same right to their characteristic names as any other of our citizens. They should not be nicknamed. The one thing we must insist upon is that they take family names so that relationship will be indicated. At present three brothers are called, 'White Shield,' 'Brave Bear,' and 'Red Eagle,' with nothing to show their connection. So far as possible their own musical personal names should be retained and a family name adopted. In this I have the agreement of the President. The worst feature of the situation is that the lands have been allotted to almost all of our remaining red men and they appear on the rolls with silly or disgusting translations of their proper names. It should be possible, however, to apply the white man's system to those tribes whose lands are still held in common."

The outcome of this conference was not entirely to my liking. The commissioner said, "You must compose a circular which can be used as a guide to the agents, teachers, and interpreters."

Being in so far, I could not refuse to go farther in the matter. I went through with it. I not only designed such a leaflet with sample family and personal names; I also asked the President to appoint Dr. Charles Eastman, a well-known Sioux, as a special worker to see that our plan should be carried out so far as the rolls would permit. To this Roosevelt agreed, and Eastman went among his people and worked for two years along the lines laid down by my circular.

However, the plan received but half-hearted support on the part of the officials in the field, and only a partial application of it was ever made. The custom of giving one man a fanciful name like "Red Cloud" and his brother a disgusting one like "Scabby Back Bull" persisted, leaving relationships undefined; so that endless confusion and litigation have followed and will grow worse as time goes on. On the school rolls some attempt to indicate family ties was made by the use of such names as "James Red Horse" and "Jennie Red Horse," brother and sister; but their mother remains "Yellow Leaf" or "Blowing Cloud."

(The following letter from Franklin K. Lane in April, 1913, indicates how the plan faded out into a routine and futile gesture: "The plan has, as you say, never been fully carried out, but the difficulties in the way should be borne in mind. Under the instructions of the circular to which you allude, this work has so far been left chiefly to the superintendents of the various schools, and it appears probable that, in the press of other duties, this matter has been somewhat overlooked. Your offer of coöperation is appreciated, and any suggestions from you will be considered.")

III

On the night following my afternoon in the office of the Commissioner of Indian Affairs, my wife and I were present at a musicale in the White House. We met many of our friends there. Some of them had come from New York City to meet the President and to hear Paderewski play the piano. Mrs. Roosevelt delighted us all by her grace and air of modest self-possession. She and the President mingled with their guests with the unassuming dignity which was their habit at Sagamore Hill.

When I clasped hands with Paderewski, he lifted my huge paw and studied it closely. "What strength! What breadth!" he said.

"Yes," I replied, "it was broadened by the spade and the plow."

I don't know how much he understood of my reply, but if he had known that many of his distinguished auditors were sons and daughters of farmers or mechanics, it might have cheapened them in his estimation. Not knowing this, he was tremendously impressed by his surroundings. To him it was a hearing at court— and surely he could not have failed to admire the bearing of his host and hostess. They were natural aristocrats. He was at his best that night, at the height of his fame and in the fullness of his powers. I never afterward heard him play with equal brilliancy. Inspired by his surroundings and his audience, he was almost magical in effect.

(In these later days as I see his picture—that of a gray-haired old man striving to rebuild his shattered

country—I think of him as he was that night, his shock
of tawny hair radiating electrical flames, while his
broad, white hands compelled the rigid ivory keys to
sing!)

This was a high point in my own career. I was happily married, my latest book was being acclaimed
beyond all my hopes, I was at the White House as a
personal friend of the President, and surrounded by
those who accepted me as one of the elect—and yet
when brought down to the hard, cold measurement of
the dollar, my success was illusory. My wife and I
lodged in a small suite of rooms in an obscure hotel,
and on the following day returned to our humble home
in Chicago. I am certain Roosevelt never knew how
slender my income really was. It wouldn't have changed
his attitude toward me if he had realized my poverty—
unless to make him still more considerate of me.

His liking for my "Captain of the Gray Horse
Troop" went far to compensate me for its relatively
small sales. Although the most successful of all my
books, its sales were meager compared to those of
"Eben Holden." Fifty thousand copies of a book scattered among one hundred million people is, after all,
a rather pitiful showing. However, I had a vague hope,
that night, that it might be more widely accepted than
any of my previous books; and in that hope I continued, for a year or more, to live. It is still selling after
nearly thirty years.

CHAPTER NINE

COLONEL LOWDEN'S CHALLENGE

I

FROM my meetings with President Roosevelt in the executive chamber, and my work as his special commissioner, and from a musical evening in the East Room of the White House, I descended with an awakening jolt to the prosaic level of my routine in Chicago. In New York I felt myself to be a man of letters, in Washington, an officer of the government, but in Chicago I was just another literary pioneer.

Oklahoma was calling me, and in my diary I find this entry: "April 8, 1902. It was six o'clock of a cold, cloudy morning when I alighted from the train at Fort Reno and started to walk to the agency some two miles across the prairie. I had not gone far when I heard a loud coughing behind me. Looking around, I perceived a large, good-humored half-breed Cheyenne hustling along as if to overtake me. On drawing near he began to talk. Although evidently somewhat inebriated, he was clear-headed and good-natured. Keeping close to my side—too close to please me—he went on to ask if I was a friend of the agent, and when I replied that I was, he said, 'Hagent good man but he cut rations too soon. Injun go hungry.'

"As I passed through the sleeping village, I observed

a woman building a fire beside her tepee and caught the pleasant smell of baking bread. Mongrel dogs sniffed and snarled at my heels, and at the moment Washington and the White House seemed ten thousand miles away. However, as I am to consult with Major Stouch and Captain Seger concerning the renaming of the red man, my presence here is not illogical."

I ate my breakfast at a wretched little hotel in company with several half-breed employees of the agency and two full-blood Cheyennes. The food was not so bad, but the rooms were unswept and the walls grimy. "How hopeless it all is! I do not wonder that missionaries and agents fail to maintain standards. Stouch is doing his best, but there is so much to do.

"April 10. Seger's Colony. This day was a record rain-maker. Hiring a saddle horse this morning I set out to visit my new farm. The rain fell in torrents; and as I sought shelter with my tenant, a typical poor white, I found him without sufficient food for himself, so I went on to the next house (almost as barren and ugly), which offered shelter from the storm, but no food. At last in despair of a clear sky I set out in a wild gallop toward the colony. All the ravines were belly-deep in water, and twice sudden showers forced me to dash into roadside barns for shelter. Eventually I reached Seger's fire, wet, weary, and hungry. However, I am not discouraged—on the contrary, I shall buy more land."

One of the objects of this trip was to urge Seger to make record of his experiences among the red people. After obtaining his consent to talk in the hearing of a shorthand reporter, I set about finding one. Knowing that he could not write his story—his spelling was unlike any other man's spelling—I thought that he might tell it to me.

"Once in type you can revise and shape it," I said.

Although disturbed by the knowledge that his words were being taken down, he talked for an hour or two each day, and in ten days I succeeded in obtaining a chronicle, more or less consecutive, of his most valuable experiences. In the intervals I rode with Neatha, his son, in search of other farms.

It was a joy to gallop over the shining prairie swells watching the green hills roll away like waves of an emerald sea. It was good to look the sun in the face and to feel the force of my horse as he drummed across the sod. Young Seger, a fine, modest young fellow, made an interesting companion. Unlearned in books, he possessed an enormous fund of knowledge of the red man. "The red children were my playmates," he said. "I was named after one of them. A brave boy he was. All my life I have been a neighbor to the Cheyennes and they are just like other folks"—and yet the department was making no use of this knowledge. My talks with him and his father carried me back into the early history of Indian territory.

Seger's memory for details was prodigious, but he had no power of construction. He could not write— and his talk was repetitious. The pile of manuscript accumulating under the hand of the typewriter was a confused mass of raw material, valuable only for its historical data. At the end of my stay I turned over to him the carbon copy of this manuscript, but kept the first copy with intent to help him put his book into readable shape. "I will find a publisher for it if I can," I said.

On the last day of my stay, I acknowledged a reluctance to start North. "Last night was marvelous—so still, so absolutely dreamlike was its silence and its beauty. The moonlight lay upon the ground like a flood of liquid pearls, and when I turned my face upward, a subtle essence seemed falling from the sky in cataracts of radiant fire. I cannot tell why these nights should seem so magical. There is something exotic in them. The soft air is Southern, the bird songs Southern."

Two days later I witnessed a display of the fury of this climate. "I am on the train riding east from El Reno. A furious wind is blowing, a powerful, relentless-sounding wind from the south; a wind that screams at the windows of the train, uproots the grain in the fields, and fills the air with dust—a wind which withers and destroys. The sound of it, so sinister, so foreboding, so relentless, brings back to me a thousand remembered sorrows, and suggests the sure approach of other ills. The Indian tepees stand unmoved amid the blinding clouds of dirt—it is unaccountable, but they do! The spring-sown lands are gray with dust. No man is abroad. The train drives on like a ship in the grasp of a hurricane—a merciless, all-invading, destroying tempest. It is incredible that I should have been enchanted last night by a moonlit landscape. Such are the moods of the plain."

As I ran over this manuscript of Seger's talks I was repelled by its lack of cohesion. It was a confused tangle of valuable material. I saw that to make it acceptable to an editor I must rewrite it and I could not afford to give the necessary time. There could be no great sale for it even though I gave a year to it and

I was already started on another novel of Colorado. I wrote all this to Seger and urged him to take it up with Neatha and comb out the tangles in it. This he promised, over and over, to do, but alas! Each year made the job more difficult. With his consent I used a few of the incidents as suggestions for short stories, but the huge manuscript still lies in my desk awaiting the man or woman with time and patience to untangle its lines and give sequence to its pages.

As compensation for the suggestions he gave me, I bought a farm and helped him make a home upon it after the department had dropped him from its rolls. He wished to live near the colony he had founded and I did my best to have him retained as teacher of farm-ing—a position in which his lack of education was not a serious handicap. For years he wrote me regularly, always saying, "I am going to take time off and go over my book," but he never did. I shall present the manu-script to some historical society. It is a most valuable mass of source material.

It was good to get back to the green serenity of Illi-nois, and to the comfort of my desk in Chicago. I had two books in my mind: one a novel dealing with the miners' war in Cripple Creek; and the other a volume of short stories in which the red people should be the chief characters. To continue my studies for both these books, I at once began to plan another summer in Colorado and Wyoming.

"The papers to-day contained news of the death of Sterling Morton of Nebraska, whom we met at Col-orado Springs last summer (and for whom we had formed a real affection), but almost coincident with the passing of this great pioneer, Mary McLane, a young woman from Montana, received ten times the space devoted to this ex-Governor of Nebraska, the friend and confidant of Grover Cleveland. Mary McLane of Butte is the latest Chicago sensation.

"April 29. In reading, 'I, Mary McLane,' the very remarkable book which Herbert Stone has just issued, I am convinced that its author is entering upon a startling career. This book will open for this girl the gates of both heaven and hell. She can take her choice. She will be deluged with exhortations and warnings along with offers of marriage and a place on the stage, but as she seems to have already declined these offers, there is nothing to be said.

"The most remarkable of her powers (to me as to Fuller) is her crisp, clear, unhesitating use of English. It is annoying to find that an unlettered young girl can write with such precision and such power. Critics are already comparing her confessions with those of Marie Bashkirtseff; but in truth this Montana maid has no need to fear the comparison. In this Fuller agrees. He said to-day, 'Mary has a remarkably firm grip on the English language. There is more in her 'yawp' than mere 'eroticism gone mad,' as some of the critics are saying."

Although I did not meet this rebellious young writer, I heard much of her from Lucy Monroe, who was at once her editor and her mentor. Fuller reported that Mary was not as insolent in personal contact as she was in print; "but she is not a shrinking fawn even in the most exclusive literary circles."

(She was not with us long. Chicago soon proved too

small for her. Moving on to New York, she flared forth in the metropolitan press in greater front-page glory. The *World,* indeed, made her a full-page celebrity for a week or two.

With something of Stephen Crane's native flair for an original choice of words, she entered New York almost at the precise time of his passing. She, too, was a genius without capability of development. One by one the editors lost interest in her, and in a few months she dropped from sight, leaving an impression of girlish audacity and not much else, a literary rocket exhausting itself in a flare of light. Her glory passed and she was left to suffer poverty and the darkness of neglect. Many years afterward I heard of her living in obscurity in Chicago, old and bitter, meditating suicide, befriended by Harriet and Lucy Monroe, who remained faithful through all her vicissitudes. To reread her insolent girlish defiance of the world as expressed in her small book, in the knowledge of her tragic failure, is to re-value her endowment.)

While in the midst of packing to leave Chicago for the summer, I saw a performance, by Anna Morgan's dramatic school, of Shaw's "Cæsar and Cleopatra," the first performance of it in America, and my impression of it now has a certain chronological value. "The play appeals to me with great power. It is one of the most original dramas of our day, so unconventional, in fact, that the ordinary hearer has no means of measuring its true value. It starts from the stump, disregarding all accepted notions of Cleopatra and Cæsar but is wonderfully human and vitally interesting—manifesting the author's wide outlook and his courage. I was delighted with its lines and with its characterizations, although a farcical 'slam' at England embodied in the character of Britannicus seemed out of place."

This was Saturday. On the Sunday following I reported the Reverend Dowie, preaching in the Auditorium, to this effect:

"I heard Elijah Dowie this afternoon. He is a queer little man of vast conceit but of undoubted power. He is bald, bearded, and of stentorian voice. His audience was a singular one, well-dressed, decorous, but weak-chinned, and wistful. To see such people sitting in the boxes and looking down over the orchestra with the glances of aristocrats is shocking. Dowie, a fiery little Scotch orator with a high, nasal voice, is not eloquent in the ordinary use of the word, but he sways his audience! He blares curses and commands like a militant monk of the Middle Ages. People call him a charlatan, but he enjoys the admiration and allegiance of many thousands of people. He has created a city—Zion City—on the north shore of Lake Michigan, over which he rules like a rajah."

The University of Chicago having again invited me to give a series of lectures, I went out to the artists' camp to prepare these addresses, taking with me the tepee which the Cheyenne women had made and blessed to my use. There was a certain appropriateness —it seemed to me—that my writing should be done in such a lodge. I therefore raised its white walls on the edge of the wood, and set to work revising a manuscript volume of essays which I had written years before with intent to use them as the basis of my lectures.

"May 13, Eagle's Nest Camp. In spite of my determination to do nothing but work on my addresses for the university, I find myself putting in a large part of each day sawing, hammering, painting, and picking up stones. My hands are worn to the quick and feel like sawdust bags. Nevertheless last evening while the Heckmans were here I read to the camp the second section of my volume of lectures. It was a little like a session of the Brook Farm Circle. The big dining room, lit by a wide fireplace, the small lamp at my elbow, the dimly seen faces of my listeners, and the occasional word of question or approval, made up a singularly impressive hour. As Charles Francis Brown said, 'Brook Farm has nothing on Eagle's Nest Camp. I am reminded of some of the chapters in the Blithedale Romance.' "

I found myself alternately admiring and deploring these essays of my earlier years. "Audacious and illogical as they are," I said to Fuller, "their meanings are never obscure. Some of my judgments must be revised —others hold their place. The dignity and truth of Bryant's verse is incontestable, but his effect is too often marred by his moralizing habit. He is American, however, a noble foundation stone in our characteristic literature."

In reading Higginson's "Life of Margaret Fuller," I found her an altogether stronger person than I had thought her. She had her impossible period, but her later comment on American writers (in 1845) is singularly clear-headed. She did not hesitate to question the oracular Emerson when time and chance served. No one writes such letters now, and they are valuable despite their high-flown phraseology. A letter with her was an epistle, penned with full intention of literary permanence. She has a special claim upon the members of this camp, for she spent a summer here and named "Ganymede Spring."

II

In response to a wire from Duneka I closed my tepee and hurried to New York to help the *Harper* editors entertain the Booksellers Association. On arrival in New York I went at once to Franklin Square, where I found Howells, Clemens, Kendrick Bangs, Edward Townsend, Robert Chambers, and several others of the Franklin Square writers prepared to welcome and amuse the merchants whom Colonel George Harvey had invited to meet us. They came at last, in procession, not unlike a political convention, each man wearing a blue badge. They attacked the champagne and sandwiches with the gusto of politicians, and a love feast followed. Harvey made a neat introduction, Howells a fine, incisive, but brief address, and Clemens followed with a very funny speech. My own was highly disappointing to me, but my auditors cheered me at the close, perhaps because I closed. I was a bit bewildered by this party. It did not seem worth the long journey I had made to share it, and it was by way of compensation perhaps that Colonel Harvey invited me to go with him down to Deal, his home on the Jersey coast.

I am free to confess that I did not at this time take Harvey as seriously as he deserved. He did not impress me as a man of letters—in fact I could not think of him as a publisher. I was told that he had come into the firm as "one of Pierpont Morgan's men," and that the arrangement was only temporary, hence I did not associate him with the literary side of the house. He came late to the office (Duneka reported him a great diner out), and so far as I could see he gave little thought to the making of books. He was, however, keenly interested in the *North American Review* and in *Harper's Weekly,* and wrote for both of them copiously and well. He appeared to know all the great financiers and many famous politicians and was nightly in their company. He was generous in his entertainment of authors—perhaps by way of publicity—but Duneka and Leigh were the actual managers with whom I came in contact.

Harvey was not my kind of a man, and on this ride down to Deal I found myself working hard to interest him. I don't think he had read a line of my "The Captain of the Gray Horse Troop," but he knew that Duneka and Leigh were featuring it, and wished to show me honor. Furthermore, as this was my first automobile ride with him, I was distraught by the reckless speed with which he ran along the crowded highways. I had less faith in him as driver than as publisher.

His home in a charming little seaside town was colonial in line—not at all imposing even to me—and Mrs. Harvey, a familiar type, was New England in manner and a kindly hostess.

In the evening Arthur Brisbane of the *New York Journal* came to call and we had much talk concerning "yellow journalism," of which he was even then a renowned representative. I had never seen him before and I was observant. "He is a smallish man with a protuberant brow and a confident tone. He talked vigorously and shockingly of the power which he claimed his

paper wielded. He said, 'We control the proletariat.'
Harvey remained unimpressed, saying dryly, 'I doubt
whether you and Hearst wield as much power as you
imagine.' I took the ground that the *Journal* could be
much better than it was and still retain its circulation,
but Brisbane laughed at the idea. He was quite frankly
the pessimist and the egoist. I had never met Hearst,
but meeting his chief editor gave me a disturbing insight into the editorial policy of the *Journal* office."

From this meeting with Brisbane and his talk of yellow journalism I returned almost at once to the artists'
camp at Eagle's Nest, and to a talk with Daniel Burnham, a great idealist, on the lawn of Colonel Frank
Lowden's noble farm at Sinissippi.

Burnham, one of the most renowned of our architects, was the opposite of Brisbane. He was a grave,
thoughtful, farseeing artist, and I rejoiced in this opportunity of becoming better acquainted with him. He
liked Lorado Taft and believed in him both as man
and sculptor; and it was due to this liking, probably,
that he opened his heart to us that day. He outlined
his grandiose design for improving the Chicago lake
front, and explained his plans for making Washington
the worthy capital of a great nation. As he talked, I
felt in him the dreamer and the poet. The breadth of
his culture was evident. "His designs are academic
rather than creative in quality, but there is something
moving in the fact that he considers us all fellow ideal-
ists, working toward the enrichment of American art.
For all his fame, his responsibility, he showed himself
companionable—a nobly serious elder brother, whose
visions we were honored to share." (Whenever I ride

down the outer drive in Grant Park to-day or pass by the portico of the station in Washington, I think of him as he showed himself to us that Sunday afternoon.)

Our neighbor, Frank Lowden, although he looked like an English earl, had been raised on a farm in Iowa and delighted to talk of it. "I am the real farmer," he declared to the artists with a smile on his handsome face and a chuckle in his voice. "Garland is a literary man making capital of it. He is the kind of farmer who brags of mowing grass in November and of corn husking in June. I'm going to make a test of his powers. I challenge him here and now to a mowing contest in my timothy field next Saturday afternoon. Now, Garland, put up or shut up," he said, turning to me.

In the proper spirit and vernacular, I replied, "Done! I'll mow the heels off you—anywhere and at any time."

The camp was greatly amused, naturally, and at once took sides, some with Lowden, more with me. They had seen me chop and saw and shingle, and while they had no proof that I could swing an old-fashioned scythe— and to tell the truth I was in some doubt myself— they had faith in my training.

On the afternoon designated, the entire camp drove down to the beautiful Rock River farm where Lowden awaited us with three sharply ground new scythes, for E. A. Potter, a Chicago banker, had been included in Lowden's defiance. Stripping for battle and with a smiling "gallery" (as they call a throng of golf onlookers), we selected our tools and took our places under command of our judges, Mrs. Potter, Mr. William Angell, and the farm superintendent. The leading position was assigned to our challenger.

It had been some years since I had wielded a scythe, but as I took in after my handsome young challenger, I kept steadily in mind my father's admonition, "Keep the heel of your scythe down." I had no time to look behind at the swath I was leaving, but the sight of Lowden's ragged path was encouraging. It was a comical series of notches. I knew I had him beaten long before I had a moment's time to look back.

"Get out of my way!" I shouted in the old-time phrase. "Clear the track or I'll trim your legs off. What's the matter with your scythe? Have you turned its edge?"

He kept gamely in the lead till he reached the end of the course, then turned and rested on his tool, while Potter and I came marching up. A glance at the three swaths convinced him. "You win!" he gallantly conceded, and when Mrs. Potter, who bore the wreath of oak leaves, placed it on my perspiring brow, he added with a humorous twist of his lips, "I should enter an appeal to a higher court; this jury is 'packed,'" but Mrs. Lowden sustained the jury's decision and took a snapshot of me proudly marching at the head of the procession.

Thereafter Lowden treated me with elaborate respect. I heard no more of "farmer—for literary purposes only."

It was all a bit of jolly comedy; but as I look back upon it now, the beauty of the meadow, the laughing faces of the spectators, the sunlit youth of it all comes back upon me with a wave of wistful sadness. The faces of those who are dust return as vividly to mind as those which I still see, grown old with the years. The present is momentarily nonexistent. In my dream I am young and skillful and my circle of friends unbroken.

III

As soon as my lectures at the university were ended, I returned to my home in Wisconsin and resumed work on my new novel, which at this time I called "The Cowboy Patrol"; for in the miners' war (which was the sociologic theme of this story) a platoon of young cow hands rode up from the ranches on the plains and volunteered to act as pickets—a most picturesque feature of the strike. Each day I relived my Colorado experiences. Wisconsin had no appeal for me at this time. "I have exhausted this field, the field in which I found 'Main-Travelled Roads' and 'Rose of Dutcher's Coolly.' In coming here to live I lost perspective on its life and characters. I must return to Colorado, to the hills whence cometh my strength," I confided to Fuller who had never seen the Rocky Mountains and who was not sympathetic with my change of base.

"August 9th. En route to Colorado. This has been a hard, hot day, but nothing like as hard and hot as last year. I read Stephen Crane's 'Active Service,' and found it lacking in interest. It is not an important book. As night fell the loud cry of locusts came in at the window along with the odor of ripened grain and grasses. Leaning from the car, I studied the plain which was profoundly impressive. A deep hush lay over it—a cool, dusky hush—and on the far horizon, lightning was silently at play. As I sensed this wonderfully peaceful and solemn hour, my boyish awe of it returned to me.

Out of its dark immensity kitchen lights shone with steady glow. I knew what those homes were like. I had lived with their owners. I granted these people a desperate heroism. I marveled at their patience, their brave cheer!"

The mountains when we came in sight of them next morning gave me a strong uplift. "They are familiar presences now," I said to my wife. "And up there under those clouds the scene of my new story is laid."

The theme of this novel had been suggested to me a year before by the fifteen-year-old son of a New York acquaintance, a slender, poetic lad who had read my books and was eager to accompany me into the West. Nothing else held for him such allurement, such promise of adventure, as the Rocky Mountains. As he pleaded with his mother to let him go, I heard his sister joining in the arguments against it, and so got my start on the story. "Imagine such a lad insisting on Colorado for a summer vacation and dragging his devoted but reluctant sister into the midst of a labor war among the clouds."

I wrote the first chapter of this story before leaving Chicago; and my summer in Colorado Springs and Cripple Creek had been planned to give me new material for the remaining chapters. My chief interest was in the free miner and prospector with whom I had camped and whose outlook was somewhat like that of my boyhood heroes in Wisconsin, resourceful, humorous, and unafraid. These old trailers scorned a union. "We can take care of ourselves," they said. To them the incoming union laborer was a poor "wop" or "dago," alien to the America they knew and loved.

"If anything irritates or oppresses you—saddle up and hit the trail to the west. The gate to the sunset is always open," they said.

Without realizing it they were making their last stand here and I hoped to put some of their poetry into my novel.

Again the Ehrichs were our hosts and in a few hours I was in touch with Russell Wray; and thereafter all that came my way was grist for my mill. Meetings with bankers, merchants, and officials in the Springs gave me "The Little London" point of view, and a visit to a cattle ranch gave me the cowboy setting.

"August 22. These three days' riding on the round-up in the Sierra Blanca country have been very richly productive with me. They plunged me again into the cattleman's world, a magnificent mountain region, and I have harvested a deal of vivid impressions. It is not necessary to spend weeks in studying such a life. I came away while my impressions were keen and pleasant—before the charm of the life was lost in the pressure of routine."

CHAPTER TEN

AISLES OF GOLD AND STREAMS OF SILVER

I

WHILE at the Ehrichs' in Colorado Springs I met Walter Wyckoff, a young professor from Princeton, whose book "The Workers" had been widely commended as an account of the adventures of a scholar among tramps—a deliberate attempt to get at the worker's point of view by mingling with "the slaves of the capitalistic system." Wyckoff, a handsome and cultivated young man of the English type, was notably fastidious of dress and charming in manner. So considerate, indeed, that Alma, Ehrich's little daughter, said, "I like Mr. Garland best—he isn't so polite as Mr. Wyckoff," which may be taken as a comment on my Western bluntness or Wyckoff's New England courtesy. I quote it with some hesitation.

"Walter," as we at once called him, had come to Colorado for a few weeks' hunting; and when I recommended a tour of the White River Plateau he asked me to go in with him—a request with which I was delighted to comply. I still had my Klondike sleeping bag and tent—I never went West without them—and was able to assure a comfortable outing for us both. "We'll go in by way of Wolcott and Yampa and be gone about two weeks," I announced to my wife.

Like all my trips into the mountains in those days, this was of inspirational value to me. For example, as we were jolting up the valley in an old-fashioned stage, a young girl, riding furiously to intercept our coach, suggested the opening of a story, the "Forester's Daughter," and the mid-way house and the ranchers we met there were also grist to my mill; but over and beyond these details, I was enriched by the beauty of the landscape, the music of the streams, and the voices of birds and animals. Each mile added to the mass of poetic impressions with which my memory was stored.

The mood in which I started on this trip is expressed in this note made on September 6: "I like best the trail which climbs along the bank of a rushing stream—a stream in which trout lie at ease in amethystine pools and the water ouzel dips beneath the snow-white falls or sits on the mossy edge of a rock peering strangely into the water. I love to camp at night beside such a torrent, so close that its roar brings the noise of wings to my slumber. I am reactionary when I am here. I resent every mill that pollutes a stream, every factory that spews its sewage into a river. I oppose the ore mill which transforms a clear torrent into a rush of mud. Beauty is too precious in this world. I resent the coming in of the utilitarian."

Another note is filled with exultation over the passing of the miner. "Red Gulch is like a chapter out of Bret Harte—a deep, fir-adorned cañon with a glorious stream of water of amber and emerald and gold. Cabins hang to the sides of the perpendicular walls, crazy footbridges swing above the torrent. Vast bowlders stand in the water. Ruined and rotting machinery lies beside

huts whose sagging doors are padlocked just as when
their owners went away. Far, rounded hilltops gleam
above with gold and gray and green—and always the
whirring, rushing, laughing water is ringed with eddies,
amber-tinted—revealing its thousand-jeweled bottom
studded with strange rocks—a scene to make a miner
believe that every glittering thing which the sun
touched was precious ore."

I find two pages in my notebook which I cannot
bring myself to leave out—one is called "Cedars" and
the other "Mollie McCoy." "The road being steep and
the progress of the stage slow, Walter and I walked
on ahead and so came upon a grove of cedars. Incredibly ancient, gray, weathered into strips, half decayed,
torn by winds, scorched by lightning and the suns of
August, rooted deep in the grim and grudging earth,
old as tradition and unlovely as Egyptian mummies,
they stand around us, a sorrowful company. Some rise
harsh and bleak as the cast-off crumbling antlers of the
elk. Others are fantastic, dwarfed, and ragged as gypsy
hags. The dead and the living mingle horribly, and
when the wind arises their voices blend in a moan of
pain, of infinite despair. They seem the survivors of
another world and time—unrelated to the Colorado
around us."

Just below these cedars stood a tavern called "Mc-
Coy's"—"a most attractive ranch house of logs surrounded by red-walled hills like the Navajo country
and shaded by willows and cottonwoods. In the yard
ran a clear stream of water and a big pile of elks' antlers up which a tangle of sweetpea vines is climbing.
The house is kept by a quaint, gaunt, little old woman

and a prim, pretty girl—soon to look like her mother. To the cattlemen coming in over the hot hills, dusty, thirsty, and hungry, this place is like home and mother. The girl has the pride of rank. She dwells in a high place. She is adored and she knows it. Suitors throng about her, but they are not of the quality she cares to encourage. She is more deeply interested in the strange young men who come from the outside world, stay only for an hour, and pass on into mystery. She waited on Walter with especial care."

"Leaving Yampa with a pack outfit, Wyckoff and I rode for several hours through groves of aspen, whose yellow leaves were like burning, burnished coins, over a carpet of green and bronze and amber. I have never ridden a more celestial aisle. The lighted vistas were like those of some measureless cathedral, the landscape a miracle of color, the air like October in the lowlands. We camped that night on the bank of a rushing, glorious stream.

"September 12. We left camp this morning at eight and climbed the White River Plateau to a plain far above timber line. The view was surpassingly large, and gorgeous with autumn coloring. The golden waves of the tableland broke against royal-purple cliffs. On every side range after range of mountains rose. . . . At midday we came upon a band of over forty mountain sheep. Leaving our horses, we crept toward the flock and lay for an hour watching them at their feeding, studying their system of protection. Always some one of the rams was looking and listening. Becoming alarmed, at last, they started running toward the south and we galloped after them. They ran directly toward the edge

of the eastern precipice and dropped, one by one—
lambs and all—into the profound abyss! It was marvelous—proving all the stories we had heard of their
hardihood."

We pondered over this, and to prove that they were
uninjured, we spent several hours in riding down and
round to the foot of this prodigious wall from which
those little lambs had leaped. We found no bodies. Not
one had been injured!

"Striking our tents the next day, we took the trail
across the rocky ridges between the plateau and Pyra-
mid Peak. Part of the way we rode in a dense and beautiful forest. On coming down to the valley of the Wil-
liams Fork we made camp at about nine thousand feet
in a clump of aspen by a little rill. I have never seen
anything in the way of woodland more beautiful. Green
trees rose out of a carpet of frost-touched, golden vines
and coral-colored plants, a magical forest, of high romantic charm, yet real and filled with game. It is a
commodious wood—like the forest of Arden where
ladies in trailing robes might walk in converse with
their lovers—so smooth and orderly are its aisles, so
still and windless and scented are its glades."

"September 16. This, my forty-second birthday, was
spent in camp on Trappers Lake. Seven years ago—or
maybe eight—I stood on this very spot. I had not expected to return, but here I am after having passed
seven years of wandering elsewhere. The wind is snarling through the pines about us. We are alone in the
clearing. No one else seems to have been here recently.
I cannot understand why this exquisite spot is not alive
with campers. All that I've been through should make

material for literature of some sort, but I do not yet see in what way I can use it."

On our way out we spent the night at Wolcott and I find this paragraph: "The old postmaster. His little office was bright with new wallpaper but the ventilation was bad. He was like a man in a diving bell. So long as the cowboys did not riot in his preserves he paid no attention to their noise. Denver Dan might ride the street, whooping and popping, but the old man went calmly on with his reading, remote in his official den. All about him were men who swore, drank, gambled, and fought, whilst he, as remote from it as Carlyle (whom he resembled), lived alone, caring for his own bed and cooking his own food. He had his story—every one said so, but no one knew the story. He was musty, tobacco-stained, and unkempt, but he was a philosopher —a stoic in theory and in practice; actually, he was some kind of failure."

That this outing would bring me inspiration I knew. My hunger for it, my absorption of it, led to my enrichment. A group of short stories and a novel ultimately rose from a return to this region, which I had called "The Prairie in the Sky" in my article of ten years before.

II

Chicago was steaming under a pouring rain when we returned to it in September, a violent contrast to the High Country. Life seemed a gloomy struggle as we threaded the clangorous streets, bags in hand. The screaming tumult of the town set the sweet silences of the mountains an immeasurable distance above us.

"October 3. Each year I am more and more disgusted with cities—Chicago in particular. The trail from the radiant forests of the White River to these turbulent and greasy pavements is a descent into hell. My disgust is, of course, only a mood. Those high meadows are for a vacation—not for a home, but is it necessary that cities should be so filthy, so noisy, so ugly?

"After working all the forenoon on 'Nistina,' a little Indian tale suggested by Seger, I called on Senator Beveridge at his hotel. He was at work at a table with coat and collar off and surrounded by manuscripts, as boyish as ever. He appeared very restive. I cannot take him seriously either as legislator or author."

October 11 found me back in West Salem, the finest part of our Wisconsin autumn. "Hiring a team to-day, I drove over to Uncle Frank's just as we have done in many, many other years. As we sat under a hickory tree on the hillside the hour and the scene combined in a perfect, golden October afternoon. A delicious little valley lay below us. The fragrant nuts, the gorgeous coloring, the intermittent whispering rustle of the dead leaves, the dog watching us, the cow bells tinkling from the yellow cornstalks in the fields all joined to restore our youth."

Soon after this a lecture called me to Sioux City, where I again met Herbert Quick. "He is a lawyer of power and insight, still trying to write. On the way I read Hopkinson Smith's 'Oliver Horn,' a very interesting and charming story. It lightened my day and I feel grateful to him. I shall write him a word of thanks."

On my return I found a letter from President Roosevelt in which was an excerpt from his approaching message to Congress—a paragraph dealing with the subject of Indian education. "I send it to you for consideration," he wrote. "I shall be glad of any correction or suggestion." It was a good, frank letter as always, and I made some slight changes in the text and returned it promptly. He thanked me for my suggestions and asked me to call on him when next in Washington.

On October 25 Frank Norris died, in the midst of his beautiful, valiant, happy youth. "His taking-off in the full flush of his joyous success, in the glow of his domestic happiness and the pride of his paternity, is cruel. Nothing of late has so stirred me and grieved me. It seems that some criminal neglect must have manifested itself. Some physician must have blundered. I want to accuse some one responsible. 'See what an irreparable injury to American literature you have wrought.' "

At the request of "The Critic," I wrote a brief estimate of him, in which I said:

"The three books on which the fame of Frank Norris rests are: 'McTeague,' 'The Octopus,' and 'The Pit.' 'McTeague,' as its name implies, is an exhaustive study of one character; but 'The Octopus' is the presentation of sociologic conditions in California. 'The Pit' is a social study of Chicago.

"I began my acquaintance with Norris over the pages of 'McTeague.' The amazing particularity and unfailing interest of this grim story led me to a belief that its author could do anything—even to write a 'Trilogy of Wheat.'

"Once William Dean Howells, a very wise and gentle man, listened to a plan of my own which involved several volumes and at the end said quietly—very quietly: 'Admirable, only be sure you don't lose interest in your plan.' I thought of this when Norris first outlined his scheme for his trilogy, now to be forever incomplete, not because the author lost interest in its final volume, but because he is dead. 'The Wolf' remains only a title in Norris' last preface.

"In the place of this third volume we may set 'McTeague'—or rather it should come first, and 'The Octopus' and 'The Pit' be moved up the line—for there is little need of apology in dealing with 'McTeague.' In it is some of the best work Norris ever did, and as a whole it stands as a piece of preparative work—a superb thesis on an individual, leading to a consideration of the sociologic—the epic.

"The chronicle is inexorable in its unrelenting lifelikeness—one of the most masterly studies in our literature, but the reader is forced at the end to ask, 'What of it?'—for it does not lead even to a notion of social betterment. It is gray—gray and cold—in tone. It ends in a desert, with two of its chief characters locked in a death grapple—a touch of youthful rigor.

"Norris' interest was not that of the ethical teacher, the reformer who turns on the light. He rejoiced in McTeague and Trina as terms in a literary theorem. Their sufferings lead to no conclusions. They were studied because they appealed to his dramatic sense, his love for character.

"In 'The Octopus,' his intention was frankly sociologic. A map prefaces the story, a cast of characters is thrown upon a screen. The author is in the wheat field and concerned with wide horizons rippling with grain. He is dealing not with a few persons huddled into a flat, but with proud landowners in combination against a giant corporation. McTeague was a blind fighter, but the farmers in 'The Octopus' are rich landlords, oppressors in their own right, banding together for purely mercenary reasons; had they all been really fighting for life, as was the poor engineer turned tiller of the soil, the book would have been heart-wringing. In every chapter *wheat* is taken as the motive, the ever-recurring refrain. The impersonal is uppermost; individuals are subordinated, inexorably crushed, or senselessly exalted, as in life, by blind forces.

"At times the attempt to apply the methods of Zola is too apparent. We weary of adjectives which seem to have been taken directly from 'La Terre.' The motive is too insistent, the impersonal ceases at times to interest. The use of the refrain is Wagnerian, but it fails, ultimately, of effect. Perhaps it is not a trick, but it certainly is an artifice. Reference to Trina and McTeague was often made in words to the same effect; but in 'The Octopus,' Hilma Tree, Annixter, Behrman are all announced by almost exactly the same phrases—wonderfully good phrases, too—precisely as Wotan and Siegfried are announced by the recurring trumpet flares, adjusted to the flow of the orchestral score. This gives unity to the structure of the novel, and produces a vivid and powerful impression on the mind of the reader, but it also adds formality and fixedness—restricting free development.

"I do not know that I object to this device, but I do consider the employment of adjectives in the style of Hugo and Zola a disfigurement. Their use was

a survival of Norris' boyish literary idolatry. 'Mc-
Teague' may be said to partake of the method of Balzac. 'The Octopus' certainly was founded upon 'Germinal' and 'La Terre'; but there Norris' indebtedness
ceased. For McTeague and Annixter and Trina and Der-
rick—for the throngs of marvelously realized characters in each of these books—we are indebted to the keen
eyes, the abounding insight, and the swift imagination
of a born novelist. Norris studied life, or rather he absorbed it, without effort and without conscious design.
'McTeague' is a mine of inexhaustible riches of observation. A second or third reading gives increasing
wonder as to how the boy acquired so much knowledge
and so much discernment.

"It is not necessary to apologize at any point for Norris. It is not necessary, in criticizing some mistakes of
judgment in 'The Octopus,' to say, 'He will become a
great novelist.' 'The Octopus' is a bitter and sweeping
arraignment of impersonal conditions. It rose higher
on some sides than 'McTeague' and fell below it on others—but it showed the author's power in another way.
It demonstrated his ability to transfer his scene as well
as his characters. He was not bound to the slums of San
Francisco. As a resident of Chicago, he knew Polk
Street, and as a Californian he seems to present the San
Joaquin Valley and its life. His first novel was worthy
of his great plan. It was fairly tremendous.

"In its sequel he permitted himself a greater display
of power. He laid the scene of his Epic of the Wheat
in Chicago. Here again he was on familiar ground. His
boyhood had been spent in the great city of the Wheat
Pit. He knew certain phases of it as the keen-eyed

youth saw it, and he studied it later with definite purpose, with the eyes of the novelist, in preparation for his last book, 'The Pit.' I saw a great deal of him during the time that this story was forming in his brain, and I confess I was more uneasy over the outcome than he. He smoked his pipe and made merry and discussed everything else under the sun—confident and at ease. He said, 'I know it is, in a way, the final test of my powers,' and yet he seemed not to be taking pains. He appeared almost too confident of his future.

"However, 'The Pit' turned out to be a worthy successor to 'The Octopus.' It was sunnier and more hopeful than 'McTeague,' and less cumbrous and set of form and phrase than 'The Octopus.' It was, in fact, a superb study of Chicago on certain well-defined sides. The *wheat* is there, of course, by design, and is (to my mind) too much insisted upon, but the impersonal does not submerge and dissolve the characterization. It is there as a sound, a wind in the trees, a reminder, but the characters move to and fro, acting and reacting on one another, quite freely, quite naturally. The great speculator, Jadwin, is an admirably drawn type of Western business man—worthy to be put beside Silas Lapham. Laura Dearborn, if she has not the subtlety of emotional experience of Howells' Marcia Gaylord, is quite as vital. She does not convince at all points, but as a whole she is Norris' most important study of a woman.

" 'The Pit' does not pretend to be a society story of Chicago—it is unduly bleak on that side—but as a presentation of the ruthless forces finding expression in its business centers it is, thus far, unrivaled. Henry Fuller's 'Cliff Dwellers' is its worthiest companion piece.

"Norris' projected final volume, 'The Wolf,' would have been a more difficult problem than either of those preceding it, for it was to deal not merely prospectively with foreign material, but to involve a succession of incidents rather than a dramatic clashing of interests. Had he lived, he would have written it worthily, but its working-out offered peculiar dangers, it seems to me.

"Thus far the reader will get only the grim side of Norris; but in 'Blix,' fortunately, he is the author as we, his intimate friends, knew him—boyish, fun-loving, jocund. With us, his eyes glowed with humor. His face shone with roguery and good cheer. His antic manner was never coarse, and his jocular phrases were framed in unexpected ways. He was always and constantly interesting, and to spend an hour in his company was to find the world better worth while.

"Youth can afford to be a savage realist, for youth has boundless hope and confidence in itself. When a man begins to doubt his ability to reform the world by challenging it, he softens, allows himself to pity. Norris in 'The Pit' is more genial—that is to say, more mature —than in 'McTeague' and 'The Octopus.' Thirty-two and successful, he was entering on a less inexorable stage. Then death came. He was not written out, as perhaps Stephen Crane was; on the contrary, his mind was glowing with imagery. His ideals were fine, his life without stain, and we who knew him and loved him are confident that his small shelf of books will stand high in the library of American fiction."

I feel no inclination to change the broad outlines of this estimate now, thirty years later.

CHAPTER ELEVEN

HOWELLS GIVES A LUNCHEON

I

On my way East late in November, 1902, I bought my ticket by way of Washington and on arrival in the capital reported to the President. He invited me to lunch with him the following day. At my hotel, that night, I came in contact with the much-discussed Labor leader, John Mitchell, who, with Clarence Darrow and Henry D. Lloyd, was engaged in an arbitration conference. "They all looked worn, and Mitchell appeared sad, very sad. I was much attracted to him. He has fine, pleading eyes and a handsome, boyish face. He is carrying a big load and shows it. Darrow was almost equally haggard. Wayne MacVeagh, who was with him when I entered his room, is a dapper, adroit, and dangerously able lawyer, a subtle advocate for the capitalist. Mitchell, who was a day laborer only five years ago, is singularly modest—almost shrinkingly so—and yet has firmness of purpose. The President likes him."

I closed a very busy day by going to hear Duse in "La Gioconda," which made a powerful impression on me. "Duse is a sad woman; one who has been very beautiful and gay, but who is now disillusioned—hopeless—tragically worn and old. The play was depressing."

After a morning's work in the office of the Commissioner of Indian Affairs, I went to the White House, which was in the midst of being restored to something like its original beauty by Mead and McKim—under the direction of the President. In the midst of a raucous chorus of floor polishers and carpenters Mrs. Roosevelt met me and led the way to the small temporary dining room at the front of the house. I was the only guest (aside from Captain Cowles, who came in to talk about a big dinner which had been announced) and I rejoiced in the intimacy thus expressed. The President, perfectly simple and direct, was in abounding good health and quite buoyant despite his labors and his problems.

My record reads: "Mrs. Roosevelt, most domestic of wives, is a charming and cultivated hostess. She understands people. She reads and she observes. Her good taste makes increasingly evident the rusticity of previous mistresses of the White House. She is very sweet, large-minded, and tactful. I spoke of meeting Mitchell, and the President talked with entire freedom of him and the coal strike. I was pleased by his deference to the will of his wife. The lift of an eyebrow or a finger would arrest him in the midst of an argument. Their understanding was perfect. Miss Alice Roosevelt, a very bright girl, much like her father, was present, and I made a hit with her by saying exultantly, 'I have made a discovery. I have discovered the real ruler of the United States.' 'Who is he?' she asked. 'My hostess,' I replied with a glance at Mrs. Roosevelt. This amused her and she repeated my words to her father, who said, 'You are perfectly right. I am her subordinate.'

"He took up the criticisms, then raging, of his act in receiving Booker Washington as a luncheon guest. In substance he said, 'Booker Washington is the greatest of our black men—and I contend that recognizing his ability is aiding other aspiring negroes who are struggling up from the mire. I see no reason for alarm. If any other negro rises to the level of Booker Washington's achievement, I shall recognize him in similar fashion!'"

It may amuse my readers to know that my supper on this day was eaten at a cafeteria, which serves to illustrate the fact that my fame had far outrun my income. "To scrimp even when apparently prosperous has been my necessity. Here now I have touched the highest—or rather the widest—extreme. Luncheon at the White House, supper at a lunch counter, to-morrow a guest at the Mark Twain dinner in New York!"

This dinner to Clemens by Colonel Harvey, which was held at the millionaires' club, "The Metropolitan," was one of the noblest dinners I had ever attended. The speaking was altogether admirable. Howells was, as ever, concise, Tom Reed jocose, and Hamilton Wright Mabie eloquent—but old Mark was the king. "Old and unready at first, he warmed up soon and his wonderful humor flashed out, convulsing us all. He was deeply moving as he told of his visit to his Missouri home and to the scenes of his boyish escapades. I have never heard a finer after-dinner speech. It was a subtle mingling of the grave and the gay, the tender and the whimsical, which could come only from a mind richly stored and working along candid, homely lines. He appeared to be talking to us, phrasing with unpremeditated art. Wayne MacVeagh was at my left and Richard Le Gallienne on my right."

"November 30. A wire from Senator Beveridge called me to Washington. On the way I read two books: 'The Worldlings,' by Leonard Merrick, and 'An Imaginative Man,' by Robert Hichens. Both books are out of the ordinary, but on the whole Merrick's book is the best. Washington seems very quiet and restful after New York, which wearies me more and more. It saps my energies—eats up my time. A vast disgust seizes upon me after a few weeks of it, as if I had fed too full on rank rich food. I grow nervous and weak and apprehensive. The only way for me to live now is to sit above the tumult—to seek only what I want—otherwise I shall be swallowed up in the flood of things which do not count."

At ten (December 1) I met Senator Beveridge and his committee, and later went up into the Senate gallery to see the flower show—for that is what the chamber seemed—so abundant were the bouquets. Strachey of the *London Spectator* was there, looking on intently.

At the close of the session I went to the Ethnologic Bureau and worked on my plan for renaming the Indians, aided by Hewett, Hodge, and Mooney. "It is a curious fact, but these Algonquin names become Japanese with a little manipulation. In the afternoon I called on Dr. Hart Merriam at his office, and went home to dinner with him. We talked Indians all the evening. He showed me photographs of John Muir and his family and told me many amusing stories of the old mountaineer."

Senator Beveridge having released me from his committee, I bought tickets for my return December 3.

"New York, December 6. I still suffer from an uneasy feeling—a sense of not being at rest or at home. I went over on West Twentieth Street to look at a little flat and was much pleased with it. It was a part of old New York which I had never seen. There is a seminary over there and two or three churches. The boys were sleighing in the streets—and the whole square was like an illustration in a Christmas magazine.

"Old Joe Stoddardt was at the club when I returned. I had not seen him for years. He looked old and rather seedy, but we had an interesting talk. He told me of his first meeting with Lafcadio Hearn in an East Side attic. 'He was writing on a dry-goods box,' he said, 'a ghastly figure, hungry and hopeless! He had one bad eye and wrote bending close to his manuscript.' "

After great tribulation I found a suitable apartment in a building on West Forty-seventh Street. "It is a blessed relief to be settled in a hotel of this quiet sort. Our windows look out on snowy roofs, a blue-and-white mountainous landscape, and the steam is singing in our radiator. We hear almost nothing of the city tumult, and I foresee that I shall be able to work on my new book, 'Hesper.' The sun flooding my sitting room is an inspiration."

"December 18. At the club to-day I came upon Frederic Remington looking like a lump of raw beef. He is an enormous eater and drinker. The sirloin steak on the platter before him was enough for four men, and the tall bottle of wine which stood beside his plate was equally liberal. He is a man of power—of high talent, but is killing himself by his manner of life. He is a mystery to me. How can he work while eating and drinking inordinately? Where the soul of him resides I cannot detect, but Augustus Thomas, his neighbor in New Rochelle, admires him and loves him."

December 25 was a genuine Christmas morning, with the snow falling thick and heavy, the drab world of roof and sky made wonderful by the storm. At night we dined with Senator Jones and his family down at Stuyvesant Square, a pleasant evening among quietly luxurious surroundings. It did not seem like Christmas, however. "We are hotel guests rather than householders. Christmas makes us feel our essential homelessness.

"I have decided to stay with Harper's and to publish no second-rate matter at present. I shall try to finish 'Hesper,' which is going along very well, considering the social distractions which my wife's popularity brings to her and to me. My mornings are held for my work and unless I am out too late I succeed in doing at least a thousand words before noon."

We met the New Year (1903) at the home of Kate Douglas Riggs, in company with joyous Ruth McEnery Stuart. To fill in the half hour before midnight, George Riggs read most cleverly one of W. W. Jacobs' delightful stories, and I was greatly taken by its sly humor. Riggs suggested the dialect skillfully and we applauded him as well as the author when he closed the reading just before midnight.

Kate Douglas Wiggin, our lovely, blue-eyed, blond hostess, was in the full enjoyment of a wide acclaim. While writing mainly for girls, she was a true storyteller and had the art of pleasing grown-ups also.

Her "Cathedral Courtship," "The Birds' Christmas Carol," and "Rebecca of Sunnybrook Farm" had brought hosts of friends and a pleasant income. Her husband, although a mere business man (an importer), displayed a rather unusual interest in literature; and their home was in one of the spacious "Spanish flats" (on West Fifty-eighth Street) whose high ceilings, rich, dark woodwork, and ample drawing-room dated from an earlier and statelier era. Kate Douglas, as her friends called her, was a popular hostess, and at her teas one might meet Howells and Gilder, or Geraldine Farrar and Edward MacDowell. Her interest, like her acquaintance, was wide. Her summers were spent in a Maine village not far from Portland; but she was born in California. None of the critics took her writing seriously, and she made no pretense to greatness, but her novels were delightfully humorous and colorful. Perhaps they were more commendable than many other more pretentious volumes.

"January 6. Mrs. Herne dined with us to-day in our little room and afterward took us to see Martin Harvey, the English actor, in 'Sidney Carton.' This was a very great pleasure, for Harvey owns a singularly attractive personality. Something intangibly fine came from his face and voice. He made the old story deeply moving, and I came away with a sense of having shared those mad days of the French Revolution when human life was so cheap and theories so dear. I should like to know Harvey, and yet he might prove to be less admirable in his proper person than he seems to be as Carton. There was something in his face and voice which suggested Edwin Booth. His reading was excellent!

"Bacheller is in town and I am seeing a great deal of him, confiding to him my latest plot for a novel, and listening to his in return. I met Herman Vielé at the club, and we talked for an hour or more of the Rocky Mountain West which he had visited some twenty years before. He writes extremely well, with precision and grace, but has done only one or two small books. Apparently he is not dependent upon literature for a living. He prints little, but takes care to have that little worthy of praise. He is related to some well-known Knickerbocker families and has an air of security as regards his social position. His books are not widely known. 'Myra of the Pines' is the best of them, and a vivid, graceful book it is, with one horrible scene in it."

Mr. Howells included me in the list of his guests at a luncheon given in honor of Henry Harland, who had just returned to New York after many years of life in England and Italy. "In his note of invitation, Howells called Harland 'your rhyme'; and in truth he was much more than that—he was my embarrassment, for many kindly intentioned ladies had said to me, 'I think your "Cardinal's Snuff-Box" adorable,' forcing me to say, with a wry grin, 'It *is* a good book—I'll admit.' I wonder whether his coming will add to or subtract from this humiliation.

"Harland, who is of Jewish birth, won his fame by writing of New York with such skill that Howells at once became his kindly advocate. He still values him highly, for he assembled a very choice group of writers to meet him at a modest uptown restaurant. Mark Twain, Augustus Thomas, George Harvey, James L. Ford, Frank Crowninshield, and John Howells were the other guests, and Harland was happy in the distinction which they gave. Mark Twain dominated the circle, naturally; even George Harvey listened to the lion-headed old Missourian, and witty Augustus Thomas could only now and then shoot in a deft remark. John Howells and I were delighted auditors."

How good the talk was that noonday! and yet I could carry away and record only an occasional phrase. Mark got started almost immediately on Bret Harte, whom he heartily despised, and told some very pungent stories of Harte's early life. His drawling intonation conveyed such edge of hate that I wondered at its cause. Knowing Mark, I was inclined to discount some of his charges.

Howells at last got the floor and told of Harte's arrival at his home in Cambridge in the early 70's and of his long stay there. "He had his entire family," said Howells with a smile, "and they lived with us for several weeks, then drifted on to Boston. Bret was a careless vagabond, improvident but highly amusing, and we all liked him. He was always in debt. It fell to me on one occasion to present him as a lecturer to an audience in Tremont Temple, and when I called at his house to escort him to the hall, I found him in the custody of a constable. Harte explained, without apparent concern, that his tailor had sent the officer to collect payment for a suit of clothes and the constable said to me, 'This man shall not give his lecture without handing over his fee.' Thereupon Harte invited him to ride with us to the hall and sit on the platform.

"This he did," continued Howells, while we all laughed, "and so, as I rose to present the speaker, I had on my right hand a distinguished novelist, and on my left the constable—Harte being the least perturbed of the trio!"

I can only faintly suggest the subtle humor of this anecdote which the company enjoyed all the more as coming from the lips of a man who never exaggerated for the sake of effect.

"Mark Twain did not laugh with the rest of us. 'That was like him,' he declared, and again cursed him as a 'whelp' and a 'blackguard.' His fury of invective was almost comical. 'Do you know what that blankety-blank two-faced hound did? He came to Elmira to get my endorsement of him as consul to Glasgow, and told me with glee that he had secured the support of both parties!' "

It was apparent that Twain considered this a case of double-dealing, but to me it appeared an added proof of Harte's popularity. I may have missed the point, however.

John Howells and I remained amused auditors; and at the end of the general analysis of Harte we agreed that not much was left of him except his great fame! He still remained the author of "The Argonauts." I had a full confirmation, however, of the impression he had made upon me as a sad exile, when Harland said, "The gossip of London is, that at the time of his death he was very poor and living with a woman not his wife."

"I can believe it," said Clemens. "He deserted his wife and children many years ago, and has lived an irresponsible life in London ever since, working over the tailings of his California gold mine, till all his readers fell away from him."

As we came away, I said to Harland: "If it is true that Harte was living with a woman not his wife when he died, there must have been something finely sympathetic in that woman, for when I visited him he was a feeble, dim-eyed old man. The house looked like the home of a lady."

Harland agreed. "His last years were rather pitiful. His books had ceased to sell and he had few friends. He was little regarded by any one, so far as I know, and lived obscurely toward the last." Out of all the talk of this brilliant luncheon, I retained only this bitter commentary on Bret Harte's personal character. Howells, kindly as he was, could not gainsay Mark's accusing words nor blink Harland's testimony.

II

Ernest Seton had taken a spacious studio apartment facing on Bryant Park; and there I spent many afternoons watching the old trailer draw; while he drew, talking of Indians, bears, and birds, subjects of which he never tired. "It is not the kind of home I would have chosen for myself," he said, "but with my desk and my drawing board before me, I ignore the rumble of the elevated train."

He liked to have his friends come in of an afternoon and chat. Visitors appeared to help rather than to hinder his drawing—a fact which puzzled me. I could work only in solitude and silence.

Among those who frequently spent an afternoon hour with him were Charles G. D. Roberts, the Canadian poet, and young Emery Pottle, who was "trying to write" at this time. Pottle was a tall, blond boy

whose pleasing smile, unworried brow, and unhurried
manner led to his nickname, "The Bambino." I never
took him seriously. Some years passed before he ma-
tured to the point of writing a successful play. He had
many friends who were confident of his ultimate success, but none of them expected him to win a place
upon the stage, which he did as Gilbert Emery. Roberts,
who was a very handsome, scholarly man of forty, had
been a professor of literature in a college in Canada,
but had won success as a writer of animal stories, somewhat in Seton's vein. The best of these, to my thinking,
was his "Heart of the Ancient Wood," a picture of his
boyhood home, a beautifully written and deeply felt
sylvan romance.

Although a small man, pale and poetic of features,
he was said to be of astonishing skill as a wrestler.
One of his friends said to me, "Charles is a jujitsu
expert. He could fling me over his head with one
hand."

Despite his early training as a teacher, his life in
New York City was wholly literary. I saw little of
him, however, but I came to know his brother, William
Carman Roberts, very well, and from him had an occasional word of his "profane" brother, an allusion to his
initials, C. G. D. He went away to England and later
to Paris, and gradually dropped out of the literary
columns of American papers. He was a skilled and
graceful writer, always, but only one or two of his
books survived the War. I liked him and regarded him
as one of the best of the "nature fakers," as Roosevelt
so vividly characterized them, for he was avowedly the
fictionist.

Hamilton Wright Mabie, like myself, was irritated by the half-hearted action of the Council of the National Institute of Arts and Letters, and we met now and again to discuss plans for action. We both felt that the nation should have an organization wherein leaders representing all of the arts should make combined effort for the good of each. "I see no reason for being timid. Why not stand for bold progress?" I said to Mabie, who agreed with me.

It was rather surprising that he should uphold me in this campaign, for he was one of the gentlest and most considerate of men. His books, held to be scholarly and graceful, were of no great originality, but he was widely known as a fluent and pleasing speaker; a preacher turned lecturer. He was a cultural rather than a creative force. I respected him and found working with him a pleasure. He was at this time editor of *The Outlook,* a semi-religious publication of wide circulation. His essays are forgotten now, but his gracious personality remains with me as with all who met him.

"January 14, 1903. Through the kindness of Mrs. Richard Watson Gilder I saw Duse, the great Italian tragedienne, in Sudermann's 'Magda.' Although she is wildly acclaimed by many critics I didn't altogether like her interpretation of the title rôle. She was too Southern—too unrestrained. Magda is Nordic, and to my way of thinking Modjeska's characterization came nearer to the author's conception. Duse's acting was superbly natural in effect, but her Magda was, after all, Italian, not German.

"My novel has now come to possess me almost entirely, and I write every morning with such concentra-

tion as my surroundings and our social engagements will
permit. Our hotel is on a busy street, but my desk, being
at the back of the house, is quiet and cheerful with
sunlight, so that I should work, and do work, to good
purpose. My corporeal self is confined in a tiny cell in
the heart of a sea-level city; but my mind ranges the
grassy shoulders of Cripple Creek."

At the annual meeting of the National Institute
which came late in January, Mabie and I again advo-
cated action, and Carroll Beckwith and William Trent
ably seconded our appeal. "The influence of a body like
this is needed to counterbalance the ever-increasing influence of the newspapers, whose hasty criticism is, of
necessity, half-baked. The National Institute should
not war against popular judgments; it should supplement them."

Our appeal went for nothing; the older men voted us
down.

The address of the evening was given by Lounsbury
of Yale, a very able, dryly humorous assault upon the
authority of dictionaries. No one but a really great
scholar could have been so wittily iconoclastic. "Who
makes these dictionaries?" he demanded. "Who but you
and I? Do they not quote us as authority?"

St. Clair McKelway followed, thanking Lounsbury
for his "ambiguity."

The dinner, which took place as usual at the Aldine
Club, was successful, but not so well attended as it
should have been, and a number of the men were plainly
half-hearted in their support of the organization.
Trained to individual thought, they failed of coöperation in any action where art and literature were in-

volved. Some of them feared newspaper comment; others were inert, content with their studios and their desks.

"William James was one of the most noticeable figures at the table. His noble head and deep, quiet gaze, his black hair, abundant and lined with gray, made him an attractive philosopher. I was glad of the opportunity of meeting him. He took no part in the speaking, although we all expected him to rise. Strange to say, the point of contact between him and me is spiritism. He, like Sir Oliver Lodge, is disposed to grant the probability of spirit return."

Shortly after this dinner, John Howells and Juliet Tompkins came to luncheon with us and we talked art and literature hard and fast. John's comments on architecture were not only clever but able and his diction was vivid, graceful, and vibrant. Small of frame, he looked exactly like some of the early portraits of his father. As a student he had traveled much in Spain and Italy, and I listened to his conclusions regarding American architecture with absorbed interest and full agreement. His principles seemed much less derivative than those of any other architect of my acquaintance. "His study of the Old World designs has not dulled his creative New World concepts; on the contrary, it has clarified them."

III

Among the most widely known of the political cartoonists of the day was Homer Davenport, a young Western man who was working for Hearst's *Journal.* His remorseless daily assaults on Mark Hanna and his

like during the McKinley campaign had made him a
terror; but he liked Roosevelt, and was much less savage in his delineation of "Teddy." I knew little of Homer
personally and had no expectation of meeting him, but
one afternoon when I joined a group of men at the
New York Central Station all en route to Frank Seaman's home in Yonkers, I found Davenport among
them and was immensely taken with him. He looked like
a Colorado cowboy and talked like one, at times. He was
a tall, pock-marked, and rough-hewn man of forty. He
knew something of me as a Mid-West historian and we
fell at once into talk of farm life. His diction was picturesque and his comment humorous without apparent
straining for that effect. We sat together and he told
me of his struggles in Idaho and of his coming to New
York on half a shoestring, and when Seaman said, "You
should see Homer's farm in New Jersey with its flocks
of wild geese and herds of Arabian horses," he only
grinned.

Seaman went on, "For a boy who started from Idaho
on a shoestring, a salary of twenty-five thousand dollars per year is a substantial achievement."

Davenport knew little of me, but my intimate
knowledge of farm life won his interest. In talking of
threshing, I said: "My highest admiration was the
'feeder,' the man who could take the 'concave' out,
reset its teeth, and put it back again."

Homer rocked with laughter. "Think of that!" he
shouted. "Here is a novelist who knows what a 'concave' is. I haven't heard that word since I came East.
This man knows a threshing machine."

I liked the big, angular, good-humored fellow, and

by the time we reached Seaman's house we were friends,
almost relations. Our somewhat similar boyhood experiences had made us kind if not kin.

Here again for the thousandth time I saw the centralizing force of Manhattan demonstrated. This man,
born in Idaho, had been drawn to the great city as to
an irresistible magnet—and in an incredibly short space
of time had risen to the top of his profession. He had
grown rich. He was one of the best known importers of
Arabian horses, and Seaman declared that his stables in
Jersey were "silver-plated." His art was not a refined
art, it was in truth a brutal and hasty art, but it had
wide appeal and in all its phases expressed the sturdy
manhood which directed its lines.

He was essentially Western in his humor, and in some
of his stories made fun of himself—an American quality. One story I set down (in outline) the following
day. He said:

"When I was about twenty—a gawky, big lump of a
farm hand—my father was living in a little town in
Idaho. Too bashful to have any hand in the social doings of the town, I went about alone, but one day, when
one of our farmer friends announced a dance in his
new barn some five or six miles out, I decided to shake
foot in it. I couldn't go without a partner—and so
in my best suit I set out to find a girl. Not one would
go with me. They were all engaged—or said they were.
Dad had agreed to let me have the old gray mare and
the covered buggy, but when the day came I had no
girl. I was desperate. I took an old friend of my father's into my confidence. 'I can't go without a girl, can
I?'

"He didn't laugh at me; he thought a minute. 'Why don't you ask my niece, Cornelia Scammon? I happen to know that she has not been asked.'

"This was astounding. Cornelia was the handsomest, proudest, richest girl in the country. I hadn't dreamed of asking her. 'She's too high and fine for a pock-marked old plug like me,' I said. 'Well, now, that's just what has happened,' he replied. 'All the young fellows have taken it for granted that she was snapped up at the very start—and so here she is without an escort.'

"On his advice I put on my best suit, 'tallered' up my boots, and went to call upon her. She was a lady. She treated me as a real beau and said, 'I am much obliged to you. I would like to go.'

"You can imagine my feelings. I was more than proud, I was exalted. I stopped being a boy that minute, I was a man. Well, the next night about eight o'clock I hauled dad's rusty old covered buggy out of the shed, hitched the gray mare into it, and drove round for my queen—and she *was* a queen! It was a clear, starlit October night and I had the prettiest girl in town beside me. I hadn't anything to say to her—she did all the talking—but I answered as best I knew how, and as for my dancing, she took the will for the deed!

"It was nearly dawn when the party broke up and we started for home—so tired and sleepy that we didn't even try to talk. By the time we reached the edge of the village, people were getting out to milk the cows; and as they saw us, they gauped for a minute, then broke into broad grins—and called something after us. I thought they were joshing me about capturing the nicest girl in town, but when everybody we met along

Main Street stopped, turned, stared, and guffawed, I grew hot. 'I'll come back and make you laugh out of the other side of your mouths,' I said to myself.

"I left Cornelia at her door and drove back along a side street—same result. Everybody I met doubled over with laughter and howled something after me, and then, to put the climax on the whole affair, dad went off into splutter. Pointing at the back of my carriage, he said, 'See what you've fetched away with you.' I got out and went around to look—and there on the hind axle sat two white hens! They had been roosting there when I pulled the buggy out of the shed and they had slept there all the way out and all the way back. No wonder the neighbors laughed—I laughed myself. But right there I decided to emigrate—this town is no place for me! I started for the East the very next day."

Although I accepted this bit of biography with some reservation, I was certain that it was based on a very momentous incident; for of such tragic experiences, the far-reaching resolutions of youth are often born. To an awkward, sensitive boy, such "joshing" as this is intolerable. Whether it really started Homer on his career or not did not matter to me. I rejoiced in his humor.

He was the life of Seaman's party, and all of us were content to listen to his talk of Indians and wild animals. Another of his stories dealt with a horse race in which the red jockeys got the better of the whites by entering a cleverly disguised famous bright bay racer as a spotted brown pony with a roached mane. "They just about broke the town," laughed Homer. "They walked away with all the money in the bank. It was Bret Harte's 'Heathen Chinee' all over again."

Davenport was a great personality, but as he made no books he is already forgotten. He left no enduring record but his political cartoons, which are no longer of general interest. Although we never met again I felt that I knew him, and when he died a few years later, I joined his friends in saying, "Homer was just beginning to live."

A few days after Seaman's party, George Bird Grinnell invited us to dinner, and my wife and I rode the full length of the city in an overcrowded street car to Audubon Park where he lived. My entry reads: "Grinnell is a singular mixture of the staid Manhattan citizen and the old borderman. No one would suspect, as they see him going about the streets of Harlem, that he is honorary chief of several tribes of red people; and that he was on the warpath with the Pawnees in the sixties. In truth he is one of the best informed writers on these subjects in America."

"In calling on Edward MacDowell (February 16) I found him mightily inspired by his trip into the West and in superb health and spirits. Again I rated him one of the brightest wits of my acquaintance—a keen and masterful intelligence. I had always felt this, but never did his fire and alertness more vividly appear than on this night. He was about to start for Pittsburgh where he is to play with the orchestra. He was very handsome, confident, and patriotic. 'My soul! this America of ours is a big country,' he said. 'I know it now. I've seen it.'"

CHAPTER TWELVE

MARK TWAIN, CARNEGIE, AND ROOSEVELT

I

LATE in February, 1903, Clemens, who had taken a house in Riverdale, invited my wife and me to dinner, an invitation which we instantly and joyously accepted, for we had never seen him in his home. We reached the Riverdale station about seven of a rainy night, and as the only conveyance in sight was a musty hack, we took it. As we clattered up the hill and through a dark wood, we seemed a thousand miles from Manhattan. We came at last to an old-fashioned mansion surrounded by tall, bare-branched elm trees—a drab and lonesome place, with which I could not associate Mark Twain. As we entered the bright hall, however, he came running down the stairway with amazing agility to meet us. He presented us to his daughters with a wave of his hand—ceremony and conventions did not much count with him.

We were the only guests, and at dinner he did all of the talking, for we were there to listen. Like Roosevelt, he monologued to some purpose, and his purpose that night appeared to be our entertainment. He touched upon cockroaches, June bugs, Mississippi River steamboats, and other subjects of humorous exaggeration, then described his recent trip to St. Louis and

Hannibal, all in characteristic drawl. "I was provided with an old sweetheart in every town," he said. "They seated these candidates beside me on the platform, nice old ladies who firmly believed they were Beckie." We laughed until our sides ached when he most deftly fought an imaginary beetle. Every sentence he uttered was salable. He loved to turn a neat phrase and his remarks were often deliciously unexpected. Our laughter appeared to stimulate him. That his daughters were almost equally amused was evident, although I wondered how they could retain their ability to laugh in the midst of such abounding, unending humor.

After the ladies rose, Mark's delightful fooling ceased. With somber intonation he said, "We are only a kind of private hospital here. Mrs. Clemens is shut away from us by the doctor's orders—I'm allowed to see her only a few minutes each day—and Jean is not well."

He led the way to his library, and after he had lighted his pipe, I started him on another tack by asking, "What are you doing?"

"I am still investigating Mrs. Eddy and her papacy," he replied. Fetching a book from his table he handed it to me. "Examine that. It's one of the early copies of her book. Did you ever see a worse job of printing? It has the quality of a seed catalogue. I'm not objecting to her theory of mental healing—I'm inclined to believe in it —but I intend to expose her business methods." He then passed into a scathing denunciation of the "close corporation" which she or her advisors had formed to exploit her book. "She has a genius for monopoly," he said, a statement which has since been amplified by Dakin's biography.

Knowing very little about this publishing scheme, I listened to his scorching diatribe without comment, but I could see that he was deep in the problem and in characteristic fashion was "making it smoke." He talked to me without seeing me—I was only an excuse for his thinking out loud. I never once saw his eyes—so deeply hidden were they under his shaggy eyebrows—and I cannot say even now what their color was.

We came away late that night, feeling that we had gained a deeper knowledge of Mark Twain. I understood some of his life problems. Thereafter he was less of the great literary figure and more of the neighbor and the friend.

I said something like this to Howells next day, and he agreed that Clemens, like many another humorist, was essentially sad. "He realizes that his wife is hopelessly ill, and Jean is a constant care. He would like to believe in mental healing and is rather prejudiced in its favor, but is infuriated with the money-making side of the organization. However, I do not share his fury. No one is *forced* to buy the books."

Howells had his own worries, for Mrs. Howells was in failing health. "Beneath his cheerful exterior," I wrote, "he, too, is a sad man. He sees his wife fading away from him day by day. She is a great care. Her trouble is physical, but manifests itself in mental unrest. She is, I think, the cause of his constant moving. She sees almost no one now and seldom goes out. She is very notional, but no one could be more tenderly patient than he. She is New England to the bone and has that mental twist which so often leads to a secluded life. She still sees me and talks gayly and keenly for a little while, then draws her shawl over her shoulders, smiles brightly, and says, 'Good night.' She is very pale and thin—a wraith of the lovely, blue-eyed girl she must have been in those far Venetian days."

One of our many artist acquaintances at this time was A. A. Anderson—a painter whose studio in the Beaux-Arts Building included the entire top floor, a suite of rooms adorned with Oriental rugs, lamps, and tapestries. One room, "the Omar Khayyam room," was ornamented with panels or shields bearing the eternity sign, and lunettes with scenes from the poem. "I have never seen anything more gorgeous. It is the farthest remove from the artist life of Chicago and Washington Square, the artist life I know most about," I made record, "but it is not to be despised on that account. It is possible to paint in noble halls. The musical program of the afternoon, rendered by the harp and organ, was superb. Such entertainment is possible only in the greatest of cities."

This studio was not in the least in accordance with the popular notion of an artist's workshop, and in truth it didn't impress me as such; it was like a stage setting, and Anderson himself, a pleasing and generous host, was very far from being the tousled, toiling artist. He made me think—by way of contrast—of a studio and home I had recently visited on lower Fifth Avenue— where the painter and his wife were not only in need of furniture and clothes but of food. "His easel stood in the corner of a dusty, ratty den and he looked like a tramp, but he is a craftsman! His paintings are as bitter and as repellent as himself, but they have sincerity and crude power."

On the last day of February, we dined with the Setons, and afterward viewed the Sportsmen's Show at Madison Square Garden. The cantata of "Hiawatha" was being given there with the huge central tank for a river. "It interested me keenly as a spectacle, and some of its music was nobly beautiful. 'Fiendish' as the red man is reported to be in all our histories, he has added enormously to our romance, our poetry and our song."

We met Frederick Burton, the composer. "He is as prosaic in appearance as an agent for a canoe, but is a very real musician. Our words of praise pleased him and he asked for suggestions as to the best use of the music he had adapted. We saw very little of the show other than the Indians and the pageant which fitted in well with the display. At one or two points the scenes were most impressive. The passing of Hiawatha was especially fine and the music which accompanied it majestic in its suggestion."

On March 5, we met at dinner Edwin Winter, the vice president of the Brooklyn Rapid Transit, a slender man, youthful in appearance, and singularly fine in all ways—a soul of energy and concentration done up in a small and very handsome package. A pale, grave little man, who made me think of Kirkland, the author of "Zury."

We saw Long and Belasco's play, "The Darling of the Gods," which proved to be an intense and moving drama. "I sat rigidly through it all. My imagination was stirred at a hundred points. It is in many ways a profound innovation—perhaps it is the advance courier of a new drama uniting the East and the West, the old and the new. Blanche Bates and George Arliss were the leading actors. Arliss was especially fine, as the crafty, remorseless old councilor."

"March 12. Thomas Bailey Aldrich was at the club to-day, looking old and fat, and florid with food and drink—not at all the poet in appearance. I did not speak to him and no one else did. He seemed to be waiting for some one to come in and so remained for an hour seated alone by the fire. Later I was told that he had come over from Boston to see his poetic play 'Judith' performed at one of the theaters. No one else recognized him and I did not feel moved to make myself known to him. I recalled the resentment with which I received his letter declining my youthful article on Edwin Booth for the reason (as I thought at the time) that he was going to write a similar article on Booth himself. He has never done so.

"In a walk down Fifth Avenue which was very gay, we stopped in at an exhibition of William M. Chase's paintings and met Cecilia Beaux looking very keen, very vigorous, and quietly assured. Her own exhibition has been most successful. She is considered one of the strongest of our women painters at this time, and in this we are agreed."

One day in late March I received from Andrew Carnegie a handsomely engraved invitation to a dinner which he was giving at his home in honor of Sidney Lee, the English Shakespearean scholar. That "the Iron-master" aspired to be a literary arbiter, and that he had been giving a series of literary dinners, I knew, but I had never met him. I could not believe that he had ever read a line of my writing, and to be included in the list of his guests surprised me and aroused my curiosity. I accepted the invitation, suspecting that my name had been suggested to him by Gilder or Mabie.

On my way to the Carnegie mansion on Fifth Avenue at Ninetieth Street (which seemed very far uptown at that time), I fell in with Ernest Thompson Seton who, though less surprised, was equally curious as to the millionaire's purpose in giving this dinner.

He received us in his vast reception hall, a beaming, small Santa Claus, not at all the kind of steel-and-granite superman I had expected to encounter. No one had described him to me as he now appeared, a diminutive Scotch dominie, ruddy, white-whiskered, and kindly. I could not find in him the slightest sign of the power and insight he was reported to possess.

The guests were assembled in the noble hall on the Fifth Avenue side of the house, and I was amazed to find there many of my distinguished literary friends, Howells, Burroughs, Matthews, Gilder, Stedman, Mabie, university presidents, together with the heads of several newspapers and a group of weighty financiers. The more I studied the situation the more I resented this patronization of literature on the part of an iron merchant. By what authority did he bring these men of arts and letters to his palace?

Led by a group of glorious Scotch pipers we marched out to dinner, all smiling with pleasure in the theatrical side of it. To most of us it was a play—a pageant. The dining room was spacious and splendid and the huge table was covered (as we learned later) with a cloth especially woven to cover it. Mrs. Carnegie, the only woman present, sat at the head of the table and our host explained that she wished each of us to write our names, in our accustomed way, on the cloth before our plate. "Mrs. Carnegie will then embroider your signatures in silk," he added.

Mrs. Carnegie, a plain, modest, housewifely person, looked precisely like a woman who would take pleasure in such needlework, and my feeling of resentment did not extend to her. She assumed no airs of patronage, made no pretensions to grandeur. Aware of her democratic origin, she was proud of her intellectual guests.

My resentment softened as I studied the host. He had a vein of humor, slender, but very real, and his introductory speech displayed an inherited veneration for scholarship which disarmed me. He was Scotch in this regard. Granting that he had no intention of passing judgment upon the literary quality of his guests, he was nevertheless in a false position. That his introductions were prepared for him I could not doubt, and in some cases it was clearly evident that he would have been helpless without the actual text of his commendation.

The responses by his guests were able and tactful— just the kind of literary commerce I would have reveled in had it not been for a persistent sense of our host's helplessness. Why didn't he ask Gilder or Matthews to act as toastmaster? Why pretend to a knowledge he did not possess?

What gave me most concern was the conviction that money could command genius and genius would obey.

"Any reputable millionaire could bring to his table the most illustrious men and women in America, that is evident," I said. "Carnegie can do what Howells cannot do for lack of servants, dining hall, and bank account." If I sensed the attitude of my fellow authors correctly they, too, felt the relationship here shown to be false. "Carnegie without his millions would not have interested any of us," I said to Burroughs. "I appreciate the kindliness and hospitality of the old ironmaster, but I decline to take him seriously as a patron of the arts."

In reflecting upon it afterward, I made this record: "After all, I prefer to be patronized by Carnegie rather than by some woman with nothing but the power of inherited wealth. The ideal situation would be to have a great artist like Sargent and a great fictionist like Howells acting as hosts in a palace, calling to their tables the noblest intellectuals of their time—but such combinations do not form. We must be content with our Carnegies, grateful for their willingness to play the rôle of patron, and applauding them for playing it so well."

To show the spirit in which we all left the place, I quote this entry: "It happened that Seton, Burroughs, Gilder, and I slipped out together and as the doorman inquired solicitously about our carriage, I said, 'Gilder, you should have saved the situation for us by ordering a cab.'

"'I *have* saved it by wearing a silk hat, the only one in the party,' he replied, and in this mood of democratic scoffing we left the portal of our Iron Duke!"

II

In leaving for the West a few days later, I took, for reading on the train, Gorky's "Barefoot Brigade."

"This is the antithesis of all that Carnegie's house and his dinners expressed," was my comment. "It is a very powerful book—a harsh, unlovely book, quite unlike any other Russian's work, yet of the Russian genius."

Two days later I was back in prosaic little West Salem, Wisconsin, where the plum and cherry trees were in bloom, the apple trees in bud, and the sward irradiated with dandelions. "The strawberry patch is flecked with blossoms. The mourning dove is calling and butterflies adorn the grass. The bees are working like harvesters—so busy, so eager that they tumble over one another. The forests on the hills are billows of pink and amber and purple. I have never known a more ecstatic spring day. Our commonplace village is transformed by this heavenly bloom.

"Inspired by the glory of the morning, I wrote an entire chapter in my novel, and for the remaining afternoon lazed in the hammock absorbing the peace and beauty of the garden. I opened every avenue to the light, the odors, the sounds as I have not done before this year. The air invited it. It was gracious to the heart—concealing no dangers."

In this peaceful, prosperous scene I finished reading "Foma" by Gorky, a most depressing, unsatisfactory story, but a book of power. "The chief character is very Russian," I wrote; "no other nation has his like. The whole volume seems directed against the merchants who sprang from the peasants, but ceasing to work like peasants, found insufficient outlet for their physical vitality and so rushed into vice. Their sons and daughters wander the world in search of a key to life's riddle. Such writing now seems useless to me.

"To-night sitting on our porch and quietly absorbing sound, color, light, I am for a moment filled with a sense of completeness, of having at hand all the elements of happiness. A comfortable home over my head and before me a luscious valley with spreading trees, flowers, moonlight, and a lovely horizon line. Fundamentally these are the things to which most Americans return for rest and recreation—and yet, at times, my neighbors depress me. The small town of the West has become the old people's home, a refuge into which our prosperous farmers and their wives drift when they are bent and gray, to wear out a few years of increasing decrepitude."

Surrounded by these melancholy derelicts of a more heroic day, I welcomed another invitation to give a series of lectures at the University of Chicago. A summer in my native town would have palled upon me.

In preparation for this work I got out the manuscript of my youthful unpublished volume on "The Art of Edwin Booth," and selected Macbeth and Hamlet as two of the five addresses I had agreed to give. I decided on "Poets of the New Eldorado" for the third, and "Sidney Lanier" for the fourth, and for the finishing number I announced a reading from my own stories of the red people.

The Booth lectures proved unexpectedly successful. They appealed especially to the dramatic editor on the *Tribune,* who gave a column or more to their discussion. The lecture on Lanier was applauded by all the Southern teachers, who were numerous among my auditors, and at the suggestion of George Vincent, the manager of the Assembly at Chautauqua Lake, I arranged to repeat these talks in his course of lectures. These summer assemblies were a feature of many localities at this time and a host of "entertainers" flitted from tent to tent to supply their demand for diversion. I had grave doubt of Vincent's wisdom in calling for me, but I went!

Leaving the train at Lakewood, I crossed by bus to the boat landing and sailed up the lake—a disappointing experience, so tame were its shores and so populous. The annual plague of sand flies was at its worst, and my lecture that night (ill-suited to the enormous auditorium and my audience) was delivered amid a cloud of these pests. They fluttered about my head in millions and my auditors were so busy fighting them that my words were lost. Uneasy folk came and went noisily, and I ended by shouting the sentences I had so carefully composed.

George Vincent, a handsome, rapid-fire speaker, who presided over the educational side of the program, was idolized by his camp, and I shared this admiration. To see these work-worn women from tasteless village homes listening to his inspiring voice and to the really fine music of the programs in the auditorium, was pathetic. "Such women are not easy to define; they read—read studiously, and yet they cannot be called artistic or literary. They are strivers, seekers after knowledge of some sort—any sort, timid seekers, halting and conservative, housewives who feel the need of inspiration and have come here to share in an intellectual 'protracted meeting.' Vincent understands this and sympathizes with it. He is their shepherd."

Notwithstanding Vincent's support, I knew that my addresses were of little interest to these worthy souls. The speakers they liked were those who mingled comic instances with wise saws, giving instruction in sugared doses. My serious, carefully phrased essays bored the majority—only a few held on to the end. I left with a full knowledge that I had been a failure and that Vincent would never experiment with me again.

My self-respect was partially restored by another invitation from President Roosevelt to luncheon at the White House and I find in my diary this entry:

"August 27. Taking the noon train for Oyster Bay I reached Sagamore Hill at one. A group of politicians were at the President's table, but after I came in he talked mainly of the Rocky Mountains and of his Rough Riders. 'They all call me "Colonel," ' he said with humorous inflection, 'and they ask for all kinds of queer favors. One man wrote requesting me to get him out of jail. 'I'm in for shooting my wife,' he said, 'but, Colonel, I didn't go for to do it. I was shooting at another lady.' This appealed to the literary side of the President. The use of the word 'lady' was delicious.

"He was quite happy and fairly bulging with physical power. His shirt, a blue negligée, was rumpled, he wore no vest, and his tie was sadly crumpled. His rather short legs were clothed in khaki-colored leg-o'-mutton riding trousers and leather leggings. Altogether he looked as if he had just come in from a hard ride—

which was the fact. His vigor is unabating. We talked of wild animals, the Rocky Mountains, and of our mutual friends, Burroughs, Seton, and Muir. Later we fell upon a discussion of Lincoln's reported fondness for 'smutty' stories and Roosevelt said, 'That has always grieved me sorely. Grant's refusal to have such stories told in his presence is greatly to his honor.'

"Roosevelt's campaign against 'nature faking' was just beginning and I was desirous that he should not include Seton. To make a test of this I bluntly said, 'I hope you are not including "Wild Animals I Have Known," among the books you are condemning.'

"He reflected for a moment in consideration of my friendship for Seton, then said slowly, 'As *stories* based on wild animal life, I have no criticism to make of that book, but Seton in his preface goes too far in emphasizing the scientific value of his tales. If he had brought the book out on its merits as fiction—as a free transcription of animal life, no one would have accused him of "pulling a long bow." As stories they are admirable and in general they are based on accurate observation.'

"Unable to take exception to this kindly judgment, I went on to describe Seton's long shelf of notebooks filled with sketches, measurements, and notes stained with the mud and snow and blood of the field. 'He is a prodigious worker,' I said, 'and leaves as little to memory as a zoölogist. He makes his notes as he trails. His influence on the young people of the day is enormous and altogether wholesome!'

"'I grant all that,' Roosevelt replied; 'but he should draw the line more clearly between his fiction and his zoölogy.'"

On my return to Seton's home I told him substantially what the President had said, and while it was not as favorable as he had hoped, I think he felt relieved. To be included among "The Nature Fakers" by Roosevelt and Burroughs was no joke.

During the evening while Seton sat drawing, some remark of mine started him on the story of his career and he talked till after midnight—an absorbingly interesting chronicle. Concerning it I wrote the next morning: "His life has been most extraordinary in its vicissitudes. Some day he will write it and it will be a gloomy, bitter tale. 'My father, harshly pious, was a stern parent and a rigid disciplinarian. He came from the north of England with his family and settled in Toronto. Naturally I drifted over the line into Dakota, then back into Manitoba,' he said. He has made his own way, as I have, but he has gone much farther than I. His courage and his ability in three lines of endeavor make my powers seem feeble."

While staying at his home, I wrote and rewrote the concluding chapters of "Hesper," the novel which was to follow "The Captain of the Gray Horse Troop." Duneka and Leigh both liked this manuscript and said it might outsell anything I had ever done—not excepting "The Captain." This gave me such ground of assurance that I took one of the fast trains for home feeling a little like a successful author. Harper's in their advertising of "The Captain" had made my name known to a wide public. "People will know of me whether they buy my books or not," I wrote to Duneka.

"You stay with us," he replied, "and we'll see that people read what you are writing."

On the train I read "A Little Journey in the World" by Charles Dudley Warner, a curious mixture of the old and the new in fiction. I also read "Balaam and His Master," a book of short stories by Joel Chandler Harris. "One of these tales, which dealt with the pathetic life of a faithful negro, put a big lump into my throat—and the fiction which does that for me, these days, must needs be vitally true. Harris is a genius."

I had good reason for rejoicing in the success of "Hesper." I was now a father, with a daughter to consider. I counted my days of controversial writing at an end. As a householder I was in league with the capitalistic forces of society. Like the Irish reformer in the old story I found myself changed.

"Pat," said the judge, "if you had two million dollars, would you give away half of them?"

"I would that."

"If you had ten houses, would you give away five of them?"

"Sure I would."

"If you had two goats, would you give away one of them?"

"I WOULD not—I *have* two goats."

CHAPTER THIRTEEN

ANOTHER WINTER IN NEW YORK

I

OCTOBER 22, 1903, found me again in New York City as one of the guests at another dinner to Mark Twain at the Metropolitan Club, with Colonel Harvey presiding. The company was not as notable as that which greeted Mark on his seventieth birthday but it was a distinguished circle when all were counted. Colonel Harvey presented the speakers in the dryly humorous fashion he loved to employ. Pretending that he was speaking for Mark who was unable, for some reason, to speak for himself, he began, "I know what Mr. Clemens is thinking and I shall report it to you." Some of this introduction was witty and some of it was labored.

It appeared that the dinner was in celebration of a very important contract which Harper's had just made with Clemens; and John Pierpont Morgan was at Harvey's left as a silent partner of the publishing firm. I had never seen the great banker before and I studied him with care. "He is a large man with inflamed eyes and a huge nose—a terrible nose, knobby, misshapen, and repulsive. I had heard of this deformity, but had formed no conception of its terrifying ugliness. It is a frightful affliction. Aside from this abnormality, however, he looked the part of a great financier, powerful, brooding, lionlike. He is no small Carnegie or Harriman; he is a giant. He smiled rather grimly during Mark's speech, wherein he boasted of hiring his own lawyer in order to hold his own with his publishers. "For the first time in my life," he declared, "my interests have been fully protected."

He was amusing in the terms of his candid and savage exultation, and Harvey and Duneka both smiled at it, but to Morgan it was not so funny. He was a bit uneasy under it—so was Howells for another reason. "All that Mark said was true, but was it politic to have it so set down?" he said to me afterward. My own comment reads:

"This is Clemens' high-water mark. He is out of debt. His books are selling enormously, and by this new contract, he is assured the lion's share of the profits—and yet, beneath his bragging, ran a current of darker meaning. He is an old man and a sad man—with a dying wife, an ailing daughter, and a growing sense of his own failing fires. I am glad of his moment of triumphant security."

Another of the public men in New York who interested me, but whom I had never met, was Seth Low, who had been President of Columbia University and mayor of the city. Moved by the talk of his reëntrance into politics, I went up to the Central Palace to hear him speak. My comment at the time was: "He is a calm, rather cold, speaker. His choice of words is unusually good but he has nothing of the flamboyant orator in tone or phrase. I fear he is *too* fine, *too* level-headed, too much the gentleman to be re-elected. He is a noble

American and we would be in luck to have him for mayor of this new and greater New York but the chances are against it. The smaller man will get the nomination—that's the way a democracy works out."

"October 29. In reading Henry James' 'Bostonians' to-day, I was carried back to the Boston I knew in 1884—the South End of Boston. What a drab, ratty, crack-brained place it was! How decayed and moth-eaten and smelly those old houses on the side streets were. All kinds of 'isms' developed there, and James has recorded some of them. John Finley was at the Players and we ate luncheon together. He is greatly pleased by his selection to be the head of the University of New York, although it will take him out of his lovely home in Princeton. He is one of the finest Americans I know. Like Roosevelt, he is a compound of East and West. I wish he were not in the opposing political camp."

For several weeks my wife and I were guests of Katharine Herne at "Herne Oaks," the home which James A. had completed just before his death. It was a large frame house on the shore of Peconic Bay, about seven miles north from Southampton Station on the Long Island Railway, and although it took three hours to "commute" I did so gladly both for the beauty of the place and the pleasure I took in Katharine and her daughters.

On these trips I usually carried a book and read till I got clear of the dreadful Long Island side of New York. One of the books I read at this time was "Sister Carrie" by a writer named Dreiser. "It is a relentless, plodding, powerful book not unlike Norris' 'Mc-Teague'—a serious, well-intentioned book but wholly in the French school of Zola. It has no grace, no evidences of cultivation, but it has verity. The author is unknown to me. From his name I take him to be the son of a German."

One day at the club I had Owen Wister for table companion and as we met but seldom (he was a home-keeping Philadelphian) I welcomed an opportunity to renew our acquaintance. I set down my impression of him in these words:

"He is a singularly engaging personality—fine, self-contained, yet modest. He has a curiously shifting yet keen glance—a little like Howells in this. He is not a man who invites confidences or wins regard easily, from a stranger. Handsome, graceful, and of vigorous frame, I can easily imagine his being quickly 'spotted' by cowboys as an Eastern dude or tourist. His cultivated voice and courteous manners betray him. He is immensely worth while. His head and shoulders remind me of Roosevelt—of whom, by the way, he is a close friend and admirer."

One of the plays which I saw at this time was "Major André," by Clyde Fitch. Much was expected of it, but according to my record it turned out to be "a poor, flimsy play; Chrystal Herne as the girl character was pretty and interesting in spite of the lines. We all went home with Katharine Herne, who opened a bottle of champagne in order that we might drink a toast to her as the proud mother of a talented daughter. It was a jolly party and, in the glow of it, Chrystal seemed entering at last upon a brilliant career. She was greatly excited, for it was the best part she had ever had. 'I can't sleep,' she confessed. 'I must lie awake and wait for the morning papers.' Katharine was radiant, like her old self—and Jeanette Norris and my wife were lovely as roses."

Alas! the papers next day were harshly critical. They damned the play unanimously and gave Chrystal but scant praise. It was a gray morning for us all. "How characteristic of the stage all this is!" I wrote. "Last night the actress, radiant with hope, intoxicated with applause, owned the city. To-day she is in black despair, and yet she is big enough to say, 'They are right!' Being young she has abundant time to prove them wrong—so far as she is concerned."

Again I was a guest at a Colonel Harvey dinner—this time in honor of Lucy, the editor of *Punch*. "He is a funny-looking little man and (like his paper) not as comic as he appears. He made a great deal of his acquaintance with Mark Twain. I sat beside William Merrill of the *World* and had much talk with him. He had the appearance of a handsome clergyman but swore like a pirate. He was very amusing and put into words many bright ideas of journalism. 'Come down and see me. I'll show you how the *World* is edited and printed,' he said, and this I promised to do.

"These dinners of Harvey's, I begin to suspect, are in reality 'on the house,' and serve a publicity purpose. They are notable in their guests and interesting in their speaking, however, and I shall continue to accept whenever he includes me in his list."

"November 30. Henry Harland was at the National Institute dinner to-night, and his 'extroinery' English accent was comical. He spoke quite like the caricatured Englishman of our comedy stage. He is completely expatriated now and unpleasantly aggressive in his defense of England and English ways.

"Lounsbury was present and asked me to come to Yale. 'I want you to talk at one of my smokers,' he said, and this I took as another evidence of my 'success.' Henry van Dyke confirmed this judgment by renewing a request that I come to Princeton to meet his English Club.

"Well, if I am ever to arrive I must begin, for I am turned forty-three. Augustus Thomas, who is really prosperous, was a joyous figure, but Edward MacDowell, who sat beside me, troubled me in moments of repose by a strangely sad, almost vacant, expression, a look I had never detected before. Boyish and sparkling as ever when animated, this blank look in repose frightened me. He was like a man utterly tired out and in danger of collapse. I decided to warn Marian. To him I said, 'You are overworking.' He admitted this but added, 'I see no help for it. I must teach to earn a living.' This was in allusion to his resignation from Columbia."

II

After some rather anxious days of apartment hunting I found one on Morningside Avenue—opposite Morningside Park, just below the melancholy fragment of the cathedral, and there we settled down for the winter. With my small daughter taking the air in a basket on the fire escape, I toiled at my desk in a room overlooking the park. It was a modest place, but our faithful friends found us out and came to call. The Norrises and the Hernes were near neighbors and another advantage of the situation was the Columbia University gymnasium to which President Butler, with friendly ukase, had given me free entrance.

"December 8. We saw Shaw's 'Candida' at the Princess Theater, an amazingly good performance which gripped me intellectually, morally, and emotionally. I have not been so moved in a long time. Such a performance makes a city worth while. To me the play has something of the vague appeal of music. It is difficult to analyze the precise sources of its power, but it has deep suggestion and restrained force. I naturally recalled that the first production of it was in Chicago by Anna Morgan's School—a good reading of it."

On the Sunday following, Arnold Daly, who was producing the play, called to see me and we talked of Shaw and his work until nearly midnight. "Daly impressed me as an intelligent and forceful fellow but self-absorbed and egotistic like most of his associates. He *smelled* of the theater—but he has ideals and is willing to fight for them. He wanted me to tell him all I knew about Shaw and to aid him in getting other of Shaw's plays, which I promised to do.

"He *acted* every moment, assuming the accent and manner of his critics, his managers and his co-stars, reviving in me all the familiar sensations I used to have when in the presence of Kellerd, Lackaye, Mary Shaw, and others of my theatrical friends. I liked it when I was younger; I find it a bit boring now. Daly interested me notwithstanding my prejudice."

"January 9, 1904, the Markhams came to lunch, and confirmed us in our notions of them. They are ineradicably Western. Mrs. Markham is plain housewife, but he is as handsome as ever and somewhat less boisterous.

"He talked well and soberly, not to say learnedly, and was distinctly deferential to me—too much so. He made me feel older than I am. He took me quite as seriously as he takes himself. 'We are both men of letters,'" he said.

That night I spoke (as guest of honor) for the Campfire Club. "As the members rose and gave me three cheers and a tiger twice repeated, waving their napkins at the close (the most respectful greeting I have ever had) I almost respected myself. Dan Beard, who was toastmaster, paid me a moving tribute—indeed it was his introduction which provoked the demonstration."

"January 11. We dined last night with J. Hambleton Sears and wife, meeting Burgess Johnson and Miss Aldrich. A jolly party. Miss Aldrich, who had visited John D. Rockefeller, told us many amusing stories of the old man's parsimony. 'He burns oil to save gas, and skimps on food and fuel. He cannot bear to see anything wasted, and goes about turning out gas to cut down bills. Large in many ways, he is irritatingly small in others.' With all this care I sympathize. I don't like to see anything wasted."

One afternoon I stood for five mortal hours listening to "Parsifal."

"At the close I was 'dead on the hoof,' more exhausted than I have been at any time since my trip to the Klondike. It was a magnificent spectacle, but the music, in comparison with 'Siegfried' or 'Tristan,' seemed mild,

not to say weak. The orchestration was a disappointment. I had expected vast and splendid harmonies unrolling a continuous web like those in 'The Ring,' but
they did not come. True, I saw and heard it all under
painful physical difficulties, but it had nothing of the
robust, joyous swell of his Northern pagan songs. Its
monastic outcries were tiresome. The choruses seemed
perfunctory, like those of a church service.

"In dining at Frank Doubleday's, we met Mr. Frank
Mead, whom the President has just made General Supervisor of all the Indian reservations of the Southwest.
Mead had done good work for the Mohave Apaches and
is a vigorous, tactful, and brave citizen. He has precisely the right position, one that I have long hoped to
see filled by a man of his independent character. He is
poor and gets only two thousand per year, but this does
not daunt him. He can do and will do good work. His
story of his interviews with Roosevelt was thrilling.
'The President values Grinnell and Garland very
highly,' he said, in recounting his plea for the Pueblo
people."

"January 23. On arriving in New Haven I went
directly to the Graduate Club, where Professor Lounsbury met me. One by one others of the faculty came in
to sit about our table and drink cocktails. Dr. Jenkins
of the Philosophical School was very amusing, and so
was Dr. Smythe in a grim way. Lounsbury, rubicund
and jolly, acted as host. After dinner I gave my 'Joys
of the Trail' in the club parlors to about one hundred
auditors, mostly faculty members. The men of Western
experience were naturally most enthusiastic, and the
entire experience was highly flattering to me. Louns-

bury, my sponsor, seemed pleased with the impression I left on his fellows."

At the Aldine Club the following day, Hamilton Wright Mabie, Robert Underwood Johnson, Edward MacDowell, and I had a serious and detailed discussion of a plan for the reorganization of the National Institute of Arts and Letters. Afterward MacDowell and I called upon Howells and presented the plan which involves the election from the Institute of a Senate. We had a spirited conference. Howells doubted the wisdom of the decision, but was willing to add his name to the call for a meeting to vote upon it. I said, "It is suggested that this 'Senate' should be known as the American Academy of Arts and Letters. Mabie and Johnson are moving spirits in the plan, with MacDowell and myself as supporters."

On the following day I again met Johnson and MacDowell and we discussed Howells' objection and elaborated the plan for an Academy. At the close of our session I wrote a dozen letters in advocacy of it. "I see in it a counterbalance to the increasing vulgarity of newspaper criticism," I argued in justification of it.

At a meeting of the Sequoyah League, January 27, Seton and Grinnell both spoke and I presented the story of Frank Mead's wonderful work among the Apaches. "Charley Russell, the 'cowboy painter,' a rugged, blunt, blond man who might almost have been a Scotch half-breed, was present; J. N. Marchand, a very capable artist of Western scenes, who has illustrated some of my stories, and Miss Natalie Curtis, compact of enthusiasm and righteous indignation, were in evidence, while Edward Deming, Frederick Dellen-

baugh, and other 'cranks' on Indians added to the Wild
West character of the audience.

"Such a group is much more important than its numbers indicate, for it is composed of men and women
experienced in the West and its problems. An enormous
amount of specific knowledge was there represented.
Men like Grinnell and Dellenbaugh are especially important as historians of the plains, while Russell and Deming
are putting them into line and color, and Natalie Curtis
is gathering Amerind songs and preserving them for
future composers.

"Late in the month, while reading for the Women's
Henry George League, Miss Isabel Colbron presided
and I had for auditor my fellow citizen Ella Wheeler
Wilcox, who sat on the platform clothed in a gorgeous
gown of satin and spangles. Exotic as she looked, she
spoke of her girlhood in Madison, Wisconsin, where she
used to deliver milk for her mother. She didn't admit
this—but such is the story. At the close of this meeting I walked over to the Curtis home to meet a group
of Indian enthusiasts. Natalie Curtis sang very beautifully several wistful Hopi songs, and Mr. Loomis,
composer of Indian music, played some of his own
transcriptions, all of which showed the power which
the Algonquin has brought to bear on our art. The
spirit of the red man will come more and more into
our music as the years grow, but as MacDowell has
used it, interpreting it rather than reporting it. Miss
Curtis has the interest and support of Roosevelt in her
plan to preserve the songs of the Pueblos."

Henry Fuller came on from Chicago to attend the
Institute dinner, the first he had shared. It was a small

meeting, but important, for we discussed in detail the idea of an Academy, which seemed to meet with general approval. Some were moved to enthusiasm. Fuller was disappointed by the sparse attendance, but as he met several loyal admirers he could not complain of neglect.

He lunched with me at the club next day, and afterward called on Ellen Glasgow whom we found very alert, very charming, but quite deaf. "She manages her problem deftly, but once or twice failed to catch what Fuller said and did not ask for a repetition. Why is it that deaf people are so loath to admit their infirmity? Blind people are not so? At night, Fuller took us all to the theater to see William Gillette in Barrie's play, 'The Admirable Crichton,' a searching and original satire on English society. Amusing as it was it contained a solid shot at caste. We were all immensely stimulated by it. Gillette was most delightful in the part. What writer is so unexpected in his advance as this man Barrie? Each new work is a surprise."

Fuller was disappointed in the Authors' Club reception. "I had the hope of meeting a few authors," he said, "but there are none to be seen." As we wandered about he cynically sized up the talent present. He suggested a supercilious cockerel, as he went about, eying everybody and everything with his head on one side, maintaining a bland, expectant air, as if awaiting a revelation which never came. I was in the situation of a host who had expected to show my Western guest some of the literary men of whom I had so often written. "I can give no reason for the failure of the first-class men to attend these teas. Recalling the lively meetings of the club before it was endowed, I wonder whether we are not too comfortable."

"One afternoon we all saw Arnold Daly in 'Candida' and in 'The Man of Destiny'—a fine double performance. In the evening we attended the first production of 'The Pit,' which we found turgidly melodramatic—hardly worthy the book. The producer had seized upon the cheaper side of the story which is not quite worthy of Norris, anyhow."

III

Fuller was not included in my second invitation to dinner at Carnegie's on the 11th and I was sorry that he was not, for another fine body of literary men came together. "We are all eager to listen when money talks! The quaint, white-bearded little Scotchman again showed his power to assemble genius. His introductions of the various speakers were apt and amusing and the responses were extremely good. He called upon me after reading an introduction obviously prepared for him; but I, taken by surprise, pleaded exemption on the score that my name had already been written on the table-cloth. I really had nothing to say.

" 'Why is it?' I asked Mabie, 'that this Iron Founder can gather round him more of our distinguished writers than the National Institute's dinners can command? If he cared to do it he could organize a Literary Academy of his own.' Mabie had no explanation to offer other than 'we all like to touch elbows with millionaires!'

"Mrs. Carnegie, kindly, genial, had little to contribute; she sat at the head of the table till the speaking began, then slipped away. As the guests made adroit addresses I felt out of key with it all. 'What are we doing here? To what does this patronization of literature by fortuitous wealth lead?'—I remarked afterward to Burroughs. 'I can't quite reconcile myself to it. Roosevelt stands in different case. He is not rich and he is himself a writer—he knows! I rejoice when he assembles a group of writers at the White House, but Carnegie has only money. I shall accept no more of these invitations."

"You may not have another," said Burroughs.

One of the men who had aroused my interest while a student in Boston was a Kansas lawyer and poet, Eugene F. Ware; and although we had kept up a correspondence during these many years, I had never met him till, at a reception in the home of Albert Bigelow Paine, I found him surrounded by a throng of authors and critics. He was a big man, handsome, smiling, and quick-witted. "This is, in a sense, my literary 'coming out' in the East," he said. "I have enjoyed political recognition and legal honors in Kansas, but this is my first appearance in New York as a poet."

His verses had appealed to me strongly, but I had little opportunity to tell him so. We exchanged a few words of greeting, and then he turned to other curious or admiring guests. "The truth is he has shown unusual facility in the use of verse forms, and his lines on Kansas, his poem on the sod house, and others in his first volume have vibrant music as well as imagination."

Despite the fact of my brother's experience on the stage and my close association with the Hernes, and other theatrical folk, I had never made use of this material in fiction till now. To me one of the most astonishing phases of dramatic life had been the startling difference between the character on the stage and the actress in her home. To go from the posters of their characters to their quiet private life was reassuring as well as revealing. "Why not compose a novelette in which these contrasts shall play a leading part?" asked Fuller. "I can and I will," I replied. I called it "The Glittering Woman," but Bok, who liked it and bought it for his *Journal*, changed its title to "The Light of the Star." It was not an important work, but it had a real theme, and is one of the few of my stories which touch upon city life. Harper's were willing to publish the book and I set about preparing the copy for them.

The exact mood in which I wrote is worth recalling: "I worked at revising 'The Star' till eleven, then went down to the office to decide about the date of publication of the book. I am less impressed with the wisdom of my publishers than formerly. They know very little more about book-publishing than I do. They are all taking chances, all gambling. They *hope* this book or that book or *some* book will succeed. If none of them do, they heave a sigh and try again. They are like owners of race-horses. When they hit upon a winner, they push that particular brute to the neglect of the others. I find it all rather sickening. The 'blurb' has become repulsive to me.

"In dining at C. C. Buell's house, I came to know Oliver Herford. He was 'remote' of mood, however, and not at all as amusing as his hostess had expected him to be. He is already a kind of legendary figure at the Players and is credited with many quaint sayings, some of which he really uttered. He has come to be an institution and as a dinner guest is 'obleeged' to be funny. In truth he is a serious thinker, and a good deal of a radical."

Howells, who liked Fuller, invited him (and me) to a luncheon at the Century Club. Their talk was as literary as any I have ever heard. "I go very soon to discover England," Howells explained, "hitherto, I have visited England only in the most casual manner on my way to and from the Continent." As Fuller knew Italy as thoroughly as Howells, there was much talk of its history and its art, to which I listened with keen enjoyment.

As we came away, I said to Fuller, "Howells is not one who makes friends easily. He loves to meet people, all kinds of people, for an hour, but he is not disposed to take them into intimacy. In this he appears singular and a little uncanny. He is always critical of his visitors, although his judgments are kindly."

One Sunday night Senator Beveridge took supper at our table, and Miss Mary Fanton, who sat opposite him, was greatly amused by him. "Panoplied in all the authority and pride of the country politician, he dominated the company. His egotism is ludicrous and yet he is a fine, clean-minded, able senator. With no slightest sense of humor, he is unable to take as well as to give in conversation. He sincerely believes that the making of laws, any kind of laws, is the greatest business in the world and talks endlessly of 'the mighty legislative loads' he is bearing up the hill. He allowed small room for discussion of any subject or person other than politics and himself.

"Juliet Tompkins and Mary Fanton listened to him gravely while he discoursed on the sphere of women and the solemn duty of the Christian nations in disciplining the earth. They slyly made fun of his ideas and assumptions, asking questions which led him on to other absurdities. He was not used to women of this roguish, wit-loving kind and had no realization that they were both making game of him."

At the Canadian Campfire dinner, I met the Rev. Mr. Long whose animal stories have become bones of contention among scientists and pseudo-scientists. "He is the man who gave rise to Roosevelt's phrase, 'nature faker,' and the whole country is discussing him. He is a tall, fervid, rather boyish clergyman, just the type to imagine things which could not happen. He never had the temper of the scientist, and while he may have convinced himself that a bird bandages its own leg, he can't convince John Burroughs. I am on Burroughs' side in this controversy, although I think John is too hard and fast in his generalizations. There *are* animal heroes. I have discussed this with him, calling to his mind the differing character of individual pigs or kittens in a litter. I forced him to admit that bold pigs and timid pigs, humorous pigs and querulous pigs, exist. 'Any one who has grown up on a farm knows these characters in the barnyard. Long, however, is in different case. He pulls too long a bow!"

In dining with us the following day, Burroughs admitted to a growing regard for Seton, and was willing to exempt him from the charge of nature faking.

CHAPTER FOURTEEN

MEXICO AND ITS PRESIDENT

I

As March came on, I began to plan a trip to Mexico—to inspect a mine which I had bought, and which my brother was working in the hills near the village of Camacho. We needed more capital and with designs on Irving Bacheller I suggested that his health would be greatly benefited by a trip to this mine. He was interested and said: "I'd like to have Archer Brown, a good friend of mine, accompany us. He is a man of large affairs and a good companion."

"Just the man!" I agreed. "I am getting pretty tired of writing books. As my mind now works, I am obliged to constantly revise all my manuscripts and this destroys any pleasure I might otherwise take in them. This may be due to growing weakness, or to a sharpening self-criticism, or it may be that it is only a deepening distaste for desk work, due to my hope of easy money in a mine. Whatever the cause I want to play for a month."

In preparation for this trip, we gave up our pleasant little apartment on Morningside Avenue and my wife returned to Chicago. Just before leaving for the South I went to West Point to deliver my illustrated lecture on "The Life of the Forest Ranger." I had not been at the Academy since making my studies for my "Life of Grant"; but I found the old hotel practically unchanged, a dreary place, almost empty—warmed, in spots, by gas stoves. Colonel Dudley escorted me to the new hall, and as the boys came marching in, five hundred of them—a superb exhibition of American young manhood—they made an inspiring audience. I did my best for them, and at the close they clapped their muscular hands with such robust accord that I was deceived into thinking my "show" a worthy one. I went away next morning in a glow of self-confidence.

Returning to Bacheller's Sound Beach home I found him entertaining Senator John B. Henderson of Iowa and his wife. "Henderson is a big, blustering, good-hearted, opinionated Scotchman, much more than the country lawyer and decidedly more than a congressman. We spent the evening sitting before the fire singing old songs. Upon Irving's urging I sang 'Lorena,' 'Lily Dale,' 'Maggie,' and 'Old Black Joe,' and Henderson's face shone with excitement as he countered with an old Scotch ballad which he sang with more gusto than grace. He was saved from being 'raw' by his sense of humor." (I never saw him again and he died, not long after, leaving a fine record.)

Easter was a cold gray day which I spent indoors reading Harry Leon Wilson's "Poor Judas," a remarkable study of the modern young man's conception of the Bible—an original and very interesting book. We had another pleasant day and evening. Bacheller was the most genial of hosts. We sat before his fire like two "old coots," digging up songs and discussing plots for stories and methods of lecturing. I gave him some hints on speaking which he said were most helpful to him. He was particularly amused by my rule, "Never start your mouth talking and go away and leave it."

"I shall put that into practice," he said.

We all came in on the ten o'clock train next day and, in lunching with Duneka, I met Harry Leon Wilson, and this is my record of it: "He is a thoughtful, rather dour character, but he took my criticisms of his book in good part. He is a hard worker, but his work lacks distinction. It is good but not fine. He has not surpassed 'The Spenders,' his first success."

On April 5, Irving Bacheller, Archer Brown, and I started on our trip to Mexico and on April 9 my brother met us at Camacho, a station on the Mexican Central. He resembled a lieutenant of cavalry who had seen hard service. Under his guidance we took trail for the mine, eighteen miles away—he and I riding in a cart, Bacheller and Brown on horseback—and for hours we crawled over a perfectly flat, cactus-covered plain toward hot, dry hills.

"It is a sinister land to me, arid as Sahara, a desolate place.

"My brother's chamber and office are situated in a cave or ancient mine, but his kitchen is outside. All about on the hillside his peon laborers are waiting like hungry animals, in many cases without shelter of any kind, hoping for a job. We went to bed in the cave, a novel situation for me and an amazing one for Irving and Brown, who are both accustomed to the most luxurious living."

We were all a little frazzled next morning, but managed to inspect the mine. I had the hope (unexpressed) that Brown, who was a man of large means, would buy into our mine, which yielded in truth a very rich and handsome ore. My brother and I had no capital to invest in machinery and so continued the "gophering" methods with which it had been worked for centuries. Gophering means that the miners not only bring the ore up out of the shaft on their backs but that they climb a series of notched tree trunks in place of ladders.

"The strength of these small brown men is prodigious. One of them brought up regularly two hundred pounds of ore on his back, all for less than a cent, and around him on the hills are scores of others envious of his job. It is heart-breaking. I wanted to say to my brother, 'Hire them all,' but the cool judgment of Archer Brown held me in check.

"In a few words he disclosed our folly. 'There is no water to work the ore, no roads to transport it to the smelter, and the cost of production is more than the ore will bring.' My expectations fell to zero. I told my brother to close the mine.

"During the day we took a ride to a high peak from which we caught a wide view of the valley, glorious of color, but a place of desolation. The spiny, thorny, bitter plants—the streamless gulches, the burning sand —were appalling to me, but the mocking bird, undismayed, had the heart to sing his slender melody!"

Toward midday, the heat became terrifying, and taking refuge in our dank cavern we remained there till the cool of the evening set in. There was something relentless in this waterless, sun-baked land, and my sympathy went out to the small, dark people waiting so patiently on the hills.

After a second night in our cave with very little sleep we rose early, for our "troglodytes," as we called Brown and Bacheller, were eager to escape, and at dawn we started for the station, my brother and I in the cart, the "boys," Brown and Bacheller, on horseback.

Our ride on the train toward San Luis Potosi was smothering. With windows tightly closed in order to keep out the driving sand, our Pullman was an inferno for many hours, but about five in the afternoon the sashes were raised and we once more drew breath. Brown had suffered acutely, for he was heavy and had a weak heart—as we afterward discovered. Irving worked on a manuscript part of the time, calmly oblivious to dust.

Arriving in Mexico City at noon of a brilliant day, I found it quite as beautiful as I had remembered it, and led the way to the ancient Iturbide Hotel, where I had stayed ten years before, with a feeling of confidence that it would be unchanged.

One of my friends in the city was Frederick Guernsey, editor of the Mexican *Herald,* and as we were lunching with him at the Jockey Club (a wonderful old building) he informed us that he had arranged (through Ambassador Clayton) an interview with President Diaz. At four o'clock Mr. McCreery of the embassy conducted us to the palace which resembled a French hotel of the second class. After passing several guarded doorways we came to the audience room, a large and handsome chamber.

While we stood looking at the pictures on the wall, Diaz entered silently, swiftly. My record reads: "He is a younger man than I had expected to see and much more amiable. He is seventy-four years old but looks about sixty. He is small, erect, composed, with the bearing of a Cheyenne chieftain. His face is dark of hue but handsome in line. His grace and restrained strength are almost tigerlike in their expression."

He greeted us smilingly, while Mr. McCreery explained that we were literary men and not reporters, and at once asked us to be seated. Addressing himself to Bacheller, he talked for some time of his admiration for the United States and of President Roosevelt. At last he turned to me and said, "Mr. McCreery tells me that you have visited some of our schools."

I replied that I had happened on one or two in my sight-seeing and that I had been much amused by the loud hum which came from them. He smiled and said, "Yes, we retain the ancient method of studying our lessons out loud." Then with a grave look on his face he said, "I am educating my children in republican forms of government so that when they are grown up they can select their rulers as your citizens do, by ballot."

I then said, "I have just returned from a visit to the caverns of Cacawamilpa."

His face lightened up again. "I know them well," he replied. "I visited them when a lad. There are two chains of them, the dry chain and the wet chain. A river still flows in the lower series. I explored both of these caverns to the end. They are over twenty miles long."

"You are a tradition there," I said. "They all know that you visited the village."

He was most unassuming, dignified, and friendly. He had the air of a sympathetic physician, with a deep, underlying sadness of philosophy. I felt in him something tragic, something hopeless, the despair of an aging ruler. He impressed me as a patriot of high native endowment, a dictator with an ideal. Whatever he had been in early manhood he now appeared mellowed and softened. Natively courteous, he was the commander, the ruler of men.

"Once as we rose to go he detained us. He was especially eager to know more about President Roosevelt, whom he greatly admires and hopes some time to meet. I told him that I had heard President Roosevelt speak of him with admiration, and to this he replied, 'I thank you, señor. It is not the first time I have heard of such words by President Roosevelt.' "

"Aguas Calientes, April 21. My brother met me at the train. The town is full of peons gambling, trading, cockfighting, parading to music, and the like. With Franklin as guide, I sat in at a cockfight, but did not stay very long. The fighting was rather disgusting to me, although the little scimitars which the men fastened over the spurs of the cocks were in effect merciful. Each battle ended in death and in an astonishingly short time.

"Gambling was everywhere going on. Tables were piled with shining silver coins, and scores of dirty, ragged, malformed men crowded about these tables too absorbed to even hear the wild singing of certain slobs of women whom the management had hired to amuse them. Even the fighting cocks were of less interest than the gambling. In disgust I took the train at 8:30 for the border."

This was one of the worst days I ever spent on a train. The heat in itself was torture, but in addition to this the dust whirled in blinding clouds about the coach, and as the windows were kept tightly closed, all the male passengers sat in their shirt sleeves gasping for air. An impalpable alkaline dust filled my nostrils and brought on a severe headache. At bedtime the conditions were worse. The night was interminable. It was like going through hell.

The dust was less suffocating after leaving Torreon, and the sense of getting nearer the line helped me live through a relentless day. On arrival at El Paso I boarded a Rock Island train for Kansas City, expecting to wake next morning in a green and pleasant land.

My interview with Diaz was the high place in my tour. In later years, when he suddenly resigned, I fancied I understood him. Old and tired and disheartened, he said, "Very well. You want another kind of ruler. Create him. Have your revolution. I have done my best to make a nation of you. Now I must rest."

I felt this growing disgust and sadness in his utterance that day. The only time his face lightened was when he spoke of the caverns and his boyish exploration of them.

When next I saw President Roosevelt I described my visit with Diaz and referred to my suggestion for a meeting at the national boundary. He became thoughtful. "I should like to do that," he said. He never found opportunity to do this and not long after Diaz resigned, went to Paris and died there, an exile.

CHAPTER FIFTEEN

THE SILENT MISSISSIPPI

WHEN I crossed the Mexican line I thought: "To-morrow I shall be in a green and fertile country," but as a matter of fact, when I awoke I looked out upon another dry and dusty land filled with gaunt cattle, a lonely, desolate land. The wind was blowing hard at seven and by noon it increased to a tempest which filled the car with dust mixed with fine red sand. The coaches lurched on their tracks like a string of drunken men. The cows in the tawny pastures leaned against the blast or crouched with backs to it, waiting with elemental patience for its end. In the streets of the wretched towns nothing moved but the soil which drifts into ridges like snow. Life seemed extinct. It was horrifying.

Two days later "I am in Wisconsin—another world! A soft haze lies over the hills and through the mellow sunlight robins are singing with thrilling glee. I have been helping plant potatoes and corn. As I look back over my three days' passage from Mexico City to the Pan Handle, it seems like a journey through a tunnel of hot and dusty Pullman cars. From my present point of view the whole trip was a foolish waste of time and money, and yet it added enormously to my knowledge of Mexico and its president. My story of the caverns should pay the cost of it."

As a matter of fact it did just that. I sold the article to the New York *Herald* and so squared myself with Don Temple, who had counted upon my doing something of the kind.

When Fuller came up to spend a week or two with us I told him of my next "job." I said, "I am meditating a novel based on my twenty years of psychic experiences."

"Why not?" he replied. "It lies outside your 'main-traveled road,' but this fund of valuable material should be used. I see no reason why you should not do what interests you."

I set to work next day and wrote two chapters of a novel which I called "The Tyranny of the Dark." The plot was simple. It was the story of a young girl who as a child had been set aside by her parents as an instrument of communication between the realm of the dead and the world of the living. All her time, her vitality had been devoted to this work. She had suffered the physical and mental strain of long sittings in the dark, and was now tortured by the knowledge that, to her young companions, she was a kind of monster. She had the interests of other girls, she looked like them, but failed of their love and confidence. She was always "the medium"—something strange, unwholesome, and repellent. Lovely as she was, her playmates pitied her or avoided her.

Beyond this lay another and still more terrifying fact. She knew that she was a slave to certain unseen forces. Night after night she was called upon to lose herself in trance, to surrender her own will in order that through her the people of the shadow world might manifest. They had come to tyrannize over her. They controlled her life. She had begun to rebel against this. "I don't want to be different from other girls. I want to be like them! I want to sing, to dance, to enjoy my youth." But against this her father laid the weight of his creed: "It is your duty. God has given you this power in order that you may comfort the bereaved. How can you close the door between us and those who have passed on?"

This concept of a medium's life had been gained from many contacts with "sensititives" through a long term of years, and also from the experiences of my mother and one of her sisters who confessed that for several years the "invisibles" had made life a hell for her. I had witnessed the distressing and destructive physical effects of mediumship, and I had carried out hundreds of experiments, in the attempt to gain some explanation of the phenomena. Now I decided, once for all, to free my mind of this material, with fiction as a vehicle for its expression. I argued that the use of a psychic theme was as legitimate as that of any other phase of life. "Rightly used it can be of lasting interest," I said to my publishers.

It is significant that while discussing this dark problem, Fuller and I were walking our lovely countryside, and I find records like these: "This valley is beautiful, in its kind, beyond even the power of verse to express. Luscious green fields alternate with velvet-smooth slopes of pasture rising to wooded hills. The trees swim in a warm mist. The birds riot in song; the cattle seen through vistas of haze are like dream cattle, arousing dim memories of my childhood. On all sides the landscape expresses security, distinction, and bounteous appeal to the eye. As we walk, Fuller, groaning and sighing in a kind of ecstasy of admiration, repeats, 'All this country needs is *people*. It is as lovely as Surrey.'"

In the midst of the writing of this novel came an invitation from my friends, Mary and Fred Easton, to join them on a houseboat voyage down the Mississippi to St. Louis, and I was tempted. "It will break into my work; it may imperil my story, but the thought of loitering down that noble stream in the luxury and quiet ease of a floating bungalow is too coercive to be resisted, especially as Mary Easton assures me that I can have a quiet place in which to write."

Early in July our journey down the river began in such comfort and with such companionship that a feeling of uneasiness, a sense of guilt, disturbed me. "What have I done to earn such luxury?"

The houseboat was in effect a bungalow, some seventy feet long, with a screened-in porch at the front. Propelled by a power boat from behind, it was a floating cottage free from all noise or jar. To sit in an easy-chair on that forward deck and silently sweep down a storied water with nothing to do but doze and dream between exquisite meals was the perfection of travel. I had never known its like.

In truth the food was a source of uneasiness. As the river offered one exquisite vista after another, so our dining room three times each day offered dishes which I accepted as blessings which might never come again.

It was a lonely stream! All my life I had heard of its rafts, its canoes, its steamboats, yet here it lay, a placid, mirror-bright expanse with hardly another vessel of any kind afloat upon it. Here where the red men used to camp, here where their bark canoes had glided, no living thing appeared. Along the shore an occasional railway train rumbled, leaving the valley as lonely and as silent as when Marquette first looked upon it. "The age of electricity and gasoline has made it of no account. To me, a son of its bank, there is something sorrowful in all this. The loon, the wild swan, the painted savage were so much more poetic than the pig and the hoodlum! To me a generation of adventurous rivermen had bequeathed a store of memories—memories which are already legends."

At the fair we caught our first vision of the automobile age. Only nine years had passed since, at the Chicago Exposition, a few experimental gasoline engines and vehicles had been exhibited as curiosities. Now here in St. Louis we found a building given over to the display of self-propelled carriages and in them could be read the doom of the pleasure boat. The use of the stream for recreation was ending. I will not say that I foretold the campaign for better roads, but I did foresee increasing neglect of the river.

Our return trip was even more exquisitely dreamlike than our downward journey, for as we were going against the current we moved more slowly and absorbed more fully the valley's charm.

"Lying at ease in a wicker chair on the screened-in porch at the prow of the boat, I am being carried slowly, almost reverently, up the stream, scarcely aware of the power which propels me. This evening our course lay toward the northwest, and so (like Hiawatha) we literally sailed into the purple sunset. The splendor of orange and crimson and purple in the sky is overwhelming and reflected color lies on the water like molten amethyst. The air is as still as the stream and the boat steals forward as if hesitating to break the sacred silence of the hour. This is the perfection of travel."

As I read this to-day—after nearly a quarter of a century—I still marvel at the neglect of this mighty river by poets and painters. Lovelier to-day than it was then, the tourist sees it only from his motor car, rushing at railway speed along its bluffs. Mark Twain lived it and chronicled its life, but his pages relate only to the lower, middle sweep of its current. Those who rode its upper reaches, studied its banks, and fought its currents are passing, along with their slowly drifting rafts, their churning, bellowing stern-wheel steamboats and their birch-bark canoes, soon they will be less than memories; they will be shadows.

CHAPTER SIXTEEN

AGING PIONEERS

I

As autumn came on, I interrupted work on "The Tyranny of the Dark" and wrote two diametrically opposite stories: one "The Long Trail," a boys' book, based on my Klondike experience, and the other a short story of Wisconsin which I called "Martha's Fireplace."

Many of my readers as well as some of my critics had reproached me for not writing more "Main-Travelled Roads"; and to such letters I could only reply, "That is a work accomplished. I cannot repeat the mood in which those stories were written, and to attempt it would be folly." But now, in building a fireplace for my little daughter, I found myself surrounded by wistful-eyed octogenarians, my father's pioneer companions, recalling in the blaze of my hearth the brave days of their youth; and in the mood to record their feeling, the pathos of their sunset hours, and to depict the changes which the village life had brought to my father and mother as well as to their neighbors, I wrote a simple little story as an elegiac close to the period which my "Main-Travelled Roads" had partially depicted.

The chief figure in the sketch was Stephen Thurber, who had entered the LaCrosse Valley with his New

England bride some fifty years before. As a farmer he had prospered to the point of building an unusually spacious house, in which (in accordance with the tradition of his forbears) he had built a chimney with an open fireplace. The mantelpiece was one which Martha had brought from New England—one which her father had carved—together with the irons which had belonged to her mother's mother. In this way they made their house an altar of New England tradition.

After many happy years in this home, Martha died and Stephen married again, a brisk, practical woman much younger than he, who induced him to sell the farm and buy a cottage in the village. "I can't stand farm life," she said.

"You want to just lay back and rest," said Hiram Fox, another veteran of the plow; "that's what we're doin' and we're doin' it conscientiously. The town is full of 'tired farmers' like us."

This was the fact. Stephen found himself surrounded by a score or more of gnarled old pioneers like himself, men who had spent their youth swinging the ax and the scythe, men who had uprooted the great oaks of the hillsides and ripped the meadows into strips in order to sow their wheat—men whose muscles had once been as steel bands and whose hearts were still the hearts of warriors. They were all old now, bent and weatherworn, heavy and slow, taking their ease heroically while their wives fussed about their homes in automatic frenzy, housecleaning to pass the long days of summer, rising early to make the nights of winter short. Mostly they lived as lonely couples, for their sons and daughters, impatient of the narrow opportunities and the slow round of life in the valley, had gone to the city or to the farther West.

Stephen, without knowing it, was passing through precisely the same phases, computing the same problems. As the nights lengthened and the cold deepened he began definitely to long for the old fireplace. He mused much upon the joy he used to feel as he came in from corn-husking or rail-splitting, wet and cold, to find the fire blazing on the hearth in the old log house. He re-lived the days when the crane was newly hung and Martha sat beside him in the glow of the embers, her hand in his, while they spoke lovingly of the two little ones that died before they could speak. How the other children loved the old hearth, on which they were content to bask like puppies snuggling against his feet, asking for more bear stories. The winters of that time were made delightful by the blaze of that chimney. The roar of the branches outside carried no chill to the hearts of his children.

It ended in his building a new house on the edge of the village, avowedly for another, but in reality for himself, a spacious house in which he installed Martha's mantelpiece and andirons.

"As Stephen gazed, the spell of that which he had wrought fell upon him. The first stanza of his poem was being sung by the roaring flames. On the white walls the golden light was flickering, and along the ceiling the shadows of the tall andirons danced gro-tesquely, as of old. The mantel with its carven figures and its candles and vases seemed unaltered. The voice of the elms outside was unchanged.

"For a moment he had the exaltation of the artist

who has triumphed over time's decrees. He felt that Martha might at any moment steal into the room, light of step as of old, to sit on the arm of his chair and ask with that tenderness of sympathy which always melted his heart, 'Tired, Stephen?' and lay her cheek against his shoulder.

"He loved Serilla; he honored and cared for her as the mother of his children; but Martha was associated with the mystery of his life, the dew of its morning. The whole earth was young that marvelous May when they two adventured into this suave and fertile land. The perfume of wild honey, the song of larks in flowery meadows, clung to her name, and around her fireplace still lingered such heartiness of cheer, such neighborliness as the world no longer knew. Glorious pioneer days!"

Into this little story I put certain phases of my father's character and something of his aged companions who came in of an evening to enjoy the open fire and to talk of "the early days." They all had something of Stephen's fine simplicity and wistful sadness.

"The truth is," I explained to Fuller, "this village, like hundreds of others in the Middle West, is but a journey's-end hospice in which the pioneers of my father's generation dwell waiting for death—a melancholy grouping of the gnarled and grizzled veterans of the scythe and the plow. My Stephen is a type, as my father is a type, representing many thousands, wearing out their final years in comfort while wistfully recalling their youthful experiences as pioneers."

This led to a discussion of our own failing memories. "We hear too much and see too much," I declared.

"Our impressions come too rapidly and pass so swiftly that they fail to 'register,' as the moderns say. The people of my father's day had more time to assimilate their intake—and they were hungrier for news than we are. They pondered every item, chewing the cud of their knowledge. They had time for new concepts."

To this Fuller retorted: "We of to-day *must* forget. We can't go on remembering everything. We must drop something. Remember how enormously complex our life is. The daily doings of this village would bewilder Washington and Franklin. Forgetting is as reasonable as remembering and even more necessary."

This talk led me to add "Martha's Fireplace" to the illustrated edition of "Main-Travelled Roads," placing it as the closing tale of the volume, entitling it, "The End of an Era," for such in truth it was.

CHAPTER SEVENTEEN

ST. GAUDENS AND HIS EAGLE

I

WHILE I was still in West Salem working on my psychic novel, "The Tyranny of the Dark," Governor La Follette came to our village. As I had never seen him and as he was the chief citizen of my state, I seized the opportunity to hear him speak.

"He made a powerful plea for a direct, simple, and honest government. He was very fair, very frank, and very able—but much too serious. His Americanism is of the same stamp as that of Bryan, but he lacks Bryan's genial smile. At the close of his address, I went forward and expressed my approval. 'You are fighting our battles for us,' I declared. As a return compliment, he said: 'I have followed your career for many years. I read and admired your "Main-Travelled Roads" when a lad.' How could I criticize him after that handsome compliment?"

Election Day, 1904, found me still in the little village, rejoicing in Roosevelt's triumphant election as a vindication of his public acts and public policies. "This will silence all those who have called him 'a chance President'; he is now President by the largest majority ever given to a candidate. As I sit here with my little daughter on my knee, I am a long way from his war camps."

"November 17. In returning to my New York club I find myself still in the zone of age, surrounded by the aging pioneers of art. A. M. Palmer came in, feeble with years, an almost forgotten man. He ate alone at the central table with not one of his long-time associates to touch elbows with him. Once I thought of him as a proud theatrical chieftain; now his stage is gone, his power is gone, and his friends dead or dying like himself. Others in the club show similar decay. Augustus St. Gaudens, looking pale and sick and sad, was in a corner not far away.

"George Warner, Charles Dudley Warner's brother, who felt the change as keenly as I, said to me: 'I am trying to keep cheerful, but I find it hard work. I don't want to die. I don't want to leave this good old earth. It gives me a pang of sadness every time I think of letting go.'

" 'The truth is,' I replied, 'we have all entered the zone of the aged—the despairing.' "

John Finley, tall, strong, vital, brought another spirit to our group. "Hello, Cornhusker," he said, as he took a seat opposite me. "Let me tell you what I've just been doing. I've been lunching, with the Archbishop of Canterbury on my right and the Archbishop of Ripon on my left, and with Pierpont Morgan sitting opposite. Dramatic business for an Illinois hay-maker, don't you think?"

After quoting Warner's wistful mood, I said, "I'm growing old too, John, and I hate it."

"So do I," he returned with a smile, "but there's nothing to be done about it—so far as I know. If you find anything helpful send me word."

"November 18. I took my first ride in the subway this day, finding it amazingly swift and on the whole pleasant. The streets were still in disarray, but below all was clean and orderly. 'This ushers in a new era for the city,' everybody is saying."

My novel, "The Tyranny of the Dark," was still on my mind, and as I had use in it for some detailed knowledge on certain forms of invisible life, I accepted an invitation from my friend Prudden, head of the Bacteriological Department of Columbia University, and visited his "bug farm," as he called it.

I spent several hours in his laboratory. "He put every known germ under the microscope. Some were shaped like dumb-bells, some like tennis rackets, while others resembled threads of silk or minute flecks of oil. As I was looking at one of these tubelike bodies, he explained, 'That fellow you observe is merely a filament floating in a jellylike substance.'

" 'But what *is* the jellylike substance?' I naturally inquired.

" 'Now, now, now!' he warningly called out, a smile in his eyes, 'we can't go into that. Our job is to study these "bugs" in their relation to man, not to analyze the ultimate constitution of their matter; that is the field of the chemist—or physicist. We are concerned with what they *do* rather than what they *are*.' "

His "farm" was a place of jars, tubes, microscopes, copper ovens, and plates of glass. It was a nursery of life incredibly minute, for each of the forms shown to me was magnified several hundred times, and even then it was but a minute spot on a bar. Only the "colonies" could be seen, their billions producing faint lines on a wire, but the individuals were invisible. I got what I wanted—a sense of the dense and swarming organisms of the invisible world—and it all went to make certain parts of my novel, "The Tyranny of the Dark," the more credible.

II

Meanwhile at the Players I saw much of Augustus St. Gaudens who spent many hours at the club, wandering about in melancholy restlessness. He seemed lonely, and when I spoke to him he replied pleasantly. As I usually came for my mail about eleven, we often had an hour's talk before his artist friends arrived. We sometimes breakfasted together, two cautious dyspeptics, sharing a pot of "cereal coffee"—which we both cordially hated. Although I had long admired his sculpture, I had never before spoken with him. I agreed with Lorado Taft who said, "St. Gaudens is our chief sculptor," and yet, as he moved about the club, bored and dispirited, it was hard to imagine him triumphant. "I am here being X-rayed for some derangement of the stomach," he explained; "but I'm on the gain, so the doctors say. The worst of it is, I'm forbidden to work; and you know what that means. I have several important commissions which are being held up by my absence; but the doctors insist on keeping me here away from my studio."

One morning when I joined him at breakfast he said, "I've just been over to the White House. President Roosevelt sent for me to confer with him on some new designs for our coins. He is a marvel—probably the only President with any knowledge of art and artists. He has had the White House restored and it is beautiful. He was very amusing about the figures on our coins and made many suggestions as to the general type of the new designs, but left the final decision in my hands—just as he put the White House restoration in the hands of Mead and McKim. He knows us all—knows our work and our rank. It is amazing."

To this I replied, "He knows what the writers are about. He knows every vital man of letters. No President, except Jefferson, knew anything of architecture or sculpture—and I don't imagine Jefferson knew very much beyond what he got in France. Roosevelt's weak point is music—I never heard him express an opinion on music. He wants America to grow up in the arts, to stand on its own feet, and he welcomes every young writer whose work is essentially fine and true."

St. Gaudens sat in silence for a moment. "I want to live long enough to carry out his suggestion concerning the designs on our coins."

As he rose he groaned with pain, and I said, "What is the matter? You seem worse this morning."

His growl became a bitterly contemptuous curse. "Oh, I made a damn fool of myself last night. I ate ice cream on the train. I knew it would do me harm—it always does—but I fell. I'm like a drunkard—I can't keep clear of my poison, which my doctor says is sugar."

"You should take Willard Metcalfe for example," I urged. "I'm told he cut out *his* poison in one night."

"I know he did, but I haven't his strength of character. I oughtn't to use sweets at all, but I do. I oughtn't to touch cake or pie, but I do!"

I failed to take this complaint seriously, for under all

his snarling ran a vein of comic self-derision. His long, thin face was gray with pain, but his blue eyes still sparkled. Despite his expressed confidence in the value of his medical treatment, he continued to linger on at the club in idleness and was still there when I left.

He never recovered his health and did not complete the work he had undertaken to do. His career was American although he was of French blood. There was something exotic about his personality, but his work was essentially Puritan: the animal side of man was never stressed. His figure of the Pilgrim, his Lincoln, and his memorial figure in the Rock Creek Cemetery are all of grave nobility and masterly technique.

The public—especially the paragraph writers— made merry over the feathered legs of the eagle which replaced the old pressed chicken design, but Roosevelt stood stoutly by the sculptor. "If we are to have an eagle let us have an eagle that resembles an eagle," he said in substance. "St. Gaudens is entirely competent to design an eagle and I am content to abide by his work."

Brander Matthews was especially amusing in his description of the old design of an eagle "doing the split" with a bunch of thunderbolts hugged to his bosom. And in the end the artists won.

Up to this time I had found rest and recreation in the players, to whose dining room from time to time the most distinguished men of letters from England as well as America came—a ceaseless procession—with whom I enjoyed many luncheons and dinners, but a change had set in. In my diary I find this highly significant entry:

"November 29. Club life begins to pall on me. I talk too much, I read too much. I dare not stop to think of wife and daughter—dwelling on them makes me eager to cut and run! I have a sense of wasting time in desultory meetings. . . . My Boston friend, Jerome Elwell, who has been abroad for five years, lunched with me to-day. He was just off the boat and was soiled and rumpled, but his eyes glowed with enthusiasm and his talk was quite as literary as ever. He spoke of Whistler, of his own work, and of the exhibitions he had seen in Paris. He quoted poetry, and his face and eyes took fire as they used to do when I knew him first twenty years ago. He looked the neglected bachelor, but he had 'quality'—something which most of our commercially successful artists do not possess. By intention he is a great painter. He loves to scheme out pictures of sand dunes, scraggly forests, dragons, knights, dark towers, and phantom cities, but he has failed to make a place for himself. His critics are probably right when they say, 'He is an illustrator, not a painter;' and yet his visions interest me.

"Israel Zangwill, whom I have not seen for several years, suddenly turned up at one of the hotels and I went at once to call on him. I found him surrounded by admiring visitors with whom he was excitedly discussing the drama in America. To me he said, 'I am here to see one of my plays put on, and to write another.'

"He was uglier than ever, but kept his callers laughing almost incessantly by his witty comment. I recall an amusing remark concerning one of Shaw's stage directions. 'Shaw speaks of one character—a woman—

who enters "as if just having had a cup of tea." This
means nothing to me. If he had said, "Enter Ann looking as if she had just eaten an egg—!" ' He broke off
right there and the effect was comic. Another remark,
which I thought ill-advised, related to the claims of
professional playwrights. 'They are always saying to
me, "Oh, you novelists can't write plays—they are so
immensely more difficult to write than novels." I answer, "Nonsense. Playwriting is child's play compared
to doing a good novel. I can do a successful play in a
week.' "

Something like this was quoted by the paragraphers
and much unpleasant comment resulted.

I confess that I shared his opinion then and I do yet.
American plays are mostly ephemeral "shows," joint
products of playwright, manager, stage carpenter, and
actor. There is very little writing connected with them.
Zangwill's "Melting Pot" had an idea and was the product of a writer. It succeeded in spite of the critics.

"December 2, 1904. This night we held a meeting of
the National Institute of Arts and Letters and decided
by ballot upon the seven men who are to be the founders of the American Academy. They are William Dean
Howells, Augustus St. Gaudens, Edmund C. Stedman,
Samuel L. Clemens, John Hay, John La Farge, and Edward MacDowell. Hopkinson Smith and I acted as tell-
ers; and when Smith announced the vote, the members
heartily applauded. The list was pronounced 'perfect,'
and so it is. The vote for Howells as the leading member
was almost unanimous.

"Mabie, Stedman, and Johnson have been the chief

workers for this new organization. Mabie first spoke to
me about it, but Johnson was very active in promoting
the candidacy of the seven men and in devising the plan
whereby they are to vote in eight more. These fifteen
must select fifteen others to effect a final organization.
The limit of membership is fixed at fifty."

My own feeling was favorable to such an organization as a counterbalancing influence to journalism. Its
judgments were not those of the daily newspaper.
To be called to intellectual association by these seven
men was, in my judgment, high honor—higher than any
which an act of Congress might grant.

One of its promoters was Brander Matthews, and
when I dropped in on him a few days later we fell to
discussion of an Academy. I remarked, "Some men say,
'Why an Academy in a democracy?' "

"Why *not* in a democracy?" retorted Brander. "An
Academy is especially necessary in a democracy—as a
counterbalancing force to the snap judgments of space
writers."

These Sunday receptions of Matthews were an institution. Our host, full of good talk, invariably sat deep
in an armchair before his fire, smoking one cigarette
after another, surrounded by a lively circle of friends,
many of them former students like Clayton Hamilton,
men who had won literary distinction and had notions
of their own to express—when they could find space
for a word! At about ten o'clock, Mrs. Matthews led
the way down to the dining room, where bottles of
ginger ale, carbonated water, and Scotch whisky flanked
a large cake and a bowl of apples. This layout was always the same. It was a rather dry cake with chocolate

trimmings and the ginger ale never failed. As I grew older, chocolate cake came to be a dangerous refreshment and I sometimes suffered from it; but the talk was always worth while.

It was Matthews' joke to call me Hannibal Hamlin, and I responded by calling him James Brander; and we justified ourselves in our duplicity by revealing that Kipling's name was really Joseph R. Kipling. Brander was my loyal friend, and we had a common admiration for Roosevelt. Like Stedman he was walled in with books, but he had little of Stedman's love of poetry. His shelves were filled with volumes of dramatic criticism, literary history, and fiction. He was immensely learned in these branches—he needed to be—for he was Professor of Dramatic Literature at Columbia University, and he had written many plays, novels, and short stories. None of them had been highly successful. His mind was more analytical than creative. He knew the mechanism of play-building, but failed of "juice." Similarly his fiction was cold and formal—good but not good enough to last. He had come to realize this and to frankly admit his limitations.

His direct antithesis in many ways was Albert Paine, a valued comrade and delightful companion, although at that time he suffered the handicap of a stammer, a disability with which Matthews had small patience. I liked Paine, who was also from the Middle-West. He was a tall fellow with a smoothly shaven face and humorous glance. He regarded me as a friend and brother, and I had so much regard for his abilities as a biographer that I paid out three hard-earned dollars for his life of Thomas Nast.

Poor Nast! As I read Paine's book I regretted that I had paid so little attention to him when he was in the flesh. Somewhere in my files I have a little drawing which he made of himself, hat in hand, seeking an appointment at the hands of Roosevelt. The truth is, I could never quite associate the seedy and melancholy old man (flitting about the club) with the tremendous satirist, who had made Tweed and other evil-doers tremble, thirty years before. As a boy I had been profoundly instructed by his cartoons; and now, here he was, ready to instruct me further and I failed to listen to him! It is a tragic situation—this outliving a great fame.

Paine had tried all sorts of writing—even poetry, which he published with William Allen White while living in Kansas City. He had written a series of humorous books, half fiction, half fact, on fishing, suburban life, and other phases of his own experience—and then as his children came along he composed for them a series of stories which he called "The Hollow Tree Books" whose charm I tested on my own small daughters. They are bird and animal tales, told in the spirit of the Middle-West, in which "Mr. Crow" is the kindly housekeeper, "Mr. Rabbit" the poet and gentleman, "Mr. Possum" the glutton—and so on. They were all perfectly delightful—more appealing to my children and to me than "Uncle Remus," so human were they and so deliciously funny. I taught both my daughters to read by means of the limpid English of these books. I suspect they will go on being read long after all of Albert's other books except his "Mark Twain" are forgotten.

He was at work at this time on a careful, sympathetic, and outspoken life of Mark Twain with whom he was playing billiards almost every day—and in whose house he was staying to make his studies. The outcome of this association, combined with his skill and his enthusiasm, was a biography of high merit and of highly individual quality in its style as well as in its interpretations. It has something of Mark's own quality in the writing.

My errands in New York were accomplished early in December, for I not only sold Harper's "The Tyranny of the Dark" as a serial, but signed with them a contract for the book rights and promised them a third book. "We regard you now as one of our chief authors," Duneka said, and Leigh added, "our favorite author"; all of which was most comforting to me as I prepared for a return to Chicago and my wife and child.

CHAPTER EIGHTEEN

HENRY JAMES IN AMERICA

I

JUST before leaving (December 9, 1904), I attended another of George Harvey's big dinners—this time in honor of Henry James, who had returned to America after so many years' absence that many people had forgotten that he was alive. Naturally I was more keenly interested in seeing him than many others, for I had read most of his books and had received from him such cordial appreciation that I was eager to thank him in person as I had done by letter.

I carried but one picture of him in my memory and that was the engraving which his publishers had used for many years in their catalogue, a profile view of a handsome, bearded man of thirty-five or so; and when presented to him at the Metropolitan Club, on the night of the dinner, I was startled and a little saddened by the changes in him.

"Stout, elderly, and smooth-shaven, he was so little like *my* Henry James that I had difficulty in causing the two concepts to coalesce. As I studied him across the table, he bodied forth almost precisely my notion of a bishop of the Episcopal Church. His head was nobly proportioned, his eyes brilliant and rather prominent, and his brow serene. His expression was kindly. His lips were wide and mobile, and his voice sonorous and rich in quality, a beautiful blend of London and New England. His conversation, though lively (almost vivacious) was lacking in humor. There was no chuckle in his voice, no lines of fun lurking about the corners of his mouth. Without being solemn or portentous he was serious.

"I had no opportunity to speak with him during the dinner, for Howells and Mark Twain were naturally in his foreground; but at the close of the meal he was good enough to come round to my side of the table and take a seat beside me. He was much more alert, much younger, and more democratic in manner than I had expected him to be. He was indeed quite vivacious. With large, full, glowing eyes fixed upon me, he spoke slowly, hesitating painfully on some of his words, but always to the effect of securing the one of precisely the right color. He had a curious habit of repeating the word in hand while vaguely feeling about for another in the bush. Notwithstanding these distracting peculiarities, I enjoyed his talk.

"Several other writers drew near and we all talked, naturally, of James' books. Booth Tarkington asked a question concerning one of his short stories and James replied, 'Oh, have you read those rubbishy little tales?'

"When I named two of my favorites among his novelettes he looked at me with kind but wondering eyes. 'I have forgotten them. They are quite gone out of my mind.' This was not a pose. He really had no memory of them. His face remained serene, almost placidly expressionless, but his lips and eyes were quick with meaning. His use of words was almost as fastidious as if he were dictating an essay. Much more alert, more vigorous than I had expected him to be, he looked and acted like a man who enjoyed good food, hearty, wholesome, and substantial—a man who could walk ten miles of a morning and come in smiling. Only when he began to speak did he become the author of the "Wings of the Dove," the writer of parenthetic clauses, the fastidious artist in words and phrases.

"At times he was maddeningly hesitant, but his pauses were in no sense those of a stammerer; they were filled with an effort at finding just the precise qualifier. He appeared to grope for the exact, exquisite, ultimate adjective until, at times, I ached with his effort. But the word came—and the halt was justified! It was evident that he loathed the easy phrase, the banal judgment. He had gone beyond excusing the trite in any form."

He told me that he was going to Chicago to lecture, and I explained that I was still a resident of Chicago and that I would do my best to give him a notion of what was going on there in a literary way. I spoke of The Little Room which met in Ralph Clarkson's studio on Friday afternoons and of Lorado Taft's Camp Suppers which came at almost any moment when Taft was in town. "We shall be greatly honored if you will come to either one or both of these functions," I added.

"I will come—provided my lectures will admit and provided you will meet me and act as my guide," he replied heartily.

And in this agreement we rested.

II

By reference to my diaries I find that he did not reach Chicago till the following March, when his address be-

fore the Twentieth Century took place. His subject was
"Balzac" and the literary folk of the city were all present. He read well from his manuscript. His voice was
resonant and his utterance quite free from hesitations.
But the matter of his discourse was austerely literary—
a plea for higher standards in fiction; and in my diary
I put down these significant lines: "His address made
my own work seem small and of no account. Coming
from the centers of tradition he brought the breath
of Old World criticism to bear on American writers.
His talk was high, impersonal, and wholly unconcerned
with commercial considerations."

In answer to my note reminding him of his promise
to attend one of our studio suppers, he replied with a
provisional consent. "I am at the University Club, and
if you will call for me and bring me to the studio I
shall be very glad to have a glimpse of Chicago's artist
life."

Promptly at the hour appointed I was in the University Club, in the neighborhood of the elevator; and
while waiting for his appearance I regretted that I
had not more fully explained that our studio suppers
were very informal and that many of our guests did
not wear even dinner jackets. I feared he might be
dressing for a grand occasion.

When the elevator door opened and he stepped forth,
I smiled at my fears. "He looked like a gentleman who
had dressed in the dark. His hat of the 'bowler' type
was a little askew on his head, and a little too large for
him. His black tie also at an angle was of a piece with
his long-suffering evening suit. His vest was black and
cut in the fashion of 1898, and his trousers needed

pressing. In all ways he was the exact opposite of the exquisite artist in words whose grace and power still awed me. Perhaps I should not have rejoiced in this lack of ease and care in his dress, but I did, for I found in this neglect the evident fact that he, too, considered dress a nuisance, and had reduced it to its simplest terms. Anyhow I was comforted and put at ease."

His greeting was cordial and without a particle of condescension. "I put myself in your hands," he said after a few words of explanation on my part.

While crossing the four or five blocks which intervened between the club and the studio, I again outlined the origin of the suppers and described the artist colony of which Taft was the head. I sketched the characters of a few of the writers and artists he was about to meet. "They are the saving grace of this great city," I declared finally.

"It all sounds a bit like Paris in the days when I was a youth fresh from America," he remarked.

"It *is* a little bit of the Latin Quarter adapted to the chill winds of Lake Michigan," I admitted.

In this spirit he met my fellow workers with pen and brush. No visitor could have been more genial, more tolerant, although it was evident that he had no point of contact with any of the men except Clarkson, Henry Fuller, Oliver Dennett Grover, and Taft. All of these men knew Paris and Florence, and Grover had known Whistler.

Now and again in a hurried aside he asked me to characterize this or that man or woman in the room; and I did my best to make it plain that we were all devoted in some way to the cause of American art. His

interest was abstract. I imagined him saying to himself, "Think of it! Here are artists and writers in a city
which was a few years ago only a far-off wheat market
to me. Extraordinary!" He had not expected to find
painters and sculptors in Chicago, but when they were
presented to him he did his kindliest to believe in them.
To him we were all worthy folk, rude pioneers on the
border of the artistic and literary New World, workers
to be encouraged and rewarded.

After supper he became the center of a group of
men: Fuller, Grover, Taft, and I. He talked of Whistler
and of Sargent and Abbey in London, speaking of them
as friends and neighbors; but when Fuller and I found
opportunity we brought him back to his own work.
Again he professed—without affectation—that he had
forgotten the stories we mentioned, and this I conceded
to be true, for he had written many thousands of pages.
How could he keep them all in mind? He spoke of his
novels in vague terms as if they represented a distant
epoch in his life, things wrought out on a lower plane,
a plane he had long since abandoned. More and more
the philosopher, he was now concerned with probing
the vaguer deeps of human life.

He unbent with us—that was certain. We were to
him a reminder of his youth in Paris. He perceived in
this studio a vigorous offshoot of Paris—for without the
influence of those who had known the Latin Quarter,
these discussions could not have taken place. In this
spirit of compliance he dandled a plate of creamed turkey on one knee while holding a cup of coffee to his
lips, disposed to humor us and justly value us. His fictional enthusiasms were lost, but he still retained certain

of his early intellectual interests. "I go on writing," he said, "out of sheer momentum of habit."

He was intolerably hesitant of speech that night, but what he said was wise and helpful. He admitted that he was meeting only rich people and that he welcomed this glimpse into the artist life of Chicago. He told, with as near a chuckle as he ever uttered, of the "extraordinary close corporation" of his friends in the suburb where he had been visiting. "Most extraordinary! The first night of my stay my hosts had in some ten or twelve people to dine. A charming company. The next evening they and I dined at a neighboring house. Handsome dinner, lovely home, charming guests—but the same people, precisely, of the night before. Third night another charming home, delightful company— exactly the same group differently seated. Most extraordinary!"

We all laughed at his description, for we knew with what care he was being guarded and exploited. "If they have their way you'll see only millionaires while you are here," I said to him.

At the close of the evening I escorted him back to the University Club—which was at that time a very modest building—talking all the while of this astonishing evocation from the prairies, this huge, crude, powerful city.

At the door of the elevator he renewed his invitation to visit him in England. "I live in Rye, a very old town on the South Coast," he explained. "If you will come down for a week-end I will gladly show you about the place. Its age may interest you."

"If I come to England again, I shall certainly visit

you," I replied, "but it is a long way from Chicago to Rye and I haven't a very lively hope of reaching you."

"Nevertheless I shall expect you," he answered.

Chicago was an amazement to him. The growth of the Middle-West, the subordination of all America to New York, and the rising tide of immigration from southeastern Europe astounded and disturbed him. Later it all went into a confused and subtle book which even Fuller could not quite comprehend, although he read it to the end.

"James has not only become English in theme and outlook, he has grown away from any real understanding of the life about him. He wrote into that book only the concepts which his enormously complex and highly cultivated brain evolved. He is right. Our literature *is* cheap and newspapery in tone, our art is addressed mostly to rudimentary minds. I can imagine how we seem to him. To him literary Chicago is about as important as literary Omaha is to New York. Aren't you called upon to meet 'rising authors' and 'promising artists' in Spodunk and Prairie City? Well, James feels toward us in Chicago as you feel toward the aspiring poets of Memphis and St. Paul. What is the use of pretending? We are still in the 'hick' stage of culture. We are on our way, but we have a long road to travel. Some of us are certain to get footsore and fall out of the procession."

To this I agreed. "It all comes back to Herbert Spencer's concept. Culture is the possession of comparative ideas. What we lack is a standard by which to measure ourselves. You and I get something of it by reading and by visits to the Old World, but most of our fellow citizens know only Chicago and the small towns from which they came. Our successful artists and writers are only a little more cosmopolitan. Henry James has done us good. He has led some of us to reconstruct our estimate of American art. At present Chicago is flimsy and crude and bloodlessly derivative. Some day we may develop into a literary center, of taste as well as power. We can't logically claim to have it now."

CHAPTER NINETEEN

THE TYRANNY OF THE DARK

I

"JANUARY 11. Here I am again, back at the Players, with the companionship of John Finley, Booth Tarkington, Oliver Herford, Albert Bigelow Paine, and other of my fellow craftsmen. The cheerful fire, the attentive waiters, the pleasant dining room possess an almost irresistible attraction to me. This is my home while in New York—a home to which I hurry when cold and hungry from my business trips about the streets.

"Stedman comes in each night to dine, complaining as ever about the enormous burden of his mail—a burden which I begin to suspect is all 'in his eye,' as the old slang phrase has it. He forfeits some of my respect by reason of his complaining attitude. His lot in life has been fortunate—it appears to me. His complaining is a sign of weakness, of decay—and so I excuse it. He seems to *enjoy* doing the hard and repellent thing."

When I said something like this to Howells, he replied with a smile, "I cannot think Stedman has such a thundering flood of mail!"

One of the reasons for my return to New York at this time was a wish to share in a public dinner celebrating the twenty-fifth anniversary of the publication of "Progress and Poverty." I had been named the toast-

master soon after my arrival. Harry George came to
tell me that William Jennings Bryan was coming to our
meeting, and would be glad to speak. Harry was exultant, for at this time Bryan drew crowds like a circus,
but I was a bit disturbed. "He may run away with our
show," I warned. The committee, however, did not
worry; on the contrary, they said, "His coming guar-
antees the success of our program."

On the day before the dinner I went over to Wilmington to address the pupils of the Friends' School,
and while there, seized the opportunity to call upon
Howard Pyle (whose illustrations I had long admired)
and to urge him to come over to our dinner. We had a
candid, earnest talk about "Progress and Poverty," but
he was quite out of key with the single taxers, although
he had been a powerful advocate of George's theories.
"He is a big, athletic figure with eyes like lenses and
the face of an English curate. His is a serious spirit—a
noble spirit. I liked him and began to understand his
influence on his pupils. He almost redeems Wilmington
which grows more and more smoky and dirty year by
year." So reads my record.

The George dinner on the 24th was a success. "Some
three hundred people claimed places—a representative
throng. Bryan sat at my right and Harry George at my
left. William Lloyd Garrison, Louis Post, Edwin
Markham, Richard Burton, Ernest Seton, and other
of my writer friends were present. I was genuinely
interested in Bryan. He was kindly and unassuming
and kept very well in tone. That he was impressed by
his company was evident—in fact, he told me so. It
amused me to discover that while in correct evening

dress above the belt, his trousers did not match his coat and vest, and were baggy at the knees. His shoes were equally plebeian, square-toed and unpolished. Whether his tailor had failed him, or whether he was indifferent, I had no means of knowing. However, he looked well above the table. He was genial and gracious and made a pleasant speech of no special significance. Nevertheless he helped to make the dinner a success."

"January 25. A savage storm is raging and I am resting after my strenuous George dinner. The papers treated us fairly well this morning and the program still seems worth while."

St. Gaudens, who, like myself, was storm-bound at the club, bore it miserably. Haggard with pain he went creeping around the empty rooms, madly eager to get back to his work. "My doctors will not hear of it, and so I am staying on for treatment, chafing under the confinement and the loss of time."

Lunching at the City Club with Robert Ely, I again met Arthur Brisbane of the *Journal*, along with Professor John B. Clarke of Columbia, Simeon Patton of Pennsylvania, Dr. Hamilton Wright Mabie, Robert Treat Paine of Boston, and Dr. Thomas R. Slicer, a brainy and serious crowd. "It was evident that they counted me one of them. I don't know whether I like that or not. I don't believe I do. I'm only forty-five, and neither old nor brainy. Despite the weight and standing of the men, I got little out of their talk."

On my way back to Chicago I stopped for the night at Bok's home in Merion. He had a new baby in the house and was jubilant. "He is in the full stride of his crusade against patent medicines and the secret of his success was again revealed in our talk. He concentrates. When he has a job on hand he thinks of nothing else. The house is very beautiful to me after my long stay in a cheap New York hotel. The perfection of the service, the exquisite food, the lovely lights, the books— all make a strong appeal to the luxurious side of me. I wish I could give my wife and child some of these things, but I never shall. Bok has something, some power, which has been denied me."

On the train I read Gertrude Atherton's book, "The Conqueror," which moved me deeply in places. The death of Hamilton was especially moving. What a tragic, useless end it was! The whole book is inter- pretive, but the material does not seem to me to be equally well digested throughout. It is all worthy, how- ever, and its general effect is informative. The reader comes to know intimately the basic facts of Hamilton's life. It is instructive to consider that at the moment of his death his career was clouded by a storm of be- wildering pamphlets. His fame had grown with the years and this was a sad anticlimax.

My interest in "The Conqueror" led me to write the author and a little later an invitation to tea came from her. I found her to be a plain, businesslike woman of about my own age, blunt of speech and with something of a man's indifference to personal comment. She said, with humorous inflection, "I have been described by an audacious reporter as a middle-aged lady with hair like a doughnut," and in truth the roll of her light-brown hair did suggest that. "I liked her. She is able, ambi- tious, and a student. She is a Californian and unswerv- ingly loyal to San Francisco."

"Chicago, March 18. Clarence Darrow and the violinist Spiering came to Clarkson's studio tea to-day. Darrow seemed to enjoy the party and was surprisingly genial. It amused me to see how this big, battle-scarred labor lawyer enjoyed the attentions of a group of pretty women who kept him busy answering impertinent questions. To them he was an object of curiosity. They knew something of his stormy past and delighted in uncovering it. His dark face and wrinkled brow (over which a long lock of hair fell) shone with mocking good humor. He liked these women, and yet, I fear, covertly despised them."

Some lecture dates and work on the proof of "The Tyranny of the Dark" took me to New York in April. MacDowell asked me to dine with him on the 5th, 1905. The place was Mouquin's restaurant on Sixth Avenue, and on arrival I found Henry T. Finck, the musical critic, and his wife, and John Lane, the London publisher, a quiet, able citizen, a small man reminding me at once of Henry Arthur Jones. The dinner started gayly, but as it went on something in MacDowell's look and action disturbed me, and this disturbed feeling rapidly deepened into alarm. He looked ill—seriously ill. His mind wandered and his hands were nerveless. Worst of all his face took on that empty look which I had observed once or twice before. An expression so unlike his brilliant usual self that Lane noticed it and glanced at me inquiringly.

Mrs. MacDowell chatted and laughed with the Fincks, seeing nothing amiss—apparently. To test my impressions I addressed Edward pointedly. He responded with his customary smile, but his glance was dim and remote. All his characteristic alertness and glow were gone. I think Marian took alarm soon after and ended the party.

As Lane and I walked back toward the club we discussed Edward's condition anxiously. "It was a tragic exhibition of an overworked man," Lane said. "Can't you tell Mrs. MacDowell that he must rest?"

"She must have noticed his condition," I responded. "I am sure she did. She is too alert and too devoted a wife to let him go on. Nevertheless I shall warn her."

This I did and was reassured. She said, "He *has* been overworking—and he is worried by the failure of his school at Columbia. The creative side of it did not appeal to President Butler—as you know. We are dependent now on private pupils and what few concerts we can secure. Edward feels that he *must* work."

"But he must not overwork. He showed utter weariness the other night."

"He *was* tired that day, but he is all right now."

What she said of Edward's sense of failure at Columbia was only a hint. I was with him often during his controversy, and although he laughed and jested about it—and talked of resignation as "a blessed release from daily grind," I knew that he was suffering. Proud and sensitive, a genius of the first rank, he could not see a dream turn into drab fog without a heartbreak. He read me one of the letters which he had written concerning the school of American music he had hoped to establish, in which he said: "If I can turn out one really fine creative musician every five years, I shall be satisfied."

This was a high ideal—too high for a huge institution becoming each year more "practical," more vocational. MacDowell's ideal was something vastly more important than even a cultural college. Like Walt Whitman, he aimed to create natively great composers —creators from the soul outward, not merely cultivated singers and skillful players of instruments. To have this ideal shattered was a shock—like a blow from a bludgeon. All this I reviewed as I rode away to the West, wondering whether I should find MacDowell alive when next I came to the city.

I was suffering a depression myself. For a week I had been working over the final revision of my novel and my state of mind is indicated in this note made just before I took the train: "I am either becoming more critical of my work or I am less assisted by my subliminal self. I suspect old sub-self is not only becoming weary but disgusted with me. For good or ill the book is done and I must take the consequences of its faults. I have less confidence in it than in 'The Captain.' "

In this I was right. "The Tyranny of the Dark" was a wandering from the main line of my course. I had been tempted by the possession of a fund of psychic material and had put it into fictional form although it lay outside the landscape and climate of all my other writing. It interested me and I gave much thought to it, and now most of my friends were saying, "It isn't like you."

They had said something very like this of my mountain stories, advice which I had ignored. Why should I confine myself to writing stories of the plains? I had done that. My novels of the mountains were logical. But to turn aside from a sunlit landscape and explore dark chambers of religious controversy was, I now confess, a mistake.

In less than a month I was back again in New York (on my way to speak in Boston or rather Chelsea) talking with Howells, who had just returned from Wales, filled with joy of its beauty. "It is my ancestral home," he explained. "I went to the village in which my great-grandfather lived." Then he added somberly, "I am done with these trips abroad. I am getting too old for travel—and it is well that my last voyage should be to the village in which my grandfather was born. I visited the mill which my great-grandsire owned."

"April 22, 1905. After a rather aimless forenoon I lunched at the club and went for a walk up Fifth Avenue. The pride and power and greed of the city made themselves felt as never before. It is very beautiful in some of its phases, but very insolent and self-centered. Here is the only American market where the man of wealth can buy to his limit. Here also is the only American city which appeals to the imagination of literary men as well as to the hope of the social climber, and yet it offers to most of us a wearisome road and a delusive goal."

Again in Boston I found myself moved by familiar sights and sounds. The city had changed. Elevated cars thundered by. Electrics howled where in other days horse cars tinkled and crept, and yet something of the old charm persisted.

Hearing that my old friend, B. O. Flower, was in

bed with rheumatism I went out to see him. He was
older and a little thinner, but he was still the intense
reformer. He told me in detail of Mrs. Flower's death,
a pitiful story. For many years she had been the victim
of an illusion which made it necessary to confine her
in a sanitarium. As I recalled her in her youth, tall,
graceful, with a lovely face and deep black eyes, I shared
her husband's sorrow.

From him I went at once to Enneking's studio, where
I found him at work, a grizzled and bent figure, surrounded by scores of pictures—few of which he was
willing to commend. He was striving as ever to do the
great thing and just about ready to finish the canvases
he really valued. He never succeeded to his highest
satisfaction, but he was a genuine artist.

My lecture to the middle-conditioned women of
Chelsea left with me a sad-colored impression. "How
uncritical I was in 1888! I did not realize that many
of my hearers were queer. I did not know how scanty
their incomes were, nor how inartistic their homes and
their dress. The houses on the hill in Chelsea are almost
unchanged except that they are older and more drab
than before."

CHAPTER TWENTY

JOYS OF THE TRAIL

I

HAVING fixed upon Chicago as my home, I made of Oklahoma my springtime playground as well as a place of investment. I rejoiced in the feeling of landed proprietorship which my constantly increasing acreage aroused and sustained. I was glad of any excuse which drew me down to my ranch. This feeling led to such entries as this:

"Oklahoma. May 3, 1905. My train reached Muskogee at noon and I met the library lecture committee at three. At four I rode out to my farm over a beautiful, green plain bright with phlox—a deep blue flower—and the creamy white blossoms of the wild pea. The sky was vividly blue and radiant with clouds. On the way I passed an immense drove of gaunt Texas cattle. At six I ate an incredibly bad dinner at the ranch.

"This is the date for the publication of my new book, and here I sit in my little ranch house after a horseback ride in survey of my crops. The land is gloriously green, the larks are singing, and on the smooth meadows the cattle are scattered like red and black beads. It is all deeply exhilarating and I would enjoy riding 'West away till the dawn of the day,' but the flesh is tender and the saddle hard. These feeble little tenants of mine depress me. They are so poor and so ineffective! The woman chews snuff, is deaf and loud-voiced, but she is a kindly soul.

"This dramatic shift is characteristic of my life. One week I am in Chelsea, Massachusetts; the next I sit with a sad Oklahoma wind complaining at my window. Bulls are bawling on the plain to the west, and one of the men is playing a sad tune on the mouth organ, while my brother is telling the story of one of our neighbors, a man from Missouri, who lost his little girl two days ago. He had buried the child on the prairie and as I listen to the cattle bellowing out there I realize how the mother must have suffered as she left her baby in a grave on this plain—so lonely and so vast."

(This incident led to the writing of a short story which was afterward published in the *Circle Magazine*.)

"May 10. There is something agitating in this sounding wind, this cloud-filled, lofty sky, and in this green and flowery plain, but I am finding benefit from it, a benefit which goes deep. It is fine to have the breeze and sun burn me brown, but my workmen are depressing. They are such sallow, dirty, little rats. Their outlook on life is essentially without hope. They content themselves with meeting the demands of the hour.

"Yesterday my brother and I went to visit the ranch of an acquaintance, a Cherokee citizen called 'Judge Moore.' I found him a man of remarkable dignity and influence, but deferring to his wife, a bustling, vigorous, flower-loving, New England schoolma'am—the daughter of a missionary.

"She showed us her lovely garden, her yard of velvety grass shaded with big trees, and her orchard, and then called us in to midday dinner. Three shy and curious cowboys and a rather pretty girl, maid-of-all-work, were seated with us at the long table. After dinner Mrs. Moore read a chapter of the Bible and then we all settled down for a long talk. The old judge, though careless of his linen, was a philosopher and something of a politician as well. He talked of the gift of Creek lands by the government to negroes of almost any origin as an outrage.

" 'After the Creeks were freed by the War of 1865,' he said, 'we were persuaded into admitting negroes to tribal membership in order that the 'Party of the North' (the loyal Creeks) might gain numerical supremacy over the 'Party of the South'—the Mackintosh party. This was an injustice. Only a few Creeks had held slaves, but the whole tribe has been bled for the action of a few of its members.' There was bitter resentment in his voice as he went on to tell of having his lands taken away by his hired herder—a negro with seven children. 'He chopped into my ranch on all sides and in the end secured more land than I.' "

This ranch and its household was like a chapter out of a novel. It was incredible, and yet it all appeared natural and logical, as I sat there in an easy chair listening to its owner.

After two weeks of riding over the prairie, so deliciously green and flowery, I gave my lecture and took the train for Chicago. On the way, I read "Dombey and Son," and set down my honest opinion. "It is a good but not exciting work. The style is less extravagant than I had remembered it to be, but the characterizations are for the most part rather poor, and certain tricks of overemphasis are annoying. My interest hardly carried me to the end."

"Back in West Salem, June 4. I have just finished Moncure Conway's book—a very interesting chronicle of great personalities. I had not realized how largely he shared the literary history of his day. I met him once, a harsh, unlovely person who related with gusto certain incidents in Lincoln's life which revealed his weak side, but the pictures he drew of Emerson, Carlyle, Hawthorne, and Tennyson were beautiful. His book is appalling, however. It is like watching a procession of noble men and women march into an abyss. . . . In the mail came a note from Stedman acknowledging a copy of my book as 'a peace offering.' It appears that I offended him by not reading his letter at the Progress and Poverty meeting in New York.

"In looking over my diaries I am dismayed to find how few of the matters noted there are of vital interest to me. Similarly my notebooks have faded. The subjects which endure are the descriptions of landscape and my contacts with my fellows. Howells once said to me, when I spoke of a theme which I was holding in reserve, 'Don't be disappointed if you lose interest in it.' How wise he was. I have done just that—I have gone past many of my plans.

"A letter from Mrs. MacDowell alarms me. Edward is in a sad state of nervous exhaustion. I fear his work is over. A poet, overworked—loaded down with the care of others and harnessed to a daily round of grinding toil. It is a horrible waste of genius."

II

Early in June while still at my home in West Salem, Wisconsin, I received a letter from President Harper of the University of Chicago inviting me to deliver the convocation address in September at the close of the summer session. To say that this was an unexpected honor is not enough. It was an unaccountable indorsement from a friend, whom I had known for fifteen years as a busy educator. We had never been intimate friends and although we met frequently, I considered myself an outsider in all his collegiate gatherings. With no college or university degrees, no official position except that of member and director of the National Institute of Arts and Letters, I was puzzled to account for this invitation. True I had given several courses of literary lectures for the university, but even these were not academic in tone or substance.

Much as this recognition meant to me, I decided, after thinking it over, to write to Dr. Harper frankly confessing that I was intimidated. "I am not qualified to address your assembly on an academic subject. The older I grow the less I feel like instructing anybody on anything. I deeply appreciate the honor and thank you most sincerely for thinking of me, but I consider it wiser not to attempt such an address."

To this he replied: "Chicago, July 10, 1905. Your letters came to my hands upon my return from the East. I was greatly surprised and troubled by the second letter dated July 4th. Your conclusion that you have no material for an address suited to the occasion of a Convocation seems to me impossible in view of your former letter. I know how critical you are of your own work, and I appreciate this. At the same time, I am sure that if you will finally accept the invitation the material will get into shape. It is not necessary for you to have entirely new material. We should like to have something which would express your own work as it has thus far been done.

"I cannot tell you how greatly interested I have been in your last book. I believe that you have done a wonderful piece of work in it. The members of the faculty to whom I had confided the fact that you were probably to be the Convocation orator were all highly delighted. I sincerely hope that you will reconsider the matter. You will excuse me for being so insistent and urgent, but I am exceedingly desirous that you shall be with us on this occasion."

To this I replied:

"If you will accept an address on a subject concerning which I am really learned, 'Vanishing Trails,' 'The Life of the Forest Ranger,' or some such outdoor theme, I will gladly come and do my best, but I feel incapable of instructing your audience on any social or economic line."

He replied cordially, accepting my suggestion. "An address on 'The Trail' is a little outside our academic field, but anything you feel like saying will do us all good, I am sure."

In suggesting an address on "Vanishing Trails" I had in mind an article which I had written just after my return from Alaska in 1898, summing up the joys and the historic significances of the trail. I believed I could put into this oration something which would apply to present-day problems, allusions which might make it acceptable to a commencement audience. Upon his agreement, I set to work upon it.

Late in August I went to Chicago and was assigned a room at the Quadrangle Club. "Chicago. Aug. 30. I am living here at the Quadrangle Club surrounded by the young men of the university who come and go busily, intent and grave. I can imagine how splendid these buildings and lawns must seem to the boys and girls who come to them from the small towns of Illinois and Indiana. To possess a comfortable room in a stone mansion, to walk on the clean campus, to eat in the big dining hall—what joy! And the girls, dimly seen, walking to and fro in white gowns, or playing tennis. Here is all the material for poetry, for romance—unless the men and maidens of this generation are vastly different from those of twenty-five years ago. There are poems here, novels and plays—will they find writers?"

As the hour of my oration approached, I was seriously troubled. I said to Dr. Harper, "My address has no educational value. It must win approval on some other basis."

He was amused by my doubts. "I trust your taste," he said.

Dining at his house that night I met a mixed group of professors and clergymen, and afterward as guest of honor donned cap and gown and stood beside him while he presented me to several hundred people. That this reception was a test of endurance for him was evident (he was reported to be hopelessly ill of cancer), but he passed the ordeal bravely.

Returning to his house that night we had a long pri-

vate conversation in which I grew to a new understanding of him and a genuine affection. He told me
that he had watched my career from the first, and that
he wished by making me Convocation orator to express
his personal appreciation of my work. He did not definitely say so, but I read beneath the lines that he would
have gladly given me a degree which I now confess I
thought should have been voted by the faculty. Just
who opposed it I never knew.

At three o'clock the next afternoon I rode to Man-
dell Hall and again put on the cap and gown. It would
be folly in me to pretend indifference as I passed
down the aisle of the beautiful hall, walking beside
President Harper at the end of a procession of the
faculty, with a grand march sounding from the organ
and the audience and graduates rising to receive us. It
was a commonplace function to the professors—but to
me who never before had shared the pomp of an academic ceremony, it was profoundly impressive as a
spectacle, and just in proportion to my appreciation of
its significance did my oration on "Vanishing Trails"
diminish in value.

I will assume that the reader who has followed me
thus far is sufficiently interested to know the precise
character of this oration, and I venture to quote a part
of it.

"Each year the numbers of those who know the trail
and its life steadily lessen, and it may be that some of
you are minded at the outset to ask: 'What is a trail?'

"On its material side it is a path, capable only of
receiving horses or men in single file. It is only twelve
or fourteen inches wide, and may be merely a smooth-

ing of the sod; or it may be a deep scar in the solid rock, the record of centuries of travel, like the burro trails of Laguna and Walpi. In the woods of Wisconsin it may be a 'carry' around a rapid; in Montana, an elk run leading to a 'lick' or water hole.

"Insignificant as a thread, far-flung upon the earth, it may unite great watersheds, linking valley to valley. To come upon it in the tangled wood is an exceeding great joy. It is a reassuring clew in the cedar swamp, a promise of water in the sand, a thread of human purpose on the hill. It is the beginning of helpfulness among animals, the evidence of coöperation among men.

"To the man of macadam it seems aimless. It wavers, appears to vacillate, uncertain of its mind; and yet it attacks most difficult places. For all its apparent irresolution, it is a brave little road, discreet and persistent, venturing where the wagon road dare not follow. It may be called the vedette of civilization.

"We are accustomed to hear it said that our Pilgrim forefathers found America a trackless waste; but this was true only in respect of wagon roads and turnpikes. So far from being a 'horrific desert,' it was, indeed, a beautiful and bounteous land, a well-inhabited country, covered by a network of intersecting trails, over which the Penobscot and the Delaware lightly trod. These paths connected rivers, lakes, and villages, and led to the most promising game fields. Fish filled the streams, and deer and partridges swarmed in the thickets. The dearth and danger lay mainly in the minds of our sires. They were unskilled in woodcraft and uninstructed of the trail. As they gained in courage and insight, they made use of the experience of their aboriginal neighbors.

"No one leader had laid out these primitive paths; on the contrary, they were the product of the combined skill of generations of men—red hunters, who camped many moons in the woods, feeling their way to new hunting grounds. The white settlers slew their guides, but followed their lead; and so in the end the wagon train and the locomotive were guided by the wisdom of the Miami and the Ute, whose bones had long since been knit into the fiber of the grasses.

"We sometimes say of a great building: 'There is the monument, unlettered and grandiose, of the bricklayer, the carpenter, the hod carrier.' So of the trails which once covered this land, from Eastport to Tampa, we may say: 'They are the fading chronicles of a race'— they and a few burial mounds, impermanent as the mark of a fallen tree. Already they seem like the paths of foxes, so little they show in wood or on the meadow.

"Philosophers remark of the human race: 'It has tried every possible way of going wrong before going right,' and so these trails were won at great cost from the forest and the mountain.

"The pioneers of Kentucky and Ohio, lured by the sunset, crossed the Alleghenies along their ancient pathways, finding the new land, like the old, marked with similar lines of tribal intercourse. Each river had its elusive, sinuous path, and on the plains, a century later, Carson and Fremont followed or crossed other well-defined arteries of barbaric trade; just as in the far Northwest, even to-day, each Hudson Bay trading post is a knot of these hesitating highways, along which the native hunters plod, bringing their burdens of furs.

Almost every stream of our own mountain West has its trails, trod only by the migrating elk, or the berry-seeking bear—and all slowly yielding to the good green grass.

"From the earliest times therefore the trail toward the sunset has stood for hope, for freedom, for imagination. Many of our songs, much of our literature, has for subject the allurement and adventure of the sunset trail. Nothing in our history approaches the heroic significance of the scenes along the pathway of the pioneers.

"It would have been a rich and grateful experience to have stood with Daniel Boone when, poised on some westward-sloping rock, he watched for the first time the sun as it set over the Ohio Valley. An experience equally splendid was his who first parted the trees on the sand dunes in the land of the Michigans, and looked out upon that vast, shining inland sea, reaching to the red skies of evening. It would have been worth a lifetime of labor to have shared the tranquil rapture in the bosom of the priest who first floated through Lake Pepen and down the Mississippi River to La Crosse; but I sometimes think I would rather have been one of the exultant, intrepid men who, with Lieutenant Pike, first detected across the barren, russet, upward-sloping plain the looming purple-and-silver summits of the Rampart Range—because with the uprisen majesty of the Rocky Mountains the western continent was rounded, made complete.

"With that discovery the symmetry of the new Atlantis was disclosed. The imagination of the explorer took wing! These heights became at once his allurement, if not his uplifting. Behind those distant ranges, what new vales spread, what stranger peoples dwelt, what hidden treasures lay? The cañons opening to the west were gates of glory to the farmer boy, and when the sun went down in a smother of purple and crimson and flame color, the heart of the humblest explorer thrilled to wonder of a land in whose high thunder Jove himself might hold his throne.

"To this day these mountains are a dream of majesty to the plainsman. They complete his mental equipment. Who can estimate the effect of this path, this open gate, this trail upon American life and thought? It has un-questionably been a developer of resource, of patience, of hardihood, of adaptability. In the grim fastnesses of the mountains, on the waterless plain, the trailer was made to feel the full power of Nature. She had no anger, but also she showed no pity. She set mud, rocks, torrents, and mist to check and chill him. Never for an instant was he free from the pressure of her hand. The clouds assaulted like birds of prey; sullen streams lay in wait like dragons; and yet he found a pleasure even in this warfare—pleasure and a profound instruc-tion.

"No man can know the essential majesty of the wild till he has lain down beside his fire, in a land of pines and peaks and roaring, ice-cold water, alone and uncer-tain of his way. Swift as the turning of a hand, the pri-meval reasserts its dominion over you, and you shudder with awe and thrill with a subtle, fearsome joy. Shall a man be of less resource than the cony? Shall the cry of the brave brown robin put him to shame?

"Out of such desert experiences the scholar of the

right metal comes with fresh courage to face his work
in the world.

> Careless of wind and wolf, serene and sane,
> He faces snows with calm disdain,
> Or makes his bed down in the rain.

The voice of the puma is to him diversion, and the
snarl of the grizzly a challenge to laughter.

"It is well to consider such action, now and again.
We are getting so thin-skinned, so dependent on radia-
tors, umbrellas, and galoshes, that such a man starting
undauntedly on a journey whose circuit is ten thousand miles seems like a being from another world—
which he is! To follow such a trailer, even in imagination, is helpful. We gain new virtue, a bolder conception of life, from such confident campaigns.

"Yes, the trail brings back the ancient fortitude. It
taught our sires to endure hunger and cold and thirst
like the Algonquin. The Iroquois youth did not complain of hardship. Whatsoever nature was, that he
accepted, and so in the end a good trailer came to the
same fatalism. Weather was as the Great Spirit sent it.
Man's duty was to adapt himself to its changes, its
rigors.

"To enter this world of the trail restores the same
balance of life, fusing the hemispheres of human experience into a whole, the passing of the trail and the
cayuse, the craft of the hunter, the skill of the cowboy, the dignity of the Sioux, the hawklike celerity of
the Comanche, will leave us poorer than before.

"To be a good trailer is not a sufficient preparation
for citizenship, it is true. But the scholar who knows

and does not fear the wilderness is so much more the man; of this I am convinced. To mount the trail that braids itself upon the bosom of Sierra Blanca is to rise above the mist, to shake off intellectual miasma.

"Do you know the *splendors* of the campfire? Have you seen it bloom in the cold, gray damp of an autumn night like a mighty rose? Have you heard the chirp and whisper—the mysterious singing of the flaming pine branches? If you have, you know its splendid solace. You are able to divine the protection which that ancient good spirit, Red Flame, flung between the houseless, hairy man of the Stone Age and the evil elements swarming upon him.

"It is a child of the sun, reproducing in the midnight forest the burning heat of the noonday. It is at once a shield and a sword. It disperses mimic stars to the bleak, oppressive skies. It beats back the darkness, laughing like Loki, defying the dragons, holding the werewolves at bay.

"You make your camp late, we will suppose. The sun is long set. All is cold and desolate. Rain is falling. Snow is in the air. Chilled and bent, you grope deep among the coverts of fir, gathering a few dry cones, collecting minute tips of dead branches. These you heap in a little mound, kneeling as in the act of conjuring some hidden spirit, some good genius of the wood.

"Then of a sudden out of the blackness licks a little red flame. It is the tongue tip of the good beast Fire gnawing his way to freedom. A light arises. The shadows flee. The wind begins to snarl again, in desperate fury; but the brave blaze answers with a crescendo roar of jubilant might. The frost retreats like a circling pack

of white wolves. The flame leaps higher! The icy
branches of the trees above you suddenly appear lined
in high relief against a blue-black sky, and lo, you find
yourself glad and grateful, in a palace of scarlet and
orange and green, a house of refuge, fragile as a bubble,
but so magical that no wild beast dares to set a foot
therein. Leagued with leaping flame you are invincible!

"Fire draws a shining line between ourselves and the
beast. It proclaims man's mastery of the elements, his
kingship. Circling the centuries, you approach the
burning tree from the emberless awe of the caveman's
desolate night.

"Yes, the trail with all it subtends is fading from the
earth; and the white trailers, like the red, are dying.
They will soon have crossed the dark river, to camp
with Clark and Fremont, and to smoke the pipe of
peace with Osceola and Sitting Bull. Soon all those
whom they type will rejoin them to talk of the brave
days gone.

"Each year the flood of humdrum settlement rises a
little higher in the Colorado valleys. Each spring growing herds of cattle crowd out the elk. Year by year the
brazen clamors of the sawmills thicken. Each summer
a new irrigation ditch depletes a stream. In the cañons
of the Crestones the thunder of the miner's bomb is
heard. The mountain sheep, wariest of all the kindred
of the hills, are surrounded; they cannot escape. The
moose, victim of the ever-increasing army of those who
kill for sport, are seen no more in the high parks. The
madness to kill, to destroy, is abroad, armed and piti-
less, and a wave of plows, resistless as a glacier, grinds

at the base of Shavano. Soon the mountains like the plains will be silent, barren of life, with not even a soaring eagle to cast a shadow on their naked cliffs.

"It is not without significance that Grover Cleveland and Theodore Roosevelt, hunters and lovers of the wild, have used their power to preserve the forest lands of the West. All honor to them! By their acts some little part of our splendid heritage of pine and peak and stream is now secured for future generations, so that, when all the interior valley of the Mississippi is clipped and dusty with traffic, a breathing space will still exist on the mighty ranges of Colorado, California, and Wyoming.

"I repeat that we as Americans draw our best qualities from the stress which the wilderness laid upon our fathers. From the very first a selection has been going on, developing courage, resolution, originality, and hope. Buoyancy, adaptability, humor—these are the qualities of the trail. Our pathfinders, our engineers, sons of explorers, have been mighty conjurors, seldom disheartened and never appalled by any task. Boundless freedom, boundless opportunity, and daily discovery have lain before them from the first. We have been a nation of explorers, in spirit as in fact.

"Many of our greatest men are sons of the trail. Who shall estimate the value of the wilderness in the training of Washington, of Lincoln, and of Grant? Simplicity and directness of purpose, tenacity and resource, they certainly drew from their border experiences, and they are but shining graduates of the Pine Tree Academe. For more than two hundred years we have been schooled by the Algonquin and the Sioux. Let us acknowledge this. We killed them, we swept them before us; but they taught us as they died.

"For two centuries or more the open lands to the West have been trying the souls of our most adventurous sons and daughters. Our leaders to-day are sons of pathfinders and trail-makers. The pioneering spirit has passed into every department of our activity. None so bold as Americans in building bridges, in digging tunnels, in constructing towers; only in art and literature have we remained timid and boyish, keeping to the beaten thoroughfares, imitative and apologetic.

"By and by the spirit of the trail-maker will enter the hearts of our artists, our sculptors, and our novelists, and they, too, will be bold and free, to match with the physical reach and splendor of their fellow inventors, poets in steel and stone and bronze."

Although the audience applauded me at the close of my reading, and Dr. Harper hurried over to grasp my hand voicing his approval and his pleasure, I felt that many of the faculty had failed to see the application of an oration on "Vanishing Trails" to the problems of academic life. Nothing like it had ever been heard there!

That night, when the time came for me to go, Dr. Harper said: "You carried me far away into the shining mountains, back to the woods and valleys which I fear I shall never see again." And looking into his face, white with pain, I felt that he was in truth letting go his hold on life.

When I saw him next, several months later, he was on his deathbed, small and white, refined almost to spirit. He spoke again and with deep emotion of the pleasure my oration had given him. Closing his eyes, he said, "I can't tell you how beautiful it all was—that brilliant audience, the sun shining in, and you so full of power and enthusiasm calling up for me such dazzling pictures of the mountains——"

He could not finish, and I knew that he had spoken his farewell to those hills and streams. I tried to hide my own emotion, but in vain. I could not control my voice. The shadow of death lay heavily upon us both. He knew and I knew that this was the end. At last I rose, said good-by brokenly, and hastened from the room.

He was a brave and noble spirit. The University of Chicago did well in calling its magnificent new library the William Rainey Harper Memorial, for he was the indomitable builder of this vast and ever-growing institution.

CHAPTER TWENTY-ONE

A ROMAN HOLIDAY

I

THROUGHOUT the years lying between 1899 and 1905 I had kept up a desultory correspondence with Barrie, Kipling, Shaw, and other of my English friends, and in the spring of 1906, feeling the need of a closer contact with London and Paris, I planned a second trip to the Old World. Worn down with writing and lecturing, I consulted my doctor, who, with fine understanding of my wishes, *ordered* me to spend the summer "abroad." I've always liked that word. It dates from a time when "going abroad" meant something like an adventure into the sunrise.

Having established a reputation on one steamship line as the worst sailor the company had ever carried, I decided to make another record on a route whose steamers promised a shorter period of torture. On May 24, 1906, I left Quebec for Liverpool, amid a shipload of Scotch, English, and French Canadians, without a single acquaintance on board. My impressions are condensed into these lines: "I have stopped going to the dining room and am taking my soup and fruit in my berth. There isn't a person on shipboard who interests me—not one!"

Happily for me I found in the library a copy of

"Dialstone Lane" by W. W. Jacobs, whom I discovered
to be "a kind of English Stockton—very quaint, very
original, and quietly humorous. His characters say the
unexpected thing, and in everything they do they are
interesting. He is a genuine humanitarian and I hope
to meet him when I reach London—if I ever do. He
has made some of my hours of imprisonment pass almost
happily."

Most of my entries are bitter imprecations against
the sea, hot cabins, and worthless complaints of ship-
smells and bleak decks. One item, however, records the
fact that this boat was carrying away the last company
of English soldiers from Canada. "We have no further
use for the English army" said one of the passengers.

On the eighth day out from Montreal we landed in
Liverpool, and that night I slept at the Euston Hotel
in London. The next day I went to the Cecil Hotel,
which I found to be several degrees less splendid than
I had imagined it; and in the evening, by way of celebration, I saw Ellen Terry in Shaw's "Captain Brass-
bound." The play was a joy, but the great actress was
to me only a memory. All her grace, her lightness, was
gone. "She hesitated in her lines, and had to be helped
out again and again. It was painful to see her working
so hard to produce that which once she created without
effort."

Again, as on my arrival seven years before, I immediately sought out Bernard Shaw in his new country
place, some twenty miles from London. "If you come
soon, I'll arrange a nightingale chorus for you," he had
written, referring to my complaint that I had never
heard a nightingale.

I found him living in a rectory—a strange place for an iconoclast—in a spacious house with an equally spacious and charming garden. He was definitely older and grayer, like myself, but quite the genial, brilliant monologist that I remembered. He had just returned from Paris, where Rodin had been making a bust of him, and his descriptions of the great sculptor were most diverting. I caught a few of his phrases. "Rodin's pose is the opposite to that of the mystic. 'Work to the life,' he asserted, and then proceeded to take the most astonishing liberties with my portrait, enlarging my nose, slicing off an ear here and resetting it there. 'The larger part of my work is mechanical. It is easy to get a likeness,' he declared, 'but to get the geometry—ah, there is the task!' He measured and squinted like a mechanic to get his geometric proportions. His egotism is colossal. 'Phidias, Michaelangelo, and Rodin—they are great sculptors!' " Shaw quoted with grandiloquent gesture, dramatizing the artist's complacent pose.

During dinner I reverted to the nightingale chorus, but Shaw began to hedge. "Yes, I promised, but the nightingale is a most unreliable bird. One night he sings and the next, for some unexplained reason, he doesn't. I am hoping that this will prove his tuneful hour, but I am not assured."

It was a lovely moonlit garden into which he led me, a place for youth, songsters, and fairies, but not a chirp was heard as we furtively moved from covert to covert. Shaw took on the apologetic tone of an impresario whose soprano has become "temperamental."

"They are like German opera stars, sometimes nothing will induce them to sing—at other times they sing after their voices are gone. To-night, when all nature invites to rhapsody, they are dumb."

At last, in disappointment and chagrin, we went back to the house and resumed our discussion of things literary.

In touching upon his own affairs, he said, "My fortunes have improved since 1899, but I am by no interpretation rolling in money. My plays are going on here and there, but the runs are comparatively short."

In plain words he was a great figure in the dramatic world without being a box-office success, yet here he was, living in what seemed luxury to me and expressing a cheerful confidence in the future. He was not yet fifty and in the high tide of his creative powers.

One of the matters on which I sought his advice was my Roman holiday. "Does any one go to Rome in the summer?" I asked.

"No Englishman does, but there is no reason why an American should hesitate, the heat is nothing like that of your Mid-West. It is a good time to travel, for the hotels are empty, and the citizens busy with their own affairs. My advice is to go. Don't fail to see Toulouse, Nîmes, Carcassonne, Avignon, and Marseilles. You'll be delighted with Nîmes and Avignon. See Aiguesmortes also."

Zangwill was living at Shottermill, and in going out to spend the week-end with him I had in mind a call on Doyle who still lived at Hindhead not far away. Zangwill had married the daughter of a Scotch professor, a very intelligent and interesting young woman, and they were spending the summer in a little hip-roof cottage on the tip-top of a hill which looked across the

valley toward the Black Moor. Israel, who was deep in
the Zionist movement, had neglected his fiction and
was writing essays and letters advocating the purchase
of land in Mexico on which to colonize the Jews. I
questioned the wisdom of this. "You know perfectly
well that the Jews would rather cultivate New York
than Monterey. Furthermore, I crossed that Mexican
land. I have seen fifty sandspouts dancing over it at
one time. Some one is trying to unload a desert ranch
upon your society. Return to your muttons!"

My words gave him pause—but only for a moment.
"We are considering also a colony in Africa."

To me this was a sad waste of his time and energy
and I did my best to show him the folly of it, all to
small effect. Even as we played tennis together he would
pause to argue some point which he had overlooked.

On Sunday Doyle came over in his grand new
motor car and took us all for a long ride about the
country—a marvelous experience for me as well as for
Zangwill. Indeed he betrayed more excitement than I.
He was in ecstasy when Doyle exceeded the speed
limit, and his face shone with reckless, boyish glee. He
rode with his hat in his hand, his mop of hair fluttering
in the wind, while Doyle kept wary eye on the lurking
"cops" along the lanes. Now and then a man stepped
from the hedge and made a friendly sign of warning.
"That is one of our men signaling 'danger ahead,'"
Doyle explained as he slowed down. Another hand sig-
naled "all clear," and the car leaped into redoubled
speed.

"It was a lovely as well as an exciting ride, for our
way led through Aldershot, the heart of the British

army, and into villages a thousand years old, with ancient church towers and tile-roofed cottages surrounded by worn and lichen-spotted walls. 'These towns are as typical as any to be found in all England,' Doyle declared."

On Monday I returned to London, and again, as on my previous visit, I was an overseas guest at an authors' dinner, but my diary records a disappointment. "Hardly any of the well-known writers were present. The guest of the evening was Mrs. Thurston, author of a popular novel called 'The Gambler.' She is a high-colored, showy woman, very nice in spite of her bad taste in dress. I sat beside her and we had a pleasant chat. Doyle, who presided, paid me the compliment of a handsome little speech."

On Thursday, Kipling had me to lunch with him at Brown's Hotel. "He, too, has suffered change. He is thin and bald, but his manner is quite as vivacious as ever. We talked of New York, Roosevelt, the English dialect, and many other subjects—a lively hour. Mrs. Kipling came in about two, a quiet, matronly figure. I would not have known her had I met her elsewhere.

"With Kipling, as with Shaw and Doyle, I resumed acquaintance almost as if six weeks instead of seven years had intervened—of such quality are the friendships established in youth. Kipling is a very great figure at this time, but his writing is no longer defiant. The death of his little daughter in New York City has given him a touch of mysticism and more than a touch of melancholy. The glow of exuberant youth is gone."

One by one I met old acquaintances. Among them: Albert Kinross, Robert Barr, and Gilbert Parker.

"Parker is now a member of Parliament, highly successful, rich, and in favor at court. I hardly dared approach him, so exalted and so shining is his place. Nevertheless, he was cordial, and kindly offered a card to the House of Commons—a favor which I was glad to accept."

Meanwhile I had learned that Jacobs, my newly discovered author, had a home near Epping Forest. Upon learning my address he wrote, inviting me to spend Saturday and Sunday with him. "Arthur Morrison lives near me," he added, "and wishes to meet you."

It happened that I had an engagement to lunch with Sidney Lee, the Shakesperean scholar, on Saturday, but I planned to go to Epping immediately afterward. Lee, who was a cultivated jew of the sort Zangwill characterized in "Children of the Ghetto," did most of the talking. He talked and talked well of public men and public affairs rather than of Shakespeare. His other guest, the Canon of Westminster Abbey, had little to say and I only now and then put in a remark.

From this lunch I hurried to the station and took the train for Loughton, where Jacobs, a small, pale man, was awaiting me—speculating, no doubt, as to the kind of person I would turn out to be. I imagined a look of relief in his large and serious eyes as I announced myself to him. He was very slight of figure, unwholesome of complexion, and spoke with wistful intonation. I liked him and found his shy smile and timid voice appealing.

Mrs. Jacobs, a handsome, graceful, dark-eyed Welsh girl, spoke with what might be called an American accent and was an easy and charming hostess. Her

house was exquisitely kept and bright and tasteful—
just such a cottage as writers of similar character maintain in Cos Cob or Riverside.

Just over the hill lay Epping Forest, and naturally I
began at once to ask questions about it. Although not
typically English, Jacobs revered English traditions and
was filled with love of this historic forest. He knew
many stories of the highwaymen who used to harbor
in it, sallying from it on errands of banditry in the
brave days of horse pistols and stagecoaches.

"Come!" said he. "I'll show you the haunts of Dick
Lightfoot!"

It was inevitable that I should be disappointed in it.
It wasn't a forest at all; it was only a waste of grasses
and clumps of gorse, with occasional groves of marvelous beeches, each group forming a grotesque, natural
cathedral with gnarled and twisted columns against
which the sunset colors splashed in glory. "Some of these
trees are seven hundred years old," Jacobs declared—
and truly they were majestic. He showed me also where
the famous robber had his stronghold.

My regard for him grew. "He is a strong little man
and his home (very like that of a writer in Edgewood)
is a place of humor, insight, and idealism. I liked Mrs.
Jacobs also. She interested me by her direct, almost
brusque, speech. I had no sense of being in a strange
country as I sat with these delightful people."

II

Paris, hot and dusty, had lost much of its charm and
all of its mystery, as I reëntered it after seven years. I
found myself ready to leave it at the end of a week of

wandering about its drab streets. Its parks looked neglected and unkempt in comparison with those of England and its art bored me. I was in no mood for it. In my search of the historical I wandered out to the Troadéro and there came upon the rooms devoted to Angkor Wat. I was at once enthralled by these reproductions of designs and sculptures of a most mysterious people. I began that moment a study which continues to this day. Like Stonehenge, Angkor remains for me an insoluble psychologic puzzle. One of the most astonishing facts connected with these majestic ruins is that these builders, so skilled in carving, so noble in their plan, had not common sense enough, after a thousand years of labor, to break joints in their masonry! Similarly I have dwelt long on the psychology of the men of Stonehenge who set up those stupendous slabs of stone on Salisbury Plain and yet had not the skill to carve a single pictograph!

After walking all the regulation tourist paths in Paris, I took train for Giverny to spend the night with Frederick MacMonnies, an old friend of Lorado Taft, and one of my wife's early teachers. I found him living in a singular old building which had been (so he explained) part of an ancient monastery around which lay a fine garden. "I have no sculpture to show you," he said. "My studio is cleaned out and I am just beginning on a new commission, but I have a few canvases on the walls and I can show you the subjects which inspired others."

As we went about the garden I recognized the flower beds, the terrace, the walls which he and his wife had so brilliantly reproduced in paint. The house, although a "ruin," was, notwithstanding, a comfortable and spacious home.

That night MacMonnies and I pretty well settled the artistic future of the United States. I told him of Taft, St. Gaudens, French, and many other of his sculptor friends and urged him to come back and help make New York a greater Paris. "That," he said, "I am inclined to do."

"He is a quick intelligence as well as a very great artist," I wrote, "but his work has almost no relationship to America. It is essentially French. Not only has he been schooled in Paris, he has breathed the air and eaten the bread of France so long that his blood and his brain are French."

We talked of Monet, who had made Giverny famous all over the art world, and of my old friend, Thomas Sargent Perry, who was living near; and when I walked out into the meadows, down past the pollarded willows, I discovered (what I might have inferred) that Monet had glorified a sadly commonplace little valley. He and his gifted associates had haloed every object, lifting it to a higher quality than it actually possessed. They aureoled every haystack. It was not as beautiful as the Wisconsin Valley in which I was born, but it had been loved and studied by men of genius for centuries. "Perhaps, fifty years from now, the Mississippi River and the hills of Trempealeau will find their glorifying artists and poets."

Thomas Sargent Perry, whom I had not seen for nearly fourteen years, had declined into a tall, clean-shaven, scholarly old man. Knowing the intimate history of the valley, he took me to see Monet's farm, an uninspiring spot. "His dwelling was ordinary and his garden formal without being tasteful. The more I studied this village, the more I marveled at the transforming power of art. Precisely as James Whitcomb Riley had translated his flat Indiana farmlands into poetry, so these French painters had transformed their commonplace Giverny into a wonderland of art."

On returning to Paris I fulfilled a promise—I went to St. Cloud to visit Madame Blanc whom I had not seen for seven years. She it was who wrote of me so feelingly in *La Revue Des Deux Mondes* and who had entertained me so handsomely at Ferté Sous Jouarre in the summer of '99. I found her old and poor and sad, living with a sisterhood high on a hill which overlooked the Paris she loved so dearly and which she had no hope of reëntering. Her son had been a disappointment, she could no longer write, and her means were almost exhausted—yet she bravely faced me. "You mean very much to me," she said. "You bring to me many pictures of your brave young America—and delightful memories of my visits there, in the West, with my beloved Alice French. It is all so far away—yet so near as I listen to your voice."

There was something in her attitude toward me which reminded me of my last visit to Dr. Harper. Here again I was aware of the inexorable. I knew that when I said farewell, it would be my final word with her. She had been a noble figure in international literature. She had done much to make France aware of American writers and artists—more, perhaps, than any other woman in France—and I honored her for it.

She died soon after this interview, and is, alas!

almost forgotten by the readers of to-day. She was a
generous and helpful critic and friend to all of us in
that day.

III

The success of my travel novelette of six years
before, ("Her Mountain Lover") decided me to try
again with a sequel to be called "Jim Mattison's Old
World Pasear." Pasear is the word which the cowboys
use to mean a stroll. My plan was to take Jim on a tour
of France and Italy and record his reactions. Writing
of this sort was not as common then as it is now, and
the fact that my story of Jim in England was still selling led me to think that I could again pay my way
by means of his later comment. Therefore I immediately sketched out a beginning, and began to make notes
in anticipation of the effect of my sight-seeing. (I wrote
the narrative, but it was never published.)

My dated record in Florence reads: "I am not enjoying myself—I am working like a man in the harvest
field. With no expectation of ever coming again, I keep
on my feet from dawn till dusk. It is not a vacation;
it is a course of study. Florence is hot and dusty as
Omaha. The Arno, shrunk to a foul little stream, lies
gasping in the sand, but my enthusiastic brother-in-
law, Lorado Taft, is here and is showing me the famous
sculptures. He exhibits them with worshipful reverence
whilst I commend the cool air of the halls.

"Taft never forgets his mission. He is here to gather
esthetic sweetness for the enrichment of the home hive.
Fuller is losing courage and so am I, but Lorado, undismayed by dirt, vulgarity, indifference, and official

graft, is bending his energies to the task of making Chicago a center of American art."

Nothing will be enlarged by a detailed story of my six weeks' stay in Italy. I saw Genoa, Rome, Naples, Venice, Verona, Milan, and the glorious Lago Maggiore. I made a large number of notes, mostly of my dislikes and disgusts. The filthy habits of the proletariat in southern Italy, the clamoring hack drivers of Rome, infuriated me. The human ordure in the parks, the dark dens from which the people crept to cook their food on the sidewalks, the smells which made every picturesque ruin loathsome—these irritations obscured the beauty of sky and landscape. The sea and mountains of Italy were glorious, but the poor, embruted citizens aroused my sympathy, at the same time that I hated their tempestuous voices, their cruelty to their animals, and their beggary. (All of which has been changed, I am assured, by the all-conquering genius of Mussolini. He has cleaned the parks, abolished the beggars, and tamed the hack drivers!)

Here is my page on Venice: "It has all the vices of a show place. Its traders are of the sort who feed on the passing stranger. As I wandered about its malodorous streets and crossed its canals, noisome as sewers (bearing dead dogs, garbage, and sewage on their currents), I lost all the admiration which my first sight of the city had aroused. The leather-lunged gondoliers, the raucous bellowing of street singers, the childish, theatric, passionate, unreasoning roaring of the people (with no reserve, no dignity—always fiercely affectionate or dramatically savage) wearied me and repelled me. I can't understand how Fuller and Howells could overlook the squalor, the ceaseless turmoil, of this city. The artists have painted the same few 'bits' a thousand times and proclaimed their pictures Venice—Damn this bellowing mob!—Fifty men and women are this moment howling outside my window. They yowl and screech from the love of it.

"For three nights I have sweltered in my hotel eaten by mosquitoes and kept awake by clamoring, never-sleeping vagrants. When I close my windows to shut out the clamor I gasp for breath. When I open them the whooping, bawling, popping, spluttering voices of the street loafers endanger my ultimate salvation. I would slay them all if I could. To-day I leave Venice. I have seen it and have nearly died in the midst of it."

Just by way of contrast, I include this one made immediately on my arrival at Stressa:

"Another world! A green, wet, silent, majestic land—with mountains, huge looming masses of blue in a mist of rain. It is as far from Naples as heaven is from hell. All is still and green and blue, and in the immediate foreground of the lakescape, a castled island, darkly green, is silhouetted against the stormy clouds of the upper lake. It is as if I had been snatched from the dusty plain and suspended amid the silence and mists of an Alpine valley."

Switzerland I liked. "It resembles Glacier Park in Montana and I rejoice in the quiet stupidity of its people. By contrast with the people of Venice the Swiss are a blessed relief. Lake Lucerne surpasses anything I have seen in way of lake scenery. It is like a great poem, historic as well as beautiful."

These notes of mine have only one merit—they express the exact mood of the moment. Most Americans go to Europe to enjoy what they see and hear (and this is well) but I was out to value what I saw. I wanted to see Italy and France and Switzerland for myself. It was not a question of what I *ought* to feel, but what my reactions plainly were. After some weeks in southern Italy—Verona, Bologna, Milan, and Florence seemed northern, almost German, and on my return to France the people of Paris seemed blond!

My stay in Paris was short, for on August 5th I was in London. "Good-by to Paris! I left on the early train and am now back in the Strand. I was not sorry to leave Paris and I do not care if I never see it again. The men I met (and was forced to bargain with) destroyed the charm of the city. I am getting too old and too irritable to enjoy fighting the demands of hotel managers and cab drivers. The people of England seem very clean, and very neighborly after six weeks of Italy and France. I feel almost at home—so familiar are the streets, buildings, and 'bus traffic. The great town is ugly and drab and the climate is depressing, but I find it restful after the sunshine and clamor of Naples and Rome. I like it because it is not continental."

IV

Although of Scottish descent on my mother's side and a worshipper of Scottish song and story, I had never seen the hills and streams, the castles and battlefields which Sir Walter Scott had made glorious, and now with three weeks to spare I bought a ticket to Glasgow by way of Edinboro and Melrose. I regarded the

Highlands of Loch Gyle as the ancestral home of my
mother's clan and Loch Lomond as the jewel of the
north.

Here again I must be honest. Those days in Scott's
land and Burns' land were a voyage of discovery—and
disillusionment. It was a rereading of "The Lady of the
Lake" and "Tam O' Shanter" by the light of a modern
sixty watt lamp. I discovered that Ellen's Isle was only
about ten rods from shore and that the maiden could
have waded across at any moment. The Trossachs' "aw-
ful jaws" were only the precipitous sides of a lonely
glen out of which ran a beautiful stream, and "Poosey
Nancy's" barroom was a tiny place where four roister-
ers would have been a crowd!

Ben Lomond was entirely up to the lines of the song,
but the sun shone only twice during my stay—in fact
the skies wept almost every hour for two days, and as I
was coming back to Liverpool I heard two fellow passengers discussing "Scotch Mist." They were young
Scots returning to London. One said to the other, "Ye
must admit, Jock, it always did rain in Ayr when we
were lads." I quote this testimony from a native because I wish to be fair.

In the matter of Scotch costume, I was disappointed.
I had expected to see more of the plaids and tartans. I
went to Inverary, eager to witness the program of
traditional Gaelic sports, only to find a crowd of commonplace people in commonplace dress. The only men
in costume were the pipers and no one but a few
Americans took any interest in the games. This became
painfully apparent when a village hockey match began,
for all the audience at the Scottish tournament aban-

doned their seats and hastened to the other and more exciting contest.

The home of my ancestors was magnificent in its spread of wild water, mist-clad mountains, and rocky glens, but I understood why they emigrated to Virginia and Ohio. I understood also the inordinate use of "whisky"—one needs something to combat the outward chill. There must be sunshine in Scotland, for how else could they grow oats and barley?—but I saw little of it. Furthermore, my disillusionment only proved the potency of the poet. In Scott's lines, the Tweed flows "broad and deep" and Lake Katrin expands into a wild and stormy water. Ellen's Isle withdraws into distance and becomes an inaccessible sanctuary. "Well, why not?" I asked myself as I walked the lonely road leading from Loch Lomond to Loch Katrin. Our poets have the same license to color the Alleghenies with poetry and to fill the valleys of the Rampart Range with the figures of romance."

From the gray skies of my ancestral hills, I passed in a few hours to Carnarvon where the Eisteddfod, a traditional Welsh song festival, was in progress and I must confess I found the Welsh more loyal to this traditional bardic custom than the Scotch were to the games at Inverary. The weather was delightful, the scenery exquisite, and the people friendly. Here is a page dated August 23d: "Leaving the train at Berwyn I walked to Llangollen through an exquisitely beautiful landscape—a delicious, softly rounded, comfortable landscape—a valley alluring with all hominess. Beside my path a clear stream rippled. Above my head, in splendid trees, birds sang, and over all a pale-gold sunshine fell. It was all so harmonious, so perfect in line and color, that I was enchanted. The cottages along the river are deeply shaded by fruit trees and their gardens full of autumnal flowers. I know of nothing in America to compare with this quiet valley, except old Chester on a warm September day."

In the glow of this experience I sailed for New York.

CHAPTER TWENTY-TWO

MY OKLAHOMA NEIGHBOR

I

HENRY FULLER was in my house when I returned to Chicago in September, and in response to his eager and amused questioning I poured forth a stream of comment: "I can't understand your enthusiasm for Italian towns. You say America has no art and that our villages are utterly prosaic—which is true, but they have windows, bathtubs, electric light, and furnaces. Don't talk to me of the Italian proletariat. Whatever the Italian peasant may be, the man in the city street is an earache. After six weeks of it I longed for the zone of reserve. After Naples and Venice, Milan seemed Nordic. When I got back to England I felt like that man in Gillette's play who purchased a pair of ear plugs and suddenly found himself in a blessed region of silence."

Fuller chuckled, eying me with bright, sidewise glance. "The Italians and the French *are* noisy—according to our standards, but when I was young I didn't mind it."

"You'd mind it now! Yelping robins and groaning insects are but a soothing murmur compared to the open-air conversations of Italy—and their filthy habits! I stopped visiting picturesque ruins even in France. I wanted to turn the Rhone in on Carcassonne."

"You must not forget where the poor things live—and that they have no public conveniences of any kind. The street is their only kitchen and garbage chute."

"Well, you may have Italy—all of it. I'll take England for my place of residence hereafter. I know for myself what Avignon and Milan and Rome are like. I'm satisfied. I'm going back to West Salem for a week or two—then on to New York with a new book."

"What about your plan to write a sequel to 'Her Mountain Lover'?"

"I have given it up. If I should put into it all my disgust of the filth of Carcassonne and the dreadful tenements of Avignon, no one would print it. Jim saw nothing in Venice but the garbage floating in the canals and felt nothing but the mosquitoes. My readers would not even commend him for honesty. I will not say my summer was wasted, but it was of no fictional service to me."

Although reluctant to give up the publication of "Jim's Pasear"—the name I had chosen for the sequel to "Her Mountain Lover"—I found on rereading it that it was not, as a whole, worth while.

"West Salem, Wisconsin, October 10. Having given up my plan for a sequel to 'Her Mountain Lover,' I returned to the story of Colorado of which I had written several chapters under the title, 'Mart Haney's Mate.' The chief characters of this novel were suggested to me by a young girl, the manager of a hotel in a little Colorado town, and her lover, a big Irish gambler I once observed in Cripple Creek. I had no talk with the girl, but as I watched her in her defensive warfare against the cattlemen, drummers, and miners who fre-

quented the hotel, I wondered what would happen if
Mart Haney of Cripple Creek should chance to lunch
at the Golden Eagle Hotel."

With a quiet, spacious room in which to work, with
my wife and little daughter to employ my leisure time,
I bent to the writing of this story, which interested me.
One day while in the midst of a chapter I was interrupted by Cordenio Severance, who had brought Richard Burton down from St. Paul in his motor car. Severance, as the junior member of the firm, Davis, Kellogg
& Severance, had won great distinction in Minnesota,
but steadily refused to run for office—in honor pre-
ferring others. He was a large man of forty-five, always smiling and full of funny stories. To be with him
at dinner was to characterize him as a delightful companion, a man without serious duty, winning success on
the strength of innumerable friendships, and yet he
was a great lawyer, retained by huge corporations. He
often argued far-reaching cases before the Supreme
Court. Joker that he was, he took his cases seriously and
worked when work was demanded. He could sit all
night writing a brief—but he could put it aside for a
concert or a dinner. He and his wife, Maidie, were
something more than friends, they were intellectual
kinfolk.

They had taken the Harriman farm some ten miles
out of St. Paul and had made of it a country seat, a center of music and literature and good-fellowship. Year
by year it had taken on "wings" and "ells" till it had
become a mansion (with a pipe organ, pictures, and a
noble garden) to which came a never-ending procession
of distinguished guests. In short, Maidie and Cordenio

had created a civilized spot on the Minnesota prairie, and Richard Burton, who was at this time the head of the Department of Literature at the Minnesota State University, was a frequent guest. A motor excursion such as this of Severance's was a real adventure in 1906. There were no paved roads, and automobiles were not yet trustworthy.

It is only fair to explain that "Money Magic," as I was now calling my new Colorado story, was sadly broken in upon by the dangerous illness of my little daughter who all but died of diphtheria in November. The authorities quarantined us in our West Salem home for a month, and that my book suffered in sympathy with these distractions and anxieties is evident. Nevertheless I finished the first draft of it on December 2d. "To-day I wrote the chapter dealing with the death of Mart Haney. The book is full of faults, but some of them I shall eliminate."

II

While my novel of Cripple Creek and Colorado Springs was still in hand I turned aside to write "The Long Trail," a boy's book, based on my "Trail of the Gold-Seekers." The continued sale of "Boy Life on the Prairie," seven years after publication, had led my publishers to urge upon me the writing of another juvenile. "Nothing lasts like a good boys' book," they declared.

Early in October, at the urging of my brother, I went down to Oklahoma to advise with him. While there I learned that the Creeks were having their last meeting in the Council House at Okmulgee, and I at once seized the opportunity of witnessing these historic proceed-ings. The place of meeting was a rude stone building, somewhat like the courthouse in a backwoods country. On the first floor sat "the House of Warriors" and on the upper floor "the House of Kings." I had met Chief Pleasant Porter as a citizen of Muskogee. I now saw him as the presiding officer of the Creek assembly.

"October 10, 1905. For several hours I watched these dusky warriors conferring in their bare and grimy chambers, sensing in their voices the sadness of a vanishing race whose history was fading into myth. Their procedure was a curious mingling of town meeting and campfire. They had a presiding officer who put the resolutions to vote quite as a state legislative official might have done and a clerk recorded the result. It was very strange, quite incredible."

Porter, a big man, darkly genial, especially interested me. "He is very able, but looks like a man who has dissipated his energies and is beginning to feel it," I made record.

I now owned two farms near Seger's Colony, and this seemed a good opportunity to visit them. Seger met me as usual at Weatherford, but told me that he was dated to visit several points in the reservation and asked me to ride the circuit with him.

To this I agreed, and we set out for Cloud Chief in the midst of a hot, rushing October wind—a furious wind which rapidly grew in power till it threatened to overturn the top buggy in which we rode. By three in the afternoon, the force of the blast had become so terrifying that Seger decided to turn in at the gate of a settler, whose home, half shack and half dugout, was sheltered by a low hill. As we drew up to the door, a procession of barrels, wash boilers, tumbleweeds, and chickens went streaming past. Never even in my darkest Dakota days had I witnessed anything more sinister than this destructive blast.

At the invitation of the farmer we entered the house, which was a blessed refuge to me. The noise of the storm was diminished by the sod walls, but the rooms were dust-filled and I could feel the flutter of the roof, which seemed about to lift and whirl away.

It was a singular household. The dominating personality of the group was a deaf old woman, a newspaper reader with the gift of speech. She knew my name—had indeed read some of my stories (unfortunately), and was eager to have me pour entertainment into her upturned ear trumpet. She seemed not in the least concerned about the storm—neither was her fat daughter-in-law, who went calmly about her task of preparing supper, but a neighbor, who had also sought refuge, sat in wordless horror, certain that her own house had been blown away.

To complete the singularity of this group, our host, a grimy, bewhiskered little man, confided to me that he, too, was an author, and that he had composed several hymns. He proceeded to sing them, playing his own accompaniment on a minute parlor organ, in order that I might express a judgment as to their value. The combination was incredible. The wailing, moaning instrument, the drone of the man's voice, the smell of cooking, the half light, the pushing, shrieking wind—what a mixture of discordant elements! In all my varied experiences, I have never been plunged into such a home.

On and on the man sang, his inane hymns hammering at my ears, and no sooner did he pause than the old woman again up-ended her ear trumpet, and demanded my opinion of the political leaders of her admiration. She was a natural lawmaker. At the table she was placed beside me so that she could handily direct her horn against my lips. No one else said a word—not even Seger. I wondered how long I could endure this torture.

The wind died down at dusk and we were able to flee. We drove to Cordell by moonlight, but my afternoon in that dim, dusty farmhouse remains a nightmare of sadness and horror.

On our way to another small town, the following day, we passed near the camp of Vea-che-ato, a renowned Cheyenne chief, one of Seger's especial friends. "I want you to see this man," said Seger. "He is one of the most powerful of the old warriors. He came out here with me twenty years ago." As we were driving along a narrow lane, Seger called out, "There he is now!" Looking where he pointed I saw an aged farmer picking cotton in a field. He was on his knees between the rows and without a hat. After him he dragged a sack half filled with cotton.

Alighting from our buggy, we crawled through the wire fence and approached this toiler. As we reached him, he straightened his aching back and raised a trembling hand to shade his eyes. The sun was very hot and sweat was thick on his brown face. For a moment he studied me. Then as he recognized Seger he called out:

"Ho! Miokany!" then again fixing his dim eyes on me he signed with his hand, "Who is this man?"

Seger explained (also in the sign language) that I

was "a paper chief," and a friend of the red man. "He has come," he explained, "to see how far the red people have walked along the white man's road."

The aged Cheyenne absorbed the agent's meaning, muttering "Aye! Ah-oh!"—much as an old Scotchman might have done, and made reply by way of graceful gestures with his fine hands.

"He says," Seger explained, "that he is working here as an example to his young men."

Taking a silver coin from my pocket, I said, "Tell him that I have heard of him as a brave warrior, a man of many battles, but that I think him a greater warrior —here in his field, leading his people along the white man's road—than he ever was in the past. Tell him that I am his friend and that I give him this coin because I wish him to know that I think him a noble chieftain, and a brave leader."

As Seger put my meaning into gesture the old man's eyes misted with tears. Gratefully, wonderingly he gazed up at me. No white man had ever spoken to him like that, no man had ever given him silver for such a reason. Silent with emotion, he signed, "This white man is good. My heart goes out to him."

Leaving him there still on his knees under the blazing sun, we rode away in silence. He was nearly seventy years of age, but he was still the heroic leader, showing his people the white man's hot and dusty way. Could there be greater contrast between his proud, free life as a warrior of the plains and his action in thus dragging a cotton sack across the field? All the customs, traditions, and laws were against him—yet there he was. Such stories of the Cheyenne do not often appear. I include him in my story as an offset to the current concept of his race.

On my return to Muskogee I went to call on Pleasant Porter, chief of the Creeks, who was living in a handsome house on one of the principal streets of the aspiring little city.

"I found him sitting for a portrait, and for an hour or more, while the artist painted, the chief and I talked. He was very hoarse, but in good condition otherwise and I enjoyed my chat with him. He was a man of ability, rising at times to something like greatness. There was a philosophy both deep and sad in his outgiving. I wondered as I studied him how much truth there was in the report of his negro strain. He told me much of Creek history and discussed their future. He was kind and considerate in his treatment of the young painter and I quite warmed to him before our talk ended."

His home was simply and tastefully decorated and he himself had many of the finest qualities, although his face was that of a man who had dissipated his energies. His daughter, tall and graceful, related to me, at another time, many incidents of her life as a student of singing in New York City. "The papers insisted on calling me 'an Indian princess,'" she said with some bitterness, "and reporters tormented me so that I was forced to hide from them."

Just before the date fixed for my return to Chicago, my brother and I received an invitation to dinner at the home of Miss Alice Robertson, a well-known resident of Muskogee, in which she said, "You will meet some of our 'citizens' and I think they will interest you."

My brother told me that "citizens" in this sense meant Creeks or Cherokees and that we should probably meet a number of mixed bloods at this party. "Miss Robertson," he said, "has been here for a long time a missionary and friend to the Indians. You'll like her."

We were at work on my ranch some ten miles away and as I had not brought any dinner clothes with me and my brother had no time to dress, we wore our business suits as we drove in about half-past six. I, at least, was surprised and a little embarrassed to find all her guests in faultless evening dress. I hastened to explain to our hostess and she was kind enough to pass the explanation on. Nevertheless my brother and I were distinctly at a disadvantage. That I should be apologizing to a Cherokee for lack of proper dinner attire is worthy of record!

Miss Porter, Chief Porter's daughter, was one of the guests, and I again observed the dignity of her bearing and the essential sadness of her face. It was an interesting group and I thoroughly enjoyed the evening.

"Well, that is a lesson to me," I said to my brother, as we set out for the farm. "I knew these citizens lived well, but I didn't know they dressed for dinner."

CHAPTER TWENTY-THREE

ASSEMBLING THE CLIFF DWELLERS

I

ONE day just before Christmas my little daughter, moved by thoughts of Santa Claus, asked, "Poppie, where is our real home?"

This question went to my heart. For five years we had been living in lodgings and furnished flats. The time had come when my income would provide a modest house in the city and I began a search for it. My dream of a home in New York was ended.

Up to this time my years had been divided into three parts. One third in New York City, a second third in my native village of West Salem, Wisconsin, and the remainder divided between Oklahoma, Colorado, and Chicago, but now with an infant daughter to cherish, it became necessary to establish a permanent home. I decided on buying a house in Woodlawn, not far from the university, and quite near the home and studio of Lorado Taft, my wife's brother.

The house which I bought with much excitement early in 1907 was a narrow, three-story brick building on a good but quite unfashionable street. It offered a pleasant front room with a real fireplace, and a small but sunlit study where I could work in comfort if not in the dignity of space which I enjoyed in my Wisconsin homestead. West Salem was a lonely place—

in a literary sense. My nearest neighbor in the world of
letters was Zona Gale (who loyally clung to her home
in Portage, her birthplace) and the group of writing
folk which the State University had colonized was more
than a hundred miles to the south. La Crosse County
offered little in way of literary comradeship.

Chicago, however, after making all allowances for
local misjudgments and conceits, possessed several writers and artists of national renown, men who for one
cause or another still held out against New York, and
in their companionship I found myself fairly content—
especially as I was seldom compelled to spend more than
a few weeks at any one time in the city. My connection
with the island of Manhattan continued almost unbroken.

One of the most distinguished of my neighbors in
Woodlawn was Clarence Darrow, the celebrated "labor
lawyer," whom I had known for many years but without full appreciation of his fine literary quality—a side
of his character which I now discovered upon reading
"Farmington," an autobiographic story which he had
recently published. That this book changed my attitude
toward him is evident from these lines written at the
close of it. "This is very true, very sad, and very beautiful. Darrow has assembled many elemental facts in
a small space. He is humorous, but he is also tragic in
the hopelessness of his outlook. He voices the doubts
and the questioning of our generation, dealing genially
yet candidly with our failures. His story is only a fragment, but it is noteworthy for its diction, which has
something rich and noble in its music."

Darrow and his young wife were living in a new flat

over near Jackson Park; and there, according to my record, we dined on January 8, 1907.

"I found him quite as grave and even more bitter than his writing indicates. He talks with much of the same acrid humor. He read to us some short stories called 'The Law's Delay' which were intolerably gloomy and savage, but powerful. Their English was altogether admirable and yet I saw no sale for them. He impressed me as a man of enormous reserve powers, but his mind is uncultivated and undisciplined. As an advocate he weakens his cause by extreme expression. His uncompromising honesty of purpose and his aggressive cynicism make him repellent to many—hence he is to me a lonely figure. In all that he writes, in all that he says, he insists relentlessly on the folly and the injustice of human society. His writing is too monotonous in tone, too bitter in quality, too pessimistic of outlook to succeed, but it has in it a protest which it is well to consider. He is essentially a literary man—even in his law practice."

I urged him that night, and also at other times, to rewrite "Farmington." "You have a great theme there —but you have not made the fullest use of it," I argued.

He was moved by my interest, but only replied, "My time is so taken by other work that I cannot find time to write the books I have in mind."

I did not tell him what I really felt—which was that to rewrite "Farmington" would be worth more than all his work in defense of criminals and fools. As a lawyer he was always ready to defend the under dog, and was in sharp demand by incarcerated labor leaders, but I was not entirely convinced that his action was dictated solely by a sense of justice. "He takes a savage literary joy in striking at society over the shoulders of crime. I feel power but not high purpose in his program. We began our careers on common ground, but he has gone on—or off—into a dark and tangled forest land. He may turn out to be right, but at present he appears to me as a destructive force merely!"

II

Early in 1907, I became a house-holder in Chicago, thus definitely assuming a more responsible relationship toward the city. For something more than twenty years it had been merely a convenient center of my literary and other interests. Now as a parent and a landowner I perceived its ugliness and the barrenness with new eyes.

"Look at the situation," I said to Fuller. "Here in this city of two million people, fourteen years after the World's Fair, there is neither a high-class magazine nor a first-class publishing house. We have no club like the Players or the National Arts, where artists and writers habitually meet. Our only meeting place is Clarkson's studio on Friday afternoons. It is true that some of our architects and men of letters can be seen occasionally at the University Club, but they do not color its life."

"What can you expect from a population lately from the farm and the village?" Fuller replied. "Every attempt to found an art club or musical club in this burg has failed of support."

"Then why not take the suggestion made by Edwin Booth in founding the Players and build a club *for all* the arts? The MacDowell Club which I have lately helped to organize and the National Arts are both based on this principle. If our literary and art forces are too feeble to have separate clubs, let us combine on a home for all workers in the fine arts."

Fuller, pessimistic and elusive, refused to support me. He would have nothing to do with my plan; but Taft, Charles Francis Browne, and Ralph Clarkson joined me in making up a selected list of names representing painting, sculpture, architecture, music, fiction, and the drama, and to these men I sent a letter stating my plan and asking their coöperation. With an astuteness for which I take no credit, I not only included laymen like Charles L. Hutchinson and Frank Logan of the Art Institute, but educators like Harry Pratt Judson of the University of Chicago.

This letter brought one hundred acceptances of membership in the proposed club, and at a meeting called soon after I was elected chairman of the committee of organization. "So here I am engaged in forming two somewhat similar clubs, one in New York and the other in Chicago, while still active on the Board of Directors of the National Institute of Arts and Letters. Fuller calls me a 'club carpenter and joiner'—and it is true that I take a certain pleasure in forming these institutions which, in my opinion, are milestones in the nation's progress. They are signs not only of the integrating movement of our cities, but evidence of a developing consciousness of the value of arts and letters in American life."

What little I did was in the spirit of Emerson and Whitman, but my first concept of this union of the five arts came from a phrase uttered by Edwin Booth in his speech when founding the Players. He pointed out the value, to the actor, of association with men of other arts and other interests. "If such an association is good for actors, it is likely to be good for the writers and the musicians," I said to MacDowell when we first spoke of a club with something like the same plan of membership, and I was simply carrying out in Chicago the idea of fellowship which the Players, the National Arts, and the MacDowell Club had demonstrated in New York.

While spending the Christmas holidays of 1905 with my family in Chicago, I received a letter from President Roosevelt inviting me to luncheon at the White House early in January, and I at once prepared to go. In loading up with books to read on the journey, I chanced to include "The Valley of Decision" by Edith Wharton. My judgment set down at the time agrees with that of Fuller: "It is a great but by no interpretation a faultless book. It is almost too learned—too rich in historic details. It is very long and at times suggests the old-fashioned novel, but it is a most inclusive and interesting picture of eighteenth century Italy."

Without the slightest knowledge of her place of residence I wrote her in care of her publishers expressing my admiration for this romance, and upon reaching New York I began to ask my friends about her. No one knew her. "She spends all her time abroad and is rather unapproachable," they said. "She is reported to be entirely out of key with modern America."

(Filled with such reports, I had no expectation of hearing from her at all, and her letter when it came was a delightful surprise. She thanked me with charming sincerity and expressed a desire to meet me, an expression which I kept in mind and when (many years later) I found myself in Paris, I wrote to her again, asking the privilege of calling upon her. I cannot do better than quote my record of this meeting.

"She met me at the railway station, and as her home was but a few streets away, we walked to her gate together. She was clad in a lovely white gown and hat to match and made an almost regal figure as she faced me in her drawing-room. She is the most beautiful and distinguished woman writer of my acquaintance and wholly charming in voice and manner. I found her frank, kindly, and keenly intellectual. She treated me as a fellow craftsman, and professed pleasure in my commendation of her Italian book. She admitted that she was open to the charge of being an expatriate but insisted that she was not. 'I find it easier to write here,' she said, 'and life is more gracious. All my work now, however, is concerned with American subjects. I shall go back occasionally, but I regard France as my home, for the present at least.'

"Her summer home is in this little village about twenty miles out of Paris, but her winter home is in the south of France. She is writing now mainly of the days when she was a young girl in New York City. Her life like her books resembles that of Henry James. She is an intellectual aristocrat and finds present-day New York disheartening. She admitted that she has been away so long that she could not find the America she knew. She returns to it only in imagination. She illustrates as completely as James the danger of staying too long in Europe—however, she would not admit that such alienation is a source of regret.")

"As I entered the dining room of the White House on January 5, 1906, I found Secretaries Taft, Moody, Root, and Bacon already there. Later, General Young and Ambassador Jusserand came in with Stevens of the Canal Commission. A Mr. Murray, Dr. Maurice Egan, Peter Finley Dunne, and I were the unofficial citizens at the table. It was in effect a cabinet meeting."

Roosevelt was quite as dynamic as ever, but only once or twice addressed the whole table. He ate sparingly and drank only milk—in truth the luncheon was of the simplest sort. We had a few minutes' talk in which he made an appointment to see me alone, and then Dunne and I walked off into another room together. I had never had much talk with "Mr. Dooley" before and my entry reads: "He is the Irish humorist in all his moods, mostly sad."

In spite of my new club and my new house in Chicago, January 5th found me back in New York lunching with Gari Melchers and Charles Francis Browne.

Browne had introduced Melchers to me as "a native of Michigan but as Dutch as they make 'em"—and in my notes I find these lines: "He looked the part—a fine, sturdy, manly fellow with blond hair and gray eyes, blunt of speech and self-contained of manner. His paintings are like him in technique. He represents a Dutch school as Hassam and Metcalfe represent a modern French school—John Alexander (with whom I am associated in the MacDowell Club) seems more American than either school. I see no virtue in having our art formed upon French or Dutch models. MacDowell, at his best, cut loose from the German influence—and that our artists should be painting in the style of Monet seems to me incongruous."

However, it was not safe for a layman to say such things in the presence of Hassam or Melchers. They held very positive opinions on all esthetic subjects, and as my appetite for argument had lost its edge since the publication of "Crumbling Idols," I seldom joined in the clamorous discussions which developed at the Players when Twachtman, Reid, Simmons, and Metcalfe formed an after-dinner circle. They were all essentially French in training, in style, and outlook on life, and just what precisely they wrangled about I never learned. Their early training had been in Paris, and their enthusiasms were all Continental. New York was merely a marketplace in which they were condemned to stay for a time, in order to earn money for a studio in France. Several maintained homes over there and painted French landscapes.

The reader should note that this refers to conditions more than twenty years ago. These men changed as the years passed; but it used to "rile" me to hear them, at that time, snarling at America. They irritated me all the more because I knew, deep down, that many of their accusations were true. America *was* lacking in "atmosphere."

There was little market for American subjects at that time. Rich New Yorkers and Chicagoans were buying bogus "old masters" of French or Italian or Spanish origin. Native art had but a sparse and negligible showing in the museums. Conditions had improved, somewhat, since my Boston days, but millionaires were still importing marbles and canvases from Europe, and copying ancient castles and manor houses. In other words, we were still an artistic province of England, France, and Holland.

"Irving Bacheller, Booth Tarkington, Mary E. Wilkins, Owen Wister, Augustus Thomas, and others in the local color group, whatever their shortcomings, have a native quality which our painters mainly lack," I argued. "It is not easy to define this native quality, but it exists and it will grow as our painters outgrow their schooling in Paris."

One of John Burroughs' intimate friends was a young portrait painter named Orlando Rouland, a handsome and boyish figure who had a charming studio on Fifty-seventh Street, and there, one afternoon, I met Julia Marlowe for the first time. Burroughs was the honored guest and many of my friends came in during the afternoon. Richard Watson Gilder and Ruth McEnery Stuart among others.

"I found Miss Marlowe to be a most interesting and intelligent woman. Her diction was excellent and her manner direct, and humorous. Her face has grown rather heavy and her shoulders stoop, but I have no doubt she is transformed, as of old, when on the stage. Rouland is a fine, boyish fellow and his wife a very bright woman. Ruth Stuart looked old and sad and is heavier than I had expected her to be. She made no allusion to the tragic death of her son, and neither did I. He was a handsome boy and she adored him. Plainly, life has lost its savor for her."

In calling on Howells at the Regent Hotel, I said to him, "It is now twenty years since our first meeting, and in some curious way there is less difference in our ages now than then. You have not grown younger and I have not grown older more rapidly than is natural, and yet I seem to have drawn nearer your generation."

He smiled. "Perhaps we have both grown wiser," he remarked.

My return to New York was mainly for the purpose of arranging with Duneka for the publication of my new novel; and while negotiations were going forward, I spent some delightful days and nights with Irving Bacheller, of whom I wrote: "There is something elementally fine in this man, something which links him with the old-time America and forecasts the new. He appeals to me in some ways as strongly as any man I know—he is bigger and finer than his writing. He is my kinsman."

Seton was at work on a huge book dealing with big game in America. Stung by the assault upon his fictional or biographical studies of animals, he had planned this volume as an answer to his critics. Into it he was putting the results of his years of study in the field. From his long shelf of notebooks (some of them stained with blood and rain and crammed with measurements and drawings of animals he had captured) he was building a monumental work which should lift him entirely out of "the nature faker" controversy.

I note: "January 8, 1907. Seton worked all day on bears, a chapter in his book on 'North American Animals'—a prodigious work, but then he is a prodigious worker. I never knew such energy. He writes all the morning and draws all the afternoon and evening, broken by a short walk and the dinner hour. It is a dark and rainy day, but the house is so cheerful with its open fire that we pay no heed to the weather."

"January 11. Last night I heard Nazimova in 'Hedda Gabbler,' an intellectual treat. She was beautiful and very subtle in the part, and the play was as great as ever—so original, so powerful, so masterly in technique that it makes current American plays commonplace entertainment. The star failed in the last act, however. She was too palpably the actress. She was acting rather than living it." I also saw her as Nora in "The Doll's House." "She was fine, but the play did not interest me as it once did."

One night I went alone down to a Fourteenth Street theater to see the so-called Belasco play, "The Girl of the Golden West." "The theater was completely filled, and so I stood, as I used to do, at the rear of the orchestra with those who smelt of cooking and washing and all the other odors of crowded and badly ventilated tenements. They were mainly native Americans, however, people to whom this picture of pioneer life especially appealed. There was charm in the theme, and also in the incidental music which was of the same date as the play—the gold-seeking era. For all its theatricality, something imperishably heroic and Western came from it. At times it was completely satisfying—stirring my imagination with the power of early association with men of similar type."

Just before I returned to Chicago I attended an important meeting of the National Institute—indeed I waited over to attend it, for Mabie expected me to lead in the discussion of plans. The attendance was unusually large. I made another appeal for action. "We have in this membership the leaders of thought in all the arts; why not exert our influence for a more indigenous art? It has taken all these years to raise certain of our members above the timid belief that there is something 'undemocratic' in a National Institute. Of course it is undemocratic—so are the Authors Club, the Academy of Design, and every other organization where membership is dependent upon skill, character, and imagination—and where candidates for admission are subject to a vote."

This fear of criticism was mostly confined to the older men—those who were still influenced by the traditions of a simpler America in which the paper hanger was an artist and the congressman an esthetic arbiter. William Vaughn Moody and John Alexander were less in awe of the newspaper men. They urged that a selective institution was needed to restore the balance of a newspaper age."

While on my way toward Chicago next day I received word of Dr. Harper's death. The papers were full of him and I relived my last visit with him, vividly recalling the sweetness of his expression when he said, "I shall never see the hills again." He was a man of singular force—almost hypnotic in his ability to secure gifts for his great plan. He has a monument such as few men in America can claim.

The funeral was impressive, but not as impressive as it should have been. There should have been at least one high, appealing address; but none such was offered. The speeches were all rather commonplace—good but not good enough. Lorado Taft could have made us feel the force of the dead man's soul, but he was not called upon to do it.

The death of Marshall Field on the day following the Harper funeral was like the sinking of another milestone in Chicago history. "He *was* Chicago—Chicago at its best. He represented the highest business probity. His name for thirty years has been a household word to me. My father used it as a symbol of commercial integrity. 'Marshall Field never cheats,' was his way of putting it."

Field left two hundred millions, Dr. Harper but twelve thousand and a great university, Edward MacDowell will leave only a handful of music scores! Which is most deserving of honor—the merchant, the builder, or the music-maker?

"It appears that I have reached the time when the changes in the world I know are insistently urging themselves upon me. The passing of the generation of writers just before me, their descent into the abyss, is now going on under my eyes—almost at my feet. Edward MacDowell, I fear, will soon pass twenty years before his time."

III

On my return to Chicago January 30, 1907, I found my literary friends talking of a strange literary visitor, a Frenchman who not only spoke English perfectly but was interested in Mid-Western America. He was lecturing at the university and I was moved to cross the Midway to hear him. He spoke eloquently and with judgment. Afterward I met him at tea in the rooms of Miss Elizabeth Wallace of the English Department. His name was Anatole Le Braz, and as Miss Wallace introduced me to him she said, "Monsieur Le Braz wants especially to meet you as a representative product of the prairie."

He was a man of good height, sturdy of frame, with black hair and beard streaked with gray. On the platform he had been intense, almost dramatic, but here, in private, he was a quiet, direct, and boyishly enthusiastic guest. "I am a primitive," he said, and smiled when I replied, "So am I—but then I was born in a primitive land."

"I am of Breton stock," he replied. "Brittany is a far country from Paris. I am more Welsh than French."

Finding him congenial I yielded to his urging and rode with him to the train, answering his many questions concerning miners, cattle kings, red men, and other Wild West characters. He wanted to know why the cowboy wore a high-crowned hat and woolly trousers, what gave rise to the sign language, and other matters upon which he believed I could speak with authority. I gave him a short lecture on the sign language, then I took off my hat and showed him how to put four dents in it. He did the same with his and at the station, in a glow of good will, he said, "You interest me. We must meet again," and I on my part set down in my record:

"Here is a Frenchman I can understand and approve."

We met at the Art Institute for luncheon (our only place where artists and writers habitually met), and nothing of the *boulevardier* appeared in him. He had the sturdy, homely virtues which I had been taught to value. He kept up a steady stream of questioning concerning all the local color art and literature of America. He liked Charles Mulligan's "Young Lincoln, The Rail-Splitter," because it was *not* academic, and because it expressed something of the New World. He agreed with me in my opposition to schooling young artists abroad. "Later, yes, but not in formative years. Europe is not interested in American derivative art."

Another European—a Hollander—lecturing on art at one of the clubs, said, "I sometimes wish that a great reef might arise in mid-ocean, shutting America off from Europe for a time, thus affording your native genius an opportunity to develop. You know too well the modes of European art. You are too subject to Old World literary fashions."

I applauded him and later supported him in a response: "Our architects are tourists, taking notes of temples and cathedrals. Our dramatists have their eyes fixed on the London stage and our musicians still compose and sing in the German manner, as our painters paint in the French manner."

Later, in New York, Le Braz came to lunch with me at the Players. "We talked mainly of Western writers, for that was his wish. He questioned me so long about my own work that I got little out of him. He was all for 'pumping' me and I found him most sympathetic and understanding of American letters. I willingly submitted to be pumped. He has seen much of America, more than any Frenchman of recent years. He went away with an armload of my books, and I am curious to see what he will find in them."

Apparently he was disappointed in them, for I never

heard from him directly or indirectly. So far as I know he never again visited the United States.

"February 9, 1907. Chicago, after some twelve or fifteen years of discussion, has come to the point of fostering a 'Little Theater movement,' and Katharine Herne has been brought on to help make it a success. A jury has been appointed to pass on plays, and Fuller is in the welter of manuscripts which the contest has called forth. 'None of them have much value,' he said, 'but one by Hilliard Booth is possible.' "

"February 11. At night my wife and I went down to hear Elgar's 'Gerontius' which bored me almost into leaving the hall. I hate all these long-drawn, oratorical agonies. This talk of blood and sacrifice disgusts me. The music, noble as it is in spots, falls so far short of being strong and high that I found myself gripping the seat in the desperate, involuntary effort to help it up the slope. I hoped it would end by voicing something new and vital but it did not."

Faithful to "the Little Room," I met with its group of struggling authors whenever I was at home. "It is decreasing. Its first-class successful members were being drawn away to the East. The parallel of Glasgow and London suggests itself every time I return to Chicago," I said to Fuller. "New York is more and more our capital. It draws off all our best or at least our 'smartest' and most aspiring. We need a real club like the Players to make life in Chicago more attractive."

"February 19. This day brought an excursion into

my past. I went to Cedar Falls, Iowa, to lecture. The
railway was rough, the coaches shabby. The town was
without touch of grace, the hotel musty, and the citizens entirely out of the dress-coat belt. The chairman
of the lecture committee, who met me, was shy, wordless, and unshaved. He wore an ancient flat-crowned
hat. The broken wooden sidewalks, the ancients sitting
on the sunny sides of the houses, the youth working
with a bucksaw, the rusty, grimy clothing of the farmers on the street, and the strong, serious faces of my
solemn audience were all of the Iowa I once knew and
which I thought had disappeared. The absence of grace,
of beauty, of interest in such a town, from my point of
view, is tragic. Mud, mud, mud! The whole land was
in the mud!"

On returning to Chicago next morning, I found it
unusually grandiose and terrifying in a mantle of snow
and smoke, a thousand miles from Cedar Falls. At
night, at the Twentieth Century, I heard Richard Watson Gilder talk on "Happy People," a whimsical, collo-
quial, and altogether charming address. He made a fine
impression. My entry concerns his audience.

"I was impressed as never before by the rough-hewn
faces of the older women, powerful pioneer types,
whose wrinkles were in sharp contrast to their gorgeous
gowns and jewels. Many were as rural in features as
those in West Salem, others, though carefully rouged,
could not conceal their essential honesty and sincerity.
All were plainly living up to the great hour. Jane
Addams sat beside me, looking rather worn and tired,
and more than usually grave. Life is always a serious
business with her."

"February 22. The town is rich in distinguished Eastern visitors: Gilder, John Finley, and Grover Cleveland. I am glad they are here. It will do them good and educate us.

"Heckman having sent me a ticket for the meeting at the Auditorium, I sat near Cleveland, the speaker of the day. He was so thin and gray that I hardly knew him. His neck, once seventeen inches in circumference, now made painful display of its sinews, and his face was equally wasted. The sullen, bulldog look of his days in the White House had given way to a wistful expression, and his voice, high and slightly nasal, had the basic sadness of his face. It was evident that he considered himself a side-liner entirely out of the political game. He looked like a man of swiftly ebbing vitality. His address was dull and verbose, but now and then he whipped out a notable phrase. In general his speech was undistinguished and disappointing. Our studio supper in the Fine Arts Building that night was made more notable than usual by the presence of Richard Watson Gilder, who seemed to enjoy the informality of the feast. He went away saying, 'This is the best thing I have tasted during my stay in Chicago.'"

CHAPTER TWENTY-FOUR

TESLA, MADAME MODJESKA, AND FORBES-ROBERTSON

I

ON my way East to attend a Longfellow dinner, February 26, 1907, I reread Howells' "Venetian Life" with delight. "It is a lovely work, one that will not go out of fashion. I also read James' novelette, 'Spoils of Poynton' during the day and found it most excellent writing, one of his most original tales. Who but he can make a country home the hero, or heroine, of a story?"

On arrival at the hotel I dressed at once and hurried to the dinner, where I found a nobly representative gathering of poets: Robert Burns Wilson, James Lane Allen, and Madison Cawein from Kentucky, William Vaughn Moody from Indiana, Edwin Markham from Oregon, Edith Thomas from Ohio, Bliss Carman and Charles Roberts from Canada, together with several others. Some good speaking followed.

"I find it profitable—this taking time to honor the memory of a man who stood for something other than war or politics. No gentler, lovelier spirit lives in our poetry. It is the fashion among certain critics of the journalistic and radical type to patronize Longfellow, but I do not sympathize with this contemptuous attitude. As an evolutionist I grant him the virtue of serving the needs of millions of people and of living the poetry he wrote. Whatever I may have said in earlier years, I now value his poems of New England as precious memories. 'Tales of a Wayside Inn,' especially their interludes, have something magical in their cadence. Like the scent of lilac bloom or the humming of bees in an apple orchard, they arouse deep-laid associations. The life he lived was cloistered, serene, and scholarly. He had nothing to do with politics or commerce and it is for these reasons that he is still the poet of millions of English as well as of American homes."

During my stay I seized the opportunity to see "Peer Gynt" as played by Mansfield. It made a tremendous appeal to my imagination, but was not entirely successful as a theatrical production. "Although dragged out thin by over-elaborate scenes, it is an astonishing *tour de force*. Mansfield played the title rôle like a young man. He tossed Peer's mother upon the roof with the action of an athlete. I am grateful to him and his producers, who must have known that the play could not possibly make money."

Under contract to revise and put my boys' book, "The Long Trail," into shape for the printer, I worked in the library of my club and against odds. "At night Whidden Graham and I went to see Louis Shipman's play, 'On Parole,' a neat little comedy of the Civil War—not a great work but entertaining. I wonder if this is the end of our dramatization of the Civil War."

"March 3. Howells showed more signs of age to-day than I had ever noted in him. His shoes were untied and his coat unbrushed; but in excuse he said, 'I have been ill of *grippe* and am not entirely recovered from it. It has left me weak and any unusual exertion leads to collapse.' He was very far from being in Stedman's condition, however. Stedman's last letter to me was piti- ful in tone as well as shocking in its weak and trembling lines.

"At Mrs. Haggin's I met Safonoff, the much ac- claimed Russian composer, and as I shook hands with him I said, 'I am a friend of MacDowell's.'

" 'Ah!' he said, his face lighting up. 'Then you are *my* friend.' He knew Charles R. Crane also and that was another bond. I found him unassuming and with a sense of humor. 'I am an American,' he said, as he drew out a fountain pen. 'See my pen. Six dollars!' "

At Mary Fanton Roberts' reception on the 4th, I met Adolph Ochs of the *Times*, and my comment upon this meeting reads:

"Ochs, who came here from Chattanooga, and who is making a great paper of the *Times*, is modestly un- obtrusive, in the midst of poets and artists. When I said, 'What a success you've made of the *Times*,' he quietly replied, 'Yes, it has been more than I expected.' He told me how low its circulation had been at that time and that the paper had been 'wished' on him. In all that he said concerning its development under his hand he was singularly unassuming. His father was a captain in the Northern army during the Civil War and he is a true American in feeling, although he has not the same background of tradition that others of us enjoy. He has made the *Times* one of the great news journals of the world."

Seeing Shaw's play, "Widower's Houses," I found it not only biting in satire and amusing, but it was played better than I had expected it to be. It was capitally presented. I left reluctantly at the end of the second act to attend a committee meeting. "At the Ernest Crosby Memorial Meeting, an impressive ceremony, I spoke on 'Crosby as Writer.' That he was much beloved was evident, for a fine, serious audience of men and women (men mostly) filled the hall. Edwin Markham, who read a poem, was a quaint figure. His trousers were too short, his coat shiny, and his hair tumbled, but his poem was received with great applause. He does these occasional verses very well indeed!"

"On the 9th I saw Sothern do Hauptmann's 'Sunken Bell' and found it very impressive despite several scenes which were too primitive for my taste. It cannot possibly obtain a hold here. It is too German in its method, and too fanciful in its subject matter as well.

"March 11, 1907. There is much comment concerning Mary Shaw's production of 'Mrs. Warren's Profession.' I saw it and was disappointed in it. I don't think the players quite rose to it. Mary Shaw characterized the title part very well but in a subdued way. Her reading was, as ever, intelligent and graceful but lacking in power. The 'Vivie', too, was not convincing, and the 'Frank' was only a comedy part. He never really became earnest. He was merely a bad boy. His remarks did not burn, as I believe Shaw intended them to do."

Hearing that John Burroughs was ill at Orlando Rouland's home, I called to see him. "He made a grand figure as he sat against the window—a dark red robe on his knees and the sun streaming over his silver head. 'I begin to feel my years,' he confessed. To me he symbolized Anglo-Saxon age, as he sat talking with me.

'There is something quietly elemental in him,' I said to Rouland. 'I am glad you are painting him.' "

At a dinner at Robert Underwood Johnson's I met Nikola Tesla for the first time. We got on famously. "After dinner he drew me to a seat in a corner and there talked for nearly an hour. He told me of his boyhood and of the marvelous skill of his mother. He related some astonishing stories of his experiments. In speaking of his inventions, he said, 'I predict that we shall soon be able to speak from one end of the world to the other without wires.' "

I listened to this as I listen to those who believe in spirit communication—and on my return to my hotel registered this judgment: "Tesla is a dreamer, to some he is a boaster—perhaps a little crazy, but he is undoubtedly a genius. He told me of many strange experiments he had made and his claims are incredible. His philosophy is drear. 'We are all automata,' he said. 'We have no souls!' I liked him even though I considered him unbalanced and visionary."

(All that he predicted that night has come true. He foresaw the radio!)

On March 15, 1907, Wall Street was reported in a panic, and feeling it my duty I went down to see what was going on. I saw little. The excitement had abated, and after calling on Allen Robinson who is doing so much to raise the MacDowell fund, I returned to the club. "I feel the need of seclusion and rest," I confessed to my diary. "Having given too much of myself lately I must now shut myself up and reflect. The fellows at the club attract me but weary me. Those who have no other home are as familiar to me as the chairs or the clock. I can tell each of them by his walk or the poise of his head even when he is at a distance; and yet I do not call them friends."

On hearing that Booker T. Washington was billed to speak on "The Negro Problem," I made a point of breaking off my work in order to hear him. It was an eloquent and sensible address entirely white in tone and diction. I met him later and had a most revealing talk with him. He gave me the impression of being a clear thinker, but not a man of high intelligence. "He is not in any sense inspirational, merely a sensible and practical teacher. He thinks as a white man thinks. He is not really a negro, black as he is.

"In some way, I cannot recall how or why, I went this afternoon to Washington Square to call on a painter by the name of Higgins, a delineator of the poor. I found his studio filled with portraits of tramps, bums, and other wretched folk. He is a powerful and savage artist, but his work is repellent. He was thin, quite in rags, and his studio, a ramshackle place, was a nest of scraps. Artistic poverty was in evidence on all sides. He was like a character in a novel—somebody else's novel. I hope he succeeds, but if he does his temper will have to change."

From this home of aspiring poverty I went to Mrs. Charles Worthington's beautiful new flat in the "Wyoming," meeting Safonoff again, George Hamlin the tenor, and others quite as eminent and interesting. Walter Damrosch played and several other musicians added to the program. It was all a long way from the Higgins studio. Once I would have glorified the painter of the poor, but I'm not so sure that he is not as false in his way as our painters of Dutch and French peasants are in theirs. He sees down-and-outs in Washington Square every hour of the day, but are they worth painting? After all, they are not typical of American life nor are they lovely.

At the request of Henry Miller, who had agreed to speak for the MacDowell Club, I called at the theater to discuss the matter. "I was reminded of Herne as I watched Miller at his make-up. The little dressing room blazing with lights and the dusky, deft valet were quite familiar. The little red parlor off the dressing room was quite as lacking in ventilation as those at which old-timers cursed. Miller again made a good impression on me. He is a man of substance and intelligence, but confessedly timid about this speech."

"March 22. This day was made memorable for me by seeing Sargent's Dramatic School perform 'The Vikings,' Ibsen's famous play. The second act was tremendous poetry—a really great dramatic document. The lines played upon a thousand strings of Nordic association. The primitive passion of all Northern races, the acceptance of fate, the grim attack upon the intricate and hopeless knot of circumstance—all were there. It was, artistically, well done. I forgot wife and child and my own struggles in the spell of these tragic scenes. I related these primitive chieftains to certain Cheyenne warriors. They carried me back to the twelfth century. Some of the lines were noble.

"March 23. Breakfasting with Frank Millet at the club I met Gutzon Borglum, the sculptor, a clear-cut, vigorous man. Millet by contrast with him appeared battered and world-weary. Borglum is clear-eyed and confident, not to say pugnacious. He is from Salt Lake, I am told, the son of a Mormon, a Dane. He is a powerful sculptor and a rugged personality. He has a brother, Solon, who is also a sculptor but of a gentler nature. Taft thinks highly of them both.

"Gutzon, a powerful man physically (like George Gray Barnard), enjoys carving the granite or marble with his own hand. He is a man of grandiose visions, and a fighter, much more interested in public men, in politics, than Taft or Barnard.

"The MacDowell Club dinner which came off last night was very successful and very handsome. The speaking was not especially brilliant, but served the purpose. I sat beside Madame Nazimova, who is a weird, graceful wisp of a woman, a Russian Jewess. She is entirely European in her vivid coloring and especially in her quick reaction to every word and gesture. The best American actresses are very like other women in private life, but Nazimova is frankly always the actress. The theater is her world. There is something exotic in her—something which she will never lose, no matter how long she lives in America."

II

On the train back to Chicago, I forgot the hours in reading a book on the red people by a man named Schultz. "My Life Among the Indians" is a most extraordinary human document. I set down this judgment at the time: "It is the truest book on the red man I have ever read. It touched me again and again almost to tears. Filled with admiration of its simple pathos, its restraint, its hopeless distrust of all that we call civilization, I read on and on to the end. I recalled that Grinnell had genially warned me by saying, 'Of course, you must bear in mind that Schultz is a romancer—he tells the truth in spite of himself.' Whatever his exaggerations, the outcome of the book is noble and moved me as few books on the red people have done."

What Grinnell, who is a careful historian, meant was "Schultz heightens his facts a little," but what facts! Going to Montana as a boy, young Schultz had made his home among the Blackfeet. He had married a Blackfoot girl and this book is his story, told very sympathetically. Whether he wrote it without aid or not, it is noble in outcome.

"Chicago, March 30. The lines are being drawn pretty closely on me these days by the editors, but I am not to be swayed—I want my work to be right. I will not be edited for the sake of pleasing the 'average reader.' Yet this is exactly what our magazine editors are more and more obliged to insist upon.

"Fuller read to us this night a story called 'Pearl McRay,' a pleasant bit of satire suggested by Mary McLane and her sensational emergence from Butte. It was very amusing and Fuller laughed when we applauded his hits. Lorado enjoyed the reading quite as much as I did. It was just the kind of subject for Fuller —no one could have done it better."

In dining at Charles R. Crane's, my wife and I met Madame Modjeska for the first time. To me this was a moving experience, for in my youth I had greatly admired her. To me she had appeared so noble, so dazzling, so remote from my way of life that I had no more expectation at that time of meeting her than I had of meeting the Queen of England. Now she was old, but still regal, still remote, a survivor of a magnificent group of stage presences.

"She still carries herself like a queen. Her dignity and her sweetness are royal; but a wistful sadness is in her face and in her voice. We talked mainly of Edwin Booth, whom she reverenced. 'He was a great artist and a princely director,' she said gravely. She is of a generation now hastening to the grave. She made me feel my own years. The mystery has gone out of her face, but she remains admirable. A pathos almost tragic lies in her decay. She was so queenly in her beautiful art!"

A few days later I met her again at her son's home. "She appeared weary of life, and her family circle, so subdued and sadly intellectual, left a somber impression on me.

"April 27. Modjeska was a guest of honor at the Clarkson studio tea to-day, and she spoke again of Edwin Booth. It was evident that her appearances with him were golden moments which she loved to recall. She remained sweetly remote, however. She heard my voice, but her mind persisted in pursuit of some thought which I had started long after another topic arose. As in a mist, she passed from one subject to another very slowly, but something darkly poetic glowed in her big eyes. Her high-bred air, her sweet aloofness, and her largeness of sympathy deepened my admiration. She is a ruin but a grandly moving ruin."

"May 3. Anders Zorn and Horace White were at the Little Room to-day. Zorn is a big man, dark of complexion at a distance, but betraying, at close range, the blue-eyed Nordic. He appeared curiously lymphatic and gentle, with nothing of the dash I had expected to see and which all his canvases show. John Alexander's paintings look like himself—refined, cultivated, graceful; but Zorn does not suggest in any degree the boldness of his brush. Personally he is without 'style' and rather disappointing as a dinner companion."

Forbes-Robertson was in town, and I met him several times. "He is a thin, sickly man of cultured personality with a noble voice. We have few men of his intelligence and culture among our actors, almost none with his cultivated background. We talked of Shaw, of James, and of Howells. His intelligence impressed me deeply. He is at home in the world of letters. His voice is especially rich and flexible and his accent combines the best qualities of the Old World and the New. He reads blank verse with taste as well as with feeling. I saw his characterization of Cæsar in Shaw's play, 'Cæsar and Cleopatra,' and found it superb. His voice reminds me of Edwin Booth. He caught the world-weary air of the great conqueror with philosophic understanding of it and voiced it superbly."

"Ranch 101," a Wild West show, came to town this same week and I took my father to see it. "I am glad I saw it, for I felt again the thrill of the plains life. These brown, hardy, resolute men belong to the heroic age my father loved. Their calm faces expressed the pride and resolution of panthers. They took desperate chances, with joy. Impassive as Algonquin warriors, they performed their feats with incredible swiftness and daring. Fifty times each day they put their lives in peril without a moment's hesitation, just as my father did at their age. They are of his type. They moved him so profoundly that he could not speak. They recalled a world he had lost. They reënacted his epic. I, too, once lived that life, or one like it in all essentials and entered imaginatively into the action.

"On the way home father talked of the epic days of '61. His life is now all in the past. He loves to relive the days when 'Grant and his staff came riding along.' His reminiscences are like those of Napoleon's Old Guard. He tells of his life on the Wisconsin river and in the pine forests with almost equal emotion.

"May 11. Fuller is getting unmistakably elusive as well as quaint. He is a vagabond, a highly intellectual city tramp. He roams at large about the city, but keeps a den at his mother's house. None of us know anything of his private life. We do not know what his income is, but we imagine that he has enough to live on. He hints that life with his family is not at all to his liking, and still complains of having to oversee plumbers and furnace men and the collection of rents. When I think of this skilled literary craftsman spending his time at such jobs I am furious. What a waste of talent!"

General Kuroki visited the university on May 31, and I was there to see him. I hung about the "Quad" for half an hour, interested in the action of the students who were shouting "banzais" in practice of the greeting which they were to chorus forth when he came. They were all very young and very crude to me, boys of the farms and small towns, able and aspiring but uncultured.

"At last Kuroki came, cheered by the crowd, and as

he passed I studied him closely. He is a short, yellow, self-contained man with a head almost clean-shaven. He has the racial prominent cheek bones of the Tartar and a very high brow like the figures in a Japanese print. Afterward I went to the reception and was named to him in the line. He appeared sadly bored, and irritated by the neglect of his aides. The Japanese consul was a bright and ugly little man; but his wife, quite Parisian in attire and whitened with powder, was a dainty little woman withal.

"June 3. To-day I finished revising 'The Silent Eaters.' It is a big theme and I have not yet made it what I had hoped to make it, a short prose epic of the Sioux race, ending in the Ghost Dance which is its final tragedy. I doubt if any publisher will ever print it, but I believe in it.

"One afternoon at Lorado's studio I saw a very curious and interesting examination of his group, 'The Blind,' by a girl who was also sightless. Her interest in the sculpture was keen, and her little hands fluttered over every inch of the model, as if seeking its full meaning. Intent, unconscious of us, she kept to her study, feeling that it was not only a work of art but something which was intended to serve in some way her fellow sufferers. She was a pitiful figure and yet her face remained sweetly patient and her voice cheerful. She went away glowing with a new emotional experience."

On June 6, I set to work definitely to organize the new Chicago Club of which I have written. Charles Crane offered his aid. Clarkson, Browne, and Taft responded enthusiastically, but Fuller remained irritatingly offish, too much the intellectual anarchist to join anything. I urged: "This may be the beginning of a noble institution. It may be that we are laying the foundation for a club like the Century of New York."

"Not in my time," he replied. "This is New York's era."

On June 7 we all went to the reception to Ambassador Bryce, who impressed me as a tired old philosopher, white and dry, a mere husk of a man. He stood passively, patiently in the line, mumbling a few words to each of us who confronted him. It was a huge throng and gave him an excellent notion of the men and women of the university.

"June 13. A group of us met and made a start on the new club. We lunched at the City Club: Lorado Taft, C. F. Browne, Charles L. Hutchinson, Ralph Clarkson, Robert Millikan, A. A. Michelson, Clarence Dickinson, Herbert Stone, Wallace Heckman, Rollin Salisbury, I. K. Pond, and I. All were heartily in favor of the idea. At night Charles came over and we made out further lists of possible names and I wrote many letters asking for support."

CHAPTER TWENTY-FIVE

GENERAL PALMER AND HIS CASTLE

I

WHILE in the midst of the formation of a new Chicago club and in possession of a new little daughter, my longing for the mountains became so keen that I set forth on a circuit which was to include Salt Lake and several national forests. "I need the change," I argued; and so shipping my little family to the Wisconsin homestead, I bought a ticket for the High Country.

"August 1. Here I am, back on the rolling plains again. The wind is in the west, cool and bracing. Flies are swarming in the car and a general air of slackness prevails. Last year at this time I was traveling in Italy and by contrast our Western civilization, with its flimsy wooden buildings, its wire fences, and its unkempt farmyards, seems very ugly and very impermanent. These towns are without charm, but their citizens enjoy a greater freedom from care, probably, than any other people in any other civilized land. After all, bathtubs and sun-lit kitchens are more important than picturesque roofs."

Again my good friends the Wrays of Colorado Springs made me happy in their lovely home, and we spent several days in talk, outlining the changes which

353

had taken place. I inquired of General Palmer and Wray said: "He is a helpless cripple. He fell from his horse while riding over one of his fields and injured his spine. He is unable to stand. Don't fail to go and see him. He knows you are here and is expecting you."

This was especially shocking news for the reason that during my previous visit to Glen Eyrie, the general had taken me on a survey of his forest, riding his horse like the trained cavalry leader that he was, erect, youthful, with straight thrust of legs and proud uplift of head. He had seemed in the prime of life, skilled and confident. "I shall go over to-morrow morning," I said to Wray, who at once telephoned the general's office to tell them of my coming. I dreaded the interview, but if he wished to see me I could not refuse to go.

I went to sleep that night with the sound of a stream in my ears. True, it was a muddy stream trained to irrigate the soil, but its voice was still eloquent of the hills from which it came. "When will it be possible for us to restore some part of the beauty of this ravaged land?"

Early next morning, I set out to visit General Palmer. Walking across the mesa, and over the ridge by way of a new trail, I found it all gloriously familiar. The blazing sun, the pungent odor of the hot pine needles, the vivid reds and sage greens of the rocks, the glowing peaks looming over the range all were as they had been when I first sensed them, sixteen years before. But I, alas! was less sensitive, less responsive to their charm.

The garden of Glen Eyrie was more beautiful than ever, and the gray towers of the mansion, rising above the soft foliage of the planted trees, stood out against the tops of the native pines of the hillside like the walls of some castle of feudal times erected here as setting for some historic American drama.

Elsie, the general's eldest daughter, received me in the great hall, which was entirely English in character. Its vaulted ceiling and decorated walls were baronial in suggestion, as the general intended it to be, for he was not only a lover of England but her grandson.

Before Elsie had time to describe her father's condition, the big doors opened and two men appeared, pushing a long, high, wheeled couch beside which walked two enormous wolfhounds. On this couch lay the old soldier, his head propped by pillows. Wagging his left hand at me, he called, "Garland, I salute you!"

Appalled by his condition, hardly able to utter a word, I stood beside his couch while he explained. "I am not entirely helpless. I can move one hand at the wrist," he demonstrated this, "and my head," he raised his head from his pillow. "I can feed my dogs as you shall see."

"How did it happen?"

"That's the ironical part of it. As you know I commanded a regiment of cavalry in 1861, a crack regiment detailed for special scouting service and I rode with my men for four years. After the war I came to Colorado and as railway engineer I surveyed these mountains before they had any trails—rode thousands of miles of trail—and then, after a life in the saddle, and while riding across an oatfield, my horse stumbles, I am pitched to the ground, and here I lie!"

As he said this, lying on that wheeled bed in the center of a magnificent hall, attended by his giant hounds, he had the stern dignity of a disabled duke in the days of Elizabeth. Turning his head, he laid his left hand on the nose of a dog. "Hungry, are you?" he asked with friendly intonation. One of the attendants put into his hand some pieces of bread and scraps of meat, which he then fed to the hounds, big, serious, courteous creatures, and I perceived that this was one of his diversions.

Knowing his history and his manifold interests I marveled at his brave acceptance of defeat, but I was soon to be further enlightened.

Suddenly he called to his attendant, "Simmons, call my aide. I want to show Mr. Garland my crops."

Show me his crops! Was his mind wandering? How could he do this? I glanced at Elsie, but as she seemed not surprised, I understood that this, too, was a matter of routine.

The servants wheeled the helpless commander to the broad stairway, and four of them, lifting his couch from its wheels, carried him down and out to the drive where a high touring car was standing. After placing the couch and the general on a specially built platform, three of the men retired, and the other took his seat as driver.

"Get in, Garland. Elsie, take your place!" commanded the general. Without a word I obeyed, in a daze of wonder, so terrifying, so dangerous did this adventure seem. What if he should die on the way?

As we started he called back to me, "I'll show you the place of my fall, my oatfield, first."

While crossing this field, we encountered a deep gully with steep banks. "Halt!" shouted the general. The machine stopped on the bank of the ravine. "Get out—all of you!" he commanded.

As I stepped from the car I said, "But, general, you are not going through that hazard?"

"Certainly," he replied, a cold glitter in his eyes. "I'm not afraid. I've given hostages to fortune. Drive on, Simmons."

Tense with apprehension, I watched the car descend into that gulch, the crippled man's head bobbing about like a ball on a string, but he was there when the car roared up the opposite bank! Whatever the pain of the passage had been he refused to display any sign of it. He possessed an unconquerable soul. As we came up to him he curtly said, "Resume your seats," and we continued in the course which he had laid out. At the end of the ride he was able to return to his wheeled couch and have tea with me.

"He suggested a great painting as he lay there on his high white couch in the midst of that magnificent hall, attended by his gigantic wolfhounds. 'I am a soldier,' he said. 'This is all a part of the campaign. So long! If I do not see you again, good luck!' and with a feeble gesture of his left hand he sent me on my way."

I never saw him again. He died soon after and glorious Glen Eyrie descended sadly into the hands of strangers.

II

One afternoon I took a car to Manitou and set off up the trail toward Pike's Peak. In less than three hours of walking I was in a gloriously wild country, beyond the tourist, beyond even the horse's track. "An exploration like this is a revelation of the bigness, the interest, and the depth of this range which seems at times, when seen from the plain, shallow in perspective and barren of verdure. By leaving the main trail and passing through a dark cañon, I have reached a silent and untroubled wilderness, where the flowers wave as they have waved for thousands of years, and the water ouzel, flitting from stone to stone in this exquisite little stream, is equally unchanging. There is something healing in this place. I got from it a peace which the plain does not give, something akin to the solace which devout tourists derive from age-old cathedrals."

On the following day, wishing to revisit Cripple Creek, I took passage on the short line amidst a mob of tourists who fought to get on the left-hand side of the car. They were all plainsmen and their interest in the scenery (which was to them as great as the Andes) was amusing to me. It recalled my own excitement thirty years before.

In the seat with me sat a big, blond, and powerful young man who told me that he was a miner from the gold camp of Victor. "My folks live in Michigan, and I've been back there on a visit." He was a rough-hewn, familiar type, and as I gained his confidence he told me of his boyhood and how he came to leave home. From this talk I got the suggestion for a short story which I afterward included in "They of the High Trails" under the title of "The Leaser." How much of it is fact and how much fiction I cannot now determine. That it is essentially true is certain.

Cripple Creek, drably weather-beaten and "all shot to pieces," was depressing. "Half the houses are empty and the streets are sparsely tenanted. An air of sullen resentment, of defense lies over it. All the confidence, all the audacity of its earlier days is gone, only a few free miners remain, dragging out their hope, haggard and unkempt. The hotels have sunk to the level of lodging houses and the business of mining has fallen into the hands of lesser men, but the hills outside the gold zone are as beautiful as ever, and the Sangre de Cristo Range is as majestic as when I saw it first."

I wandered over the hills all the morning and spent the afternoon talking with the men on the streets. "They are all quick to defend their claims and savage and bitter in resentment of the ruin which the labor war had brought. The camp is on its last legs, a cheerless and depressing ruin. Not a tree is in sight, not a garden or green lawn. It is an unnatural place—a monstrous place in which to live, a place of derelicts, men with no future. I leave it with a conviction that I shall never return, and a feeling of regret that I have seen it in decay."

At Colorado Springs I found Wray entertaining Major Aherne who had been my host at Fort Custer in 1897. He spent the evening in talking laboriously but entertainingly of the Philippines and of Cuba, drinking meanwhile immense quantities of rye, which Wray dealt out with reckless hand. "Aherne is an able soldier but a still abler forester," I said to Wray. "His work in the Philippines is important."

Miss Boaz, assistant librarian, had arranged a luncheon at the Broadmoor Club next day, and I was invited along with the Wrays. The table was very pretty, and the guests, nearly all English and Scotch or Easterners

formed on English models, were of interest to me.
Baldwin, a man from San Francisco, was building a
palace on the model of the Trianon, and when he invited me to see it, I accepted. I anticipated beauty, but
I was not prepared for a palace. "It is a marvelous exhalation from the sagebrush, a dream in marble, and
so is his log cabin—Colorado on the outside and Paris
on the inside, an incredibly dramatic contrast of camp
and château."

This was nearly a quarter of a century ago when
Colorado was famous as a health resort. All the world
was represented there.

At the polo game which followed, I sat beside Miss
Boaz and discussed Colorado Springs and its amazingly
varied population. The mountains were glorious and
the scenes on the course very spirited, especially fine
when the riders came bounding westward. "This is my
first taste of this royal sport. The swift horses, the flaming sun, the splendid purple mountains, the throngs of
gayly dressed people, the glittering motor cars, the
shouts of the players, the reeling swing of their ponies,
the fierce pursuit, the mix-up, the triumphal running
away with the ball, all these made it a gloriously exciting game for me. As a horseman I could follow every
turn."

One of the players was a cowboy, a tall, bronzed
young man who rode a cattleman's heavy saddle with
high pommel, sitting erect with straight legs. He was a
master. His beautiful riding and his marvelous defense
singled him out for our applause. He was on the Colorado team which was playing against some very famous
Eastern men, and as Wray and I were cheering for the

Western riders, we naturally took a deep interest in this man who sat his Mexican saddle with careless grace and played with such speed and precision. His position was that of defense and part of the time he sat his superb horse, waiting, chewing gum in calm unconcern until at just the right moment he dashed in, stopped the ball, and carried it back across the field so swiftly that he could not be overtaken. Again and again he saved the play and at last, to most of the spectators, he became the chief interest. The game resolved itself into a display of his amazing skill.

After the game was over, Wray, eager to have me meet this player, took me to the clubhouse, where we found him surrounded by other admiring spectators. He was very hot and very much embarrassed by the throng but listened to us with a shy grin. He was taller than I had thought, and his small head was covered with short reddish hair. He was not an intellectual type, but he was modest and manly in response. His voice, a curious, husky treble, had a boyish quality and his speech was entirely Western in quality.

After congratulating him on the game, I said, "But how in the world did you learn to play polo like that?"

He grinned as he replied, "Well, you see I train all Moncrieff's polo ponies on his Wyoming ranch."

This led to an explanation by Wray. "Malcolm Moncrieff is one of a colony of Englishmen located up near Sheridan, Wyoming. He and his brother William and his brother-in-law Oliver Wallop are the main 'lords,' as the cowboys call 'em, of the settlement. They raise polo ponies and have a polo field. Malcolm is here to-day; I'll introduce you to him."

Moncrieff, who turned out to be Scotch and not English, was quietly cordial. "If you are ever in Sheridan," he said, "you must come out and see our ranch." I mention this here for the reason that it led to a series of very interesting events which I shall record later.

(My present winter home is in Hollywood, and one of my renowned neighbors is Will Rogers, who is not only a most successful actor, but a leading player on the polo team of the Uplifters' Club, and as my son-in-law Joseph Harper is a member of this pisturesque club, I am a regular attendant upon its games. Rogers and his young sons, one only fourteen years of age, both play. Rogers is a star performer on this field as he is on the stage and platform, and the crowd always rejoices when he rides into the field. Unlike the cowboy at Broadmoor, Will plays with ringing shouts which add to the tense excitement of his rescue shots.

One Sunday afternoon when we were calling at his ranch in Santa Monica I observed, as he came to meet us, that he limped. "Have you had a fall?" I asked.

With a wry smile he pointed his thumb at a wooden "horse" which stood in the yard. "I fell off that dog-goned thing," he confessed in his provocative drawl.

"That would make a good story for the press," I said. " 'Will Rogers, noted cowboy, bronco-buster, and polo player falls from wooden horse in his dooryard and breaks leg.' What a chance for headlines!"

"It would make a good story, wouldn't it?" he replied without enthusiasm.

He made no further explanation and I am still wondering how it happened.)

III

Salt Lake was one of the few unknown cities on my map and I now set forth on a circuit which would include that alluring spot. I had a letter of introduction to Fisher Harris, secretary of the Commercial Club, and as soon as he heard of my arrival he came to my hotel and took me in hand. With him I saw much of the city and came to a clearer understanding of the warfare still going on between the Mormon hierarchy and the town boomers. I perceived the outlines of a great novel here, one which should show the elders fighting a losing battle, not with "the Gentiles" but with their own sons and daughters, who were saying, "We don't want to be Mormons, we want to be like other young people," a demand which will destroy Mormonism or any other divergent faith.

I spoke of this to Mr. Harris, who laughed as he replied, "You've hit it! No young Mormon is going to wear a uniform or a 'queer' hat. The young people are all conforming to universal American customs. In a few years there won't be any Mormons. The old will die off and the young will conform."

Another spot, a gorgeously famous spot which I had long desired to see, was the Green River Range of Wyoming; and it was with intent to explore these peaks that I dropped off the train at Granger, for from there a stage was reported to carry passengers to Pinedale at the foot of the range. I went to bed that night over a barroom filled with Chinamen, hoboes, railway men, and cowboys—a gambling, drinking, clamoring gang.

Up at dawn, hungry and sleepy, I rode back to Kemmerer, which was, as I now learned, the stage-line terminal.

The coach was gone when I got to the station, and while casting about for means to get to Pinedale, over a hundred miles from the railway, I met one of the business men of the town who introduced me to a small, kindly, farmerlike individual, saying, "This is Mr. Rathburn who lives up the road toward the Peaks. He'll be glad to take you as far as he goes and you can catch a ride on up from there."

Rathburn was accompanied by his little daughter, a round-cheeked, bright-eyed girl of ten or twelve years of age, who sat between us. I make special mention of her, for her story is of that incredible audacity which we call "typically American."

We reached the ranch along toward supper time. It was a regulation one-story log building with a dirt roof, enclosed by wire fences on which hung an ugly row of drying hides. The yard, cluttered with old machinery and horns and hoofs, was such as I had many times encountered, but the interior of the house was unexpectedly civilized. Mrs. Rathburn, who came from Kentucky, was making heroic effort to raise and educate her children in the spirit of her ancestry. Books and magazines were on her center table and a piano gave further suggestion of educated taste. "I have one daughter in Berea College now and I hope to send Olive when she is old enough."

(As I shall not refer to this again, I will set down what little I know of that shy girl's after life.

One morning, some ten years later, I received from the American Geographical Society of New York a letter which read something like this: "Do you remember the small girl who rode between you and her father from Kemmerer to a ranch, in 1907? I am that little girl. I would like to come and see you."

Curious to know how she happened to be writing on the stationery of the Geographical Society I asked her to call. She came, but I could see in her nothing of the child I had known. Self-contained, well-dressed, and delicately charming, she told me that she was the private secretary of Stefansson the renowned explorer! I was amazed. A vivid picture of her home, that lonely ranch house, surrounded with bleaching hides and decaying bones, came to mind.

"Is Stefansson a greater explorer than this small girl?" I said to my wife and daughters after Miss Rathburn had gone. "Is her story ended or has it only begun?"

Since then I have heard nothing from her.)

IV

Catching the stage next morning, I rode on to the Half-way House where I spent Sunday. The keeper of this house was entirely in harmony with his environment, a huge and grossly powerful man of fifty. He was curious about me, but concealed it under a silent, pondering scrutiny. He could have gone on the stage as the chief personage in a sheep-and-cattle war, and so could the weather-beaten, awkward cow hands who came in for Sunday dinner. They could not understand me. "Why should a man travel three hundred miles to see a range of snow peaks? He must be a spy of the government."

Gradually the landlord softened. I explained that I was interested in forestry and that I was making a tour of certain forest reservations. I said "I hate to see sheep pastured in the forests. They destroy not only the grass but the growing shrubs and lead to the erosion of the hills. They are a pest and should not be allowed on any watershed."

This won him completely. He admitted that he had been concerned in driving the sheepmen out of the country.

He described the stern measures employed. He showed me photographs of dead sheep piled in a corral. They had all been killed by the cattlemen as an example of what would happen to any other flocks which the herders were fool enough to bring in. "We drew a line on the Red Desert," my host explained, "and said to the sheepmen, 'Thus far and no farther'—and we meant it. You'll find no sheep stripping this range, in the hills or in the high valleys."

At Pinedale I fell into the hands of Wat Brandon, the young editor of the local paper, *The Round-up,* and with him I rode up into the valley of the Green River, which I found as primitively magnificent as when Captain Bonneville rode its trails. We crossed the divide and camped on a glorious stream which came down from glacial heights. During the night a rain came on, a storm which changed the next forenoon into snow, and with a fear that we might be snowed in we hastily packed and started back over the high pass.

Above timber line we rode in a blizzard precisely like those I had known in Dakota. We could not see our way. As the more experienced trailer I rode ahead seeking a path amid the rocks, taking advantage of every lull in the storm. The wet snow, driven almost horizontal by the wind, loaded our pack so heavily on one side that it slipped and we were obliged to unsaddle and repack in the midst of the blast, each moment fiercer. My fingers were numb and Brandon not much skilled in packing, but I succeeded in recinching the load and went on. Fortunately the pass was short and as we began to descend on the western side the fury of the storm abated. In an hour we were sheltered among tall firs. Two hours later, entirely below the snow, we went into camp to dry out and cook our grouse.

This trip gave me the groundwork for a story which I called "The Outlaw of Blizzard Basin" and the reader who wishes to know a little more in detail the happenings of this little pasear will find it in "They of the High Trails."

One of the strangest and most beautiful effects was the glow of the pink and yellow flowers whose tall stems sustained their blooms above the soft white blanket of snow. I have never seen anything more unearthly in its beauty.

CHAPTER TWENTY-SIX

FULLER AND THE CLIFF DWELLERS

I

ON the Sunday after my return from Wyoming, Fuller, looking seedy and depressed, came in to supper and remained to help "do" the dishes. Afterwards he went to the piano (as he often did) and for an hour played a variety of songs and "instrumental pieces" which everybody knew when we were young and to which we responded even while we smiled at their artlessness. Henry could be quite as freakish in his musical moods as he was in his comment. We never knew when he felt inclined to play or when he was about to stop. He usually sidled toward the piano reluctantly, but he could stop quicker and more decidedly than any one I ever knew. When in the spirit, however, he could play on delightfully without urging.

He was clever at improvising. "Here are the Garlands rejoicing over the acceptance of dad's new story," he would announce and then from the piano would arise a crashing, smashing, jubilant march. Ending this abruptly he would add, "Here is Uncle Henry, suffering his thirsty first editorial rejection." Thereupon bending low over the keyboard, and shrinking to the smallest possible heap, he would draw from the keys a timid, apologetic refrain, turning a whimsical glance upon us in the midst of it, just to let us know that he did not expect us to weep.

He never sang, but gladly played whilst we sang "Lily Dale," "Lorena," "Old Black Joe," or some other of my children's favorites.

One day he reported, with more profanity than I had ever heard him use, that he had spent the entire week plumbing. "I've been jacketing steam pipes like a hired man all day. I loathe my home. I loathe this town. I never expect to reach a place where I can be happy."

He had opened his heart to me, and as I thought of him, delicate artist that he was, jacketing steam pipes I was appalled. "Why do you do it?" I demanded. "Can't you let some one else play the plumber?"

"No. It's my damned New England conscience. My family expect me to do it—and so—I plumb and plaster."

Some years after, in a book of delicious humor called "Lines Long and Short," he put himself and his longing for Italy into a "poem" which I should like to quote entire, so autobiographic is it. Suffice it to say that while he walked the grimy streets of his native town, or worked in the cellar of his mother's house, he dreamed of certain beautiful Italian landscapes which he had so minutely studied, as a youth, on foot and at leisure.

The piece begins in this way:

"When Albert F. McComb
Died in his native Dodgetown
At the age of sixty-odd,
People said—the few who said anything at all—

That he had lived a futile life,
And that Europe was to blame;
His continual hankering after the Old World
Had made him a failure in the New. . . .

"Early he became a boarder,
And a boarder he continued to be . . .
But if Albert stayed single all his sisters did not.
And when he was fifty-two a group of grandnieces
Asked him to help with their grocery bills.
Albert presently perceived that not every "single" man
Can escape the obligations and responsibilities of the
        marriage state.

" 'Well, I must wait,' he said;
And he began to collect Views of the Dolomites."

In these lines, humorous on the surface, but deeply pathetic beneath, all of us who knew him well caught an indirect confession of the reasons for his discontented life. He, too, had "spent fortune on fortune abroad, before he had fairly learned to pay his way at home." He, too, suffered the imputation of failure, and lived the life of a boarder.

Nevertheless he was a strong little man. He drove himself—no one could drive him or even alter his course. He could not be scared or persuaded from a design. He and I never came to harsh words, but I displeased him when I decided that the name of the new club should be the Cliff Dwellers. I insisted on this for two reasons. First of all, it was entirely appropriate, for our only chance of having a home in "the Loop" was to

build on the top of a skyscraper. Secondly, most of
our members lived and worked in similar cliff-like
buildings, but most of all, I wished to honor Fuller
whose novel "The Cliff Dwellers" had made literary use,
for the first time, of the phrase. It was my statement of
this third reason which brought Henry into direct opposition. He had refused to act as secretary of my committee of organization and had looked on with amused
distrust of the whole project, but he had not hitherto
definitely opposed the club; now, he would not accept
membership.

I argued with him: "It isn't a matter of ten years or
your lifetime, Fuller. We are building something in
this club which will be alive and jocund when you and
I are gone, and I want its name to be characteristic
of Chicago and a reminder of you and your first fictional study of Chicago life."

"Nobody will want to be reminded of me."

"No matter. I intend they shall be whether they want
it or not. It is an appropriate name and it remains."

[As he refused thereafter to discuss it, this is a good
place to state that he never became a member and
never ate a meal there with me. Knowing that his overpowering curiosity would lead him some time to slip
in under somebody's elbow, I never referred to the
subject again.]

Two days later I launched the Cliff Dwellers. "At
four P.M. the members began to assemble and by four-
thirty, some ninety-five men representing all of the
fine arts gathered in more or less harmonious mixture.
It was a fairly representative group and the utmost
good feeling was manifest. The name was finally

adopted and the plans of the committee approved. Harry Pratt Judson called the meeting to order and Wallace Heckman served as secretary. Upon being elected president, I made a short address in which I said, 'This is a day to be remembered, somewhat as the Century Club looks back upon its humble beginnings in 1830,'" and at the moment I firmly believed that we were planting a milestone.

I was saying something like this while lunching with Howells at the Century Club on November 16 when in the midst of our talk, Thomas Janvier whom I had not seen for ten years came over to greet me.

My note reads: "His huge beard is now gray but his coal-black eyes are as lustrous as ever, and his rich, roaring Provençal voice a delight. He spoke of visiting the great poet Mistral. 'I have said to him, "You will find Garland's work faithful to the local color of the West as you are to Provence."' I thanked him and said I should like to send a message to Mistral. It is in something like his spirit I have written."

Immediately on my arrival in New York I went in to see MacDowell. "He was quite like himself mentally but not so steady on his feet. He had my 'Prairie Songs' in his hands and spoke of my verse which he strangely enjoys. Marian said, 'He carries your Songs for hours in his hand. He always intended to set some of your verses to music.'—This touched me nearly. It may be that this intention was lingering in his mind, for he spoke of it to me clearly and forcibly. When I said to him, 'In talking of your music on the platform I declare it to be Celtic-American,' he smiled and replied, 'It can be so described.'"

I had some photographs of Taft's sculptured group, "The Blind," with me and he studied them with interest. He soon turned away from them. "They are very sad," he said.

The following night I saw "The Prince and the Pauper" played in an East Side theater by the Educational Alliance Dramatic Company. The actors as well as the players in the orchestra were mainly small Jews, I recorded. "They have a facility in music which the Anglo-Saxon does not possess. That they will change the character of New York musical life is certain. These young violinists, these actors, these literary folk are to be the leaders in their lines. Mark went on the stage and was instantly surrounded by a mob of black-eyed, black-haired Orientals all eager to take his hand. His shock of white hair and his ruddy face rose grandly above them."

The Father McGlynn Memorial Meeting which came a few nights later brought me once more among the Irish who seemed very near of kin after seeing the Hebrews and Italians of the East Side. They were all untouched by the sophistication of the city. The audience might have been drawn from West Salem. They brought to my mind again the query: "Where are the Irish now? What has happened to them? They no longer dig in the streets or carry the hod." They have gone up. They are judges, clerks, policemen, and politicians."

Augustus Thomas' play "The Witching Hour" was running and I rejoiced at the opportunity of seeing it. I found it deftly written and up to date—a little ahead of date in fact. It had two noble characters, and was beautifully played. The story dealt with telepathy and I was astonished to find it so acceptable to the audience. The theater was filled and the applause cordial.

"November 20. The rage of the rich against Roosevelt was well brought out at the club to-day by a stockbroker, who convinced me that New York is an unpleasant place for those who like the President. The fury against him is shared by all the unfortunate ones who have dabbled in stocks and lost. Incidentally, there is much criticism of the new designs on our coins. St. Gaudens' realistic eagle with feathered legs is denounced as 'an awkward bird, more like a turkey than an eagle.' At Brander Matthews' to-night we discussed the matter and he said: 'We are so accustomed to the eagle doing a "split" and holding a sheaf of thunderbolts in each foot, that we are astounded when St. Gaudens designs a true eagle with rows of feathers on his legs. Once we are accustomed to the real bird, we'll wonder how we endured the pressed and dried Chinese hen which the old design resembled.' "

Everywhere I went I heard the speculators snarling at Roosevelt and at last I wrote a letter to him recording my faith in him and expressing my entire agreement with his policy. To this he responded promptly, as he always did, and with unusual fullness. I quote only a few lines, however.

The White House
Washington.
November 23, 1907.

Dear Garland:

Thank you for your letter. When hard times come, it is inevitable that the President under whom they come should be blamed. There are foolish people who supported me because we had heavy crops; and there are foolish people who now oppose me because extravagant speculations, complicated here and there with dishonesty, have produced the inevitable reaction. . . . It is just the kind of incident upon which one must count. It may produce a temporary setback for my policies in either one or two ways; that is, in securing the election, as my successor, of a reactionary or of some good man who will be the tool of reactionaries, or else through having the pendulum swing with violence the other way, so that my successor as a wild radical will bring utter discredit on the reforms by attempting to do too much.

CHAPTER TWENTY-SEVEN

EDWARD MacDOWELL

THE reader will recall that I have recorded on an earlier page my anxiety concerning the health of Edward MacDowell, a concern which was justified by an almost complete breakdown which came to him in the autumn of 1905. In my records it appears that he had taken an apartment in the old Westminster Hotel not far from the Players, and that I took a room in the same building in order to be near him.

"The immediate contributing cause of his breakdown," I wrote, "was a fall in the street—or rather an accident in the street. He was struck by a cab, so his wife tells me, and the concussion stunned him so that he was dazed for some time. He was able to walk home, but this shock, coming upon him at a time when he was worn with his teaching and suffering from his controversy with Columbia University, undoubtedly caused his collapse."

From what some of his friends told me, I was prepared to find him sadly changed, but in my diary of November 7, 1905, I find these lines: "I was instantly relieved. He greeted me with a cheery word and his familiar shy smile, and began at once to ask after my wife and my little daughter. He was dressed in a beautiful suit of light gray and looked very handsome. I could not share Marian's anxiety. On the contrary I thought her overwrought and needlessly alarmed, but as we chatted I noticed an alarming change in him. He grew tired and the brightness went out of his face."

I saw him twice on November 8 and each time my realization of his weakness deepened. "He met me in the morning with smiling interest and talked of the election returns with much of his clear judgment. He joked about the effect of the returns on Tammany Hall and touched upon other items of news in the papers." I went away confident of his early recovery, but when I went in later I found him tired, so tired and sad that I shortened my call. My entry reads: "I would leave for home to-morrow, but Marian intimated that Edward likes to have me come in and so I shall stay on. I carry him in mind constantly. To have that splendid mind show signs of decay is tragic—I spoke to him of the club of which we had so often talked and of which he wished me to be a director. I told him that we had held a meeting the night before and that I had been authorized to draw up a constitution and by-laws. This pleased him, but he soon passed into that mood of silence and sadness which comes when he grows weary. I went away with a feeling that his work was done and when I met the committee again I said, 'Let us call this club the MacDowell Club and make it a memorial organization, with the purpose of carrying out the plan he had in mind.' "

To this the other members agreed and we parted with a feeling that before we met again Edward Mac-Dowell might be among our honored dead.

On November 16, 1905, I find this entry: "Edward

was astonishingly well this morning. I found him walking about the room clad in his shapely gray suit. His smile was ready and his handclasp firm and warm. This turn for the better fills we with joy. 'I cannot believe his case is hopeless,' I wrote to my wife. 'If he can return to almost normal condition for an hour he can be aided to stay. He is not broken, he is only tired.' "

Three days later we had another meeting of the MacDowell Club Committee and adopted the plan I had drafted.

I did not see him again until in January, when scheduled to speak at the first public meeting of the MacDowell Club, I returned to the Westminster Hotel. In answer to my phone call Mrs. MacDowell answered, "Edward is worse—much worse, don't come in to-day."

"This sorrowful report gave the club meeting the tone of a memorial. 'Edward may be dying at this moment,' I thought. Ex-Mayor Seth Low, a loyal friend of MacDowell, made an admirable address and little Miss Deyo played the 'Tragic Sonata' like one inspired. She made it profoundly significant, emphasizing its somber Celtic quality till it seemed a death song written in foreboding of the fate which had already befallen its creator. Eugene Heffley's fervent introduction added to this effect. The force and power, the sinister character of those clashing chords moved me beyond measure. It was, to me, a requiem of my friend."

This feeling was with me the following morning when a call for help came from Marian. As quickly as I could I rushed to her apartment. Edward had fallen and was unable to rise, and yet as I bent over him he looked up at me with a twinkle in his eyes and a self-derisive smile on his lips as if to say, "All this is silly in me and embarrassing to you, but it can't be helped." He remained absolutely silent, but expressed to me an amused contempt of his fumbling limbs.

It was a very strange attitude—one that I could hardly analyze at the time. It was as if his brain, like his body, refused to serve his spirit. I felt that he, my friend, was within that rebellious frame and that he might at any moment regain his command of it. It was a sorrowful experience for me, but one that somehow convinced me that no matter what might happen, his brave spirit would remain untouched by any physical decay.

During 1906 I saw little of him, for I went away to Europe in May and was, besides, in low vitality myself, but I heard from him frequently. "He grows slowly but certainly weaker," my friends wrote me, and when in the summer of 1907 President James of the State University of Illinois wrote me, saying, "We are about to dedicate our new auditorium and I want you to come down and make the address on 'Edward MacDowell and American Music,'" I instantly replied, "I know very little of American music but I am well acquainted with MacDowell. I am deeply gratified by your choice of theme and honored by your wish to have me as orator. I shall do my best in tribute to my friend and hope to please you and your audience."

All the reports from the great composer were so bad that I wrote my address in the spirit of one composing an elegy. I said in effect: "All our earlier music like our literature was cultural rather than creative, derivative rather than original. We have had many scholarly composers but few who had the fire of genius. Just as in the work of our poets, painters, and sculptors, Old World modes and models were repeated, so in our music we imitated—till MacDowell came.

"As our painters were forced to live down or forget their training in Munich and Düsseldorf, so MacDowell found it necessary to free himself from Leipzig, before he could achieve an individual quality—and this individual quality was of a new world because he himself was an American." I quoted some of the many admissions and aspirations he had voiced in my hearing, and ended by expressing my belief that in thus associating his name with a noble building dedicated to music, President James had planted another milestone on the mounting pathway of New World art.

That night the Chicago orchestra presented a program of MacDowell's compositions to a great audience, and so brought to a brilliant close this deeply significant dedicatory festival. Whether Edward was well enough to read the reports which I sent him or not, I cannot say, for I did not see him again till in November of 1907.

Notwithstanding all the disheartening reports of his condition I found him so well that I was able to discuss my address with him. In his glance was something of his accustomed humor and self-analysis. Underneath his treacherous brain his soul persisted, flashing out from time to time with heartening power.

The end was approaching, however, and early in 1908, while at my home in Chicago, one of the papers called me up to say, "Edward MacDowell died this morning. Can't you give us a few words of tribute?"

I was not surprised, but I had not given up hope. Bearing in mind those amazing intervals of recovery, I had clung to a belief that he could be somehow restored to health. I replied to the editor, "I shall remember Edward MacDowell as one of the swiftest, most humorous, and most original minds I have ever known, inhabiting a body of singular beauty and manly power," and in a later tribute I made still plainer my belief that in losing him America had lost its finest composer.

CHAPTER TWENTY-EIGHT

THE VOICE FROM THE DARK

I

ONE afternoon last summer while sitting in the library of the Yama Farms Inn, I listened to Sir Oliver Lodge speaking from the platform of a hall in England, and only a week ago, while listening to my radio in New York City, I heard a nightingale singing in a London garden, and so close to my ear was the little creature that I could hear the clicking of his beak. Space for the moment was non-existent. The bird was as convincing as the great philosopher. I could feel his hesitation as I could follow every phase of the orator's thought and the subtlest inflections of his voice. It was quite as if they were "spirits" speaking from the dark interior of a cabinet!

When I recount these facts of radio magic, my hearers shrug their shoulders and say, "What will men do next?" but if I say, "Last night my grandfather spoke to me from the fourth dimension," they very properly say, "I have no faith in all that trickery."

The above paragraphs have been written as a warning introduction to a chapter dealing with a part of my literary career which many of my best friends deplore and yet my study of psychic phenomena (which began in 1891 and continues to this day) is an inescapable part of my career. I do not apologize for it; on the contrary I regard it as a most vital part of my education. The phenomena of spiritualism are, to my thinking, legitimate subjects for biological experiment. In my philosophy there is no such thing as a supernatural event. Whatever the phenomenon, it is a part of the physical universe and happens in accordance with physical law no matter how mysterious the law may seem at the moment.

One of the most important of my meetings in New York during 1907 was a dinner with John O'Hara Cosgrave, for I left his table commissioned to write for *Everybody's Magazine* a series of articles, in conversational form, dealing with my long experience as an investigator, and I was at work upon the second article of the series when the death of Edward MacDowell was announced.

Some weeks later, when my work on this psychical serial took me again to New York, I called at once on Mrs. MacDowell. I found her looking pale and sad, her brave brightness almost clouded over, but she related in detail the journey to Peterboro and the placing of Edward's body among the pine boughs of the burial vault on the farm. "He was very beautiful to see," she said. "His hands were as supple as yours as I took hold of them for the last time. . . . The country people came out in great numbers as if to show their love for him. It was an exquisite winter day. The deep grave was filled with pine branches and when the coffin was lowered into it the green boughs sprang up around the casket. It was as if he were sinking into a bed of boughs, all green. No earth appeared. I think of him sleeping there on his beloved hill like an old Norse god."

All of this is of especial significance in relation to what is to follow. Not long after my return to Chicago, I received an invitation from an old friend in Indianapolis, Mary Jameson Judah, in which she invited me to come down and visit her. "Bring Henry Fuller," she wrote, and then concluded by saying, "We have a very remarkable psychic here, a trustworthy woman. I have known her since she was a little girl. She is not only willing but eager to sit for you."

Early in March Fuller and I went down to Indianapolis to visit the Judahs who were delightful hosts, and the very next morning after our arrival I started out to visit the psychic, an appointment made for me by Mrs. Judah.

In order that the story of my experience with "Mrs. Henry" may have full value, it is necessary to explain that my mind was filled, naturally, with thoughts of MacDowell. For nearly three years I had borne him in mind consciously or unconsciously and Fuller and I had discussed him frequently, indeed just before starting out for my sitting I remarked, "By all the laws of telepathy, I should get a message from MacDowell." I said this in a tone of banter for, strange to say, with all my wealth of other phenomena I had experienced almost no cases of mind-reading. I did not really look forward to a message from MacDowell.

Mrs. Henry lived in a small, neatly painted frame cottage and her "ghost-room" as her little son called it was on the east side of the house and filled with sunshine as I entered it at about ten o'clock. It contained two chairs and a battered old table which "Coulter," her guide, especially liked.

On my way I had stopped in at a bookstore and purchased a pair of folding slates and these—at the psychic's request—I kept in my own hands. Drawing a chair up to the wobbly kitchen table, she asked me to seat myself opposite her and hold the folded slates under the table. This I did and as she grasped the opposite corner of the slates with her right hand, her left hand, like mine, remained upon the top of the table.

Almost instantly a tremendous force developed, a force so powerful, so unruly that I could not keep the slates from swinging to and fro. They cracked under the strain of my hand.

I quote from my notes: "After some time the forces began to write fragmentary bars of music on the closed slates. Not being able to read this music or record it I tried to turn the experiment in other directions, but 'MacDowell' dominated the situation. Another curious complication came with the intrusion of a design which looked like a Chinese signature."

There was a reason for a MacDowell manifestation, but I could not understand why a Chinaman should address me. Later I discovered that the psychic had just finished a series of sittings with a visiting Chinese official, and this signature was due to an influence left over from his experiments.

"After a time 'MacDowell' began to whisper to me, seemingly from a point above and to the right of the medium. Although I studied her lips while the words were forming, I could not detect the slightest motion in her organs of speech. 'MacDowell' wanted me to do something, and also wanted to communicate some music. It all seemed chaotic and fragmentary, and at last I said, 'I can't take down your music, Edward, but Henry Fuller, who is in the city, might be able to do so. I'll bring him with me when I come again."

Fuller was eager to experiment, and on the following morning at about ten o'clock we set off together. Upon taking seats at the battered little table, I said to the invisible force, "If you are my friend MacDowell, give me a page of music from one of your unpublished compositions. Such a page would be the finest test in the history of psychic research."

This the whispering voice promised to do, but we got little at this sitting. The psychic urged us to come back in the afternoon. This we did at about two o'clock. I quote from my diary: "Again 'MacDowell' came and at once resumed work on the unpublished fragment of music for which I had asked. After sketching several bars on the closed folding slates (which I had brought with me) the personality speaking from the air, said, 'Go down to the piano and work on the music there.' This we did and thereafter the 'direct voice' took entire charge of the sitting."

As the experiment went on, the psychic leaned back in her chair, and sat without stirring hand or foot. Fuller and I were in full possession of the slates. Mrs. Henry certainly had no clear knowledge of what was going on, for the discussion between Fuller and Mac-Dowell was highly technical. The voice not only made itself clearly audible; it reproduced MacDowell's manner of speech. It was swift, masterful, critical. "Play it, Fuller," he would command when a question of musical notation arose, and then, as Fuller played, he would say, "No, that's wrong. There should be a rest before that C sharp—and the B should be a sixteenth and not an eighth note."

Each mistake was instantly corrected by the invisible force *on the closed slates while entirely under our control*. Sometimes I held the slates—sometimes they were placed between Fuller and me—and through it all the psychic sat with folded hands. At the direction of the voice we drew extra bars to the score and on these lines, while the slates were closed, the necessary notes would be set with unfailing precision. Little flags would be added to the stems of the notes more precisely than Fuller could have done them on the open slates.

Once after a highly characteristic piece of musical notation, Fuller asked, "Isn't that an unusual method of expression?" the voice instantly replied in the tone of the master musician—"it is a liberty I permit myself."

In this way (absolutely without touch of the psychic) we obtained seven bars of an exquisite melody which Edward said we would find among his manuscripts. Again I quote from my records: "It was precisely as if he were present and vocally directing Fuller in the minutest particular. It was all very complicated and very beautiful. We both went away quite convinced that some marvelous occult power was present."

(My record was exact, but upon it a few days later I based a full report to which Fuller added his comment. This story became a chapter in my "The Shadow World.")

It should also be borne in mind that the psychic was not an educated woman and had only rudimentary knowledge of music, and that she had no personal knowledge of MacDowell. Furthermore, her folded hands were in view while this recording was going on, and I could not detect the slightest motion of her lips or throat while the voice was speaking to me—but even if this were a ventriloquistic trick, the writing of the music which went on within the closed slates in our own hands remains inexplicable.

There were other and still more dramatic mysteries. Once the voice said, "Fuller, we've met before."

"Yes," said Fuller. "Where?"

"In New York."

"Yes, but where in New York?"

The voice hesitated. "Well, it was down cellar."

"Yes, I know the place you mean. Who were there?"

"Well, Marian was there—and Garland—and John Lane—" then a tired sigh—"Oh, I can't remember who else."

This was correct. The dinner was at Mouquin's on Sixth Avenue and in the basement dining room—a fact which the psychic could not have known.

Another and still more startling incident was this: I had been bending forward over the table for a long time, and feeling somewhat cramped, leaned back in my chair to rest. Instantly the invisible one in anxious accents called out: "Garland! Garland! Where are you? I can't see you."

As I resumed my former attitude above the table, the spirit uttered a sigh of relief. "Oh, *now* I see you!"

Admitting that this may have been a dramatic diversion on the part of the psychic, it was a poignant and most mystifying incident. It was as if MacDowell could perceive me only when my head was within the aura of the psychic—or that a psychic spot-light was covering the table.

Another puzzling clue requires following up. At the beginning of this series of sittings, the name "Schubert" came on the slates and for a time we all inferred that Edward meant the composer and we talked along those lines, but slowly and in opposition to all our thinking, the true explanation arrived. The composer at last completed his request. "Have Shubert the publisher return a piece of my music which he has, and tell Marian to take it to Schmidt, my regular publisher"—all of which so far from being in my mind was in direct opposition to it. The "spirit" had a will of his own! He was not governed in this instance by our preconception.

I must now record the disappointing end of all this. When I read my records to Mrs. MacDowell in New York, she remained calm. "Edward never wrote a piece called 'Hungary,' and he never dealt with Shubert," she bluntly stated, and her interest was not excited till she caught sight of a certain elaborate signature on the slate.

"Where did you get that?" she asked sharply.

"It came on the closed slates, like the music, without contact," I replied. "I paid no attention to it. It isn't his writing—and it is not the way he spells his name."

"But it is!" she replied instantly. "It's exactly the way he signed his name when I first met him in Germany.

He spelled his name 'McDowell' instead of 'MacDowell'
—and he signed it with just that flourish below it."

Her statement recalled to mind the fact that I had
seen this signature at some time. I turned to a little
framed manuscript on the wall. "Why, so he did and
there it is!"

The framed manuscript was a letter certifying to
those concerned that Marian Nevins was a competent
teacher, and was signed Edward McDowell precisely as
I had obtained it on my closed slates in Indianapolis.
Did the psychic get this signature from my mind? And
if so why did she use an early signature instead of the
one more familiar to me?

With regard to the music itself, how did the psychic
produce that, without contact, on closed slates in our
own hands? Fuller analyzed the music thus: "It is Mac-
Dowell distorted by some strange influence and mingled
with certain Ute and Cheyenne melodies with which
Garland's subconscious mind is filled."

The seven bars formed a sadly sweet, haunting strain,
and Fuller, after playing it for us once or twice, refused
to do so again. "It gets into my head and will not let
me sleep," he protested.

II

My book, "The Shadow World," was published at the
close of its serial run in *Everybody's Magazine* and drew
from many scientific men letters of mingled doubt and
keen interest. One of the most interesting of all came
from William James, who said: "I have read your
'Shadow World' from cover to cover and find it valuable." Later in the year upon hearing that I was in

Boston he came in from Cambridge to see me at the
Tavern Club. His changed appearance startled me. I
had remembered him as a handsome gray-haired man
in evening dress, but he now appeared in the guise of
an old-fashioned, refined, but austere country clergyman. His necktie was awry and his coat wrinkled. His
tone and manner of speech were those of a village
professor. "He is very New England and wholly admirable," I wrote of him at the time. "He is neatly alert of
speech, and a fearless, positive thinker. He told of seeing
Mrs. Sedgwick reading a well-known book on a psychic
subject and pooh-poohing its claims. With some as-
perity he added, 'Such an attitude to-day is scandalous.
Whatever the interpretation of these phenomena may
be, no well-informed person can doubt their existence.
I envy you your wide experience. You have been more
fortunate than I.' "

My position then was, and still is, purely biologic.
"The phenomena exist," I wrote at the time, "but thus
far the evidence does not lead me to a belief that they
are caused by the spirits of those whom we call dead.
I recognize nothing 'supernatural.' No matter how
strange and mysterious any phenomenon may be, it
happens in the natural world and is subject to natural
law. We may not know the principles which govern
these astonishing sights and sounds, but no movement
takes place except in conformity with the forces which
govern the universe."

(As I look back upon these happenings now, enlightened by the radio, I can see that we were in touch with
a mysterious something which is to-day almost a commonplace. All our greatest philosophers of 1930 are

emphasizing the mystery of matter and the relativity of time, space, and motion. The phenomena which I have described have nothing to do, directly, with religion; they belong to the study of bio-physics and bio-chemistry. They are "supernatural" because the laws which govern them are at present unknown.)

CHAPTER TWENTY-NINE

THE RUSSIAN PLAYERS

I

KNOWING nothing of the social life of Manchester or Liverpool, I am nevertheless quite certain that their intellectuals in the year 1908 were subject to boredom and welcomed invasions from London and Paris, just as Chicago welcomed the coming of literary embassies from New York, or visitors from the farther East. Any man or woman whose character and opinions afforded material for conversation was tumultuously seized upon for exploitation. It may be that some of these travelers were deceived by the crowds who applauded their doings, but some of us who had lived through many similar periods of excitement, despised them while we shared them. One enthusiasm drove out another. Something new was demanded each week.

For example, on one of my returns from a tour I found all my friends applauding and discussing a troupe of Russian players whose performances, led and directed by a certain Paul Orlénieff, were declared "inspirational" and "epoch-marking." This company was presenting a Jewish play and this I must immediately see. My reactions are mildly indicated. "This play is a bloody page torn out of Russian history, done with quiet art and intense earnestness. Orlénieff and his associate star

Nazimova are exceptionally fine artists, and their subordinates are all of unusual ability. It was a poignant
performance, so true in effect that many Jews in the
audience uttered cries of pain as if some dreadful
memory had been awakened. We all went away in vast
indignation. 'How can such injustice exist in a Christian land?' That these people, handicaped by a strange
language, should so stir the city to admiration is an
artistic triumph."

In a call at Mrs. Coonley Ward's, I met Orlénieff the
director for a few moments. "He is a smallish man, very
pale and very sensitive. His manner was subdued and
he spoke but few words of English. At Mrs. Ward's request I talked to her guests about the play and the
players, and Mrs. Victor Yarros, who followed me, gave
a most interesting account of Orlénieff and Nazimova.
Naturally she exalted them.

After the speaking I was introduced to "Mrs. Smith,"
a short, plain, middle-aged woman who meant little to
me at the time. Later I learned that she was the widely-
known anarchist, Emma Goldman!

"Chrystal and Julie Herne came out to see us this
afternoon, and remained to dinner. They made me feel
middle-aged, for when I saw them first they were little
sprites playing 'paper ladies'; now here they are deep
in their own grown-up dramatic game, earning more
money than I. They are very pretty and quite as
strenuous as ever, taking life like real players, in tragic
earnest."

Emerson Hough, who was still loyal to the city, was
a resident of the South Side, and shortly after my return I shared in the pleasure of a dinner at his apart-

ment. I had never before entered his home, but I was not surprised to find it filled with bear skins, moose heads, and other trophies of the chase, for he had always been associated in my mind with hunting and fishing. When we first met he was the Western correspondent of George Bird Grinnell's *Forest and Stream,* and did his work in a small office high up in one of the downtown commercial blocks.

"He is a brusque, uneasy host," I wrote after this party; "one with whom it is difficult to converse—at least I have always found him difficult. I sense something antagonistic in him. I do not know why this should be, but I have never been able to talk with him on any subject—not even on trailing. It can't be that he is jealous of my position, for he is a far more successful writer that I. It may be that he resents my adventure into his field—a field in which I am as much at home as he. We are both Western men by birth. I think he still considers me a Bostonian.

"His 'Story of the Cowboy' was the best book on the subject at the time of its publication, but his novels, though filled with accurate descriptions, are weak in characterizations, and his style is reportorial. However, he—like dozens of others—'has the laugh' on me, for his poorest books sell five times more widely than mine. Like McCutcheon, Churchill, Major, and others of my contemporaries he has the quality which appeals to a wide audience, whereas my work is sober and slow. No, he has little cause to fear any competition from me. As I go over 'The Story of the Cowboy' to-day, I find it true in all details, but full of careless writing. It does not stand up well in comparison with the work of later men. It is essentially journalistic in quality and irritates me by its many bad phrases."

"January 15, 1908. Donald Robertson in 'Segurd Slembe' gave a fine reading of the title rôle but was poorly supported. He had no scenery or 'soldiers' and did not look the character, and yet by his fine voice, his face, and his dignity he made the characterization noble. He created the illusion almost entirely alone. He made me feel the savage dignity, the fierce hatreds, and the tragic loneliness of the grim old northern king whose sons were all given in battle. This play is a remorseless picture of the ancient Danish fighting man."

"The annual meeting and first dinner of the Cliff Dwellers took place on January 17 at six-thirty, with about ninety members in attendance. As chairman and toastmaster it was my duty to create a wave of club spirit, and I did my best to arouse the enthusiasm of the members. I succeeded—in moderate degree. Lorado Taft made a pleasing talk, and so did Harry Pratt Judson, president of Chicago University. None of them, however, quite rose to what I had hoped for. Dan Burnham sat at my left and we discussed the housing of the club, which is our next problem."

II

"March 5. On my way to Philadelphia I read 'Richard Gresham' by Robert Lovett, a serious, capable book, showing imagination and vigor. A manly, wholesome story, more like an intimate biography than a novel."

As my lecture was in Wyncote, George Horace Lorimer invited me to his house for the night. Taking me out to his country place early in the afternoon we walked for an hour or two before dinner. I record: "He is in full enjoyment of his fine house and his success with the *Post*, which is phenomenal. He and Bok have made the Curtis publications known throughout the world. How American their careers are! Lorimer, the son of a Chicago preacher, Bok a Hollander!"

One of my most interesting New York evenings, during this visit, was a dinner with the John Alexanders who took me afterward to see an East Side boys' club do a Gilbert and Sullivan opera. "All the characters were taken by lads and much of it was very funny. John is a beloved patron of this club and it interested me to see how cordially he was received by the members. He went among them in his evening clothes, wearing a high hat and a splendid overcoat, but they swarmed about him and clung to him just the same. They liked him *because* he looked the prince, their prince. His slender form, intellectual face, and musical voice set him apart from the world and appealed to their imagination."

Two days later, I joined another of Colonel Harvey's curious collections of personalities at a luncheon in honor of Mrs. Humphry Ward. "At Harvey's request I took Mrs. Ward down to the dining room, and led her to her seat which was beside mine. We talked hard—but not fast—for half an hour on real subjects. She was very serious, not to say ponderous, in manner, and I, alas! had no humor to lighten the gloom.

"She is like her books, able but rather slow; a fine mind grown old, and I would have failed utterly had not Duneka (who sat at her right) helped me out now and then. She appeared a bit in the fog as to who the guests were and why they had been invited, and I, doing my best to justify my inclusion, spoke of her books and said, 'I read and admire them'; but I did not tell her that they now seemed out of step with modern thought. That she still considered them 'advanced' was evident. No doubt she wondered especially why I should have been given the honor of sitting beside her. I was a bit puzzled myself."

At Gutzon Borglum's studio the day following I met some bright young fellows whom he had invited in to dine. These were Robert Davis of *Munsey's*, David Mannes, and Will Irwin. Davis, who had at one time been on the *New York Journal*, talked of William R. Hearst most entertainingly. For more than half an hour, inspired by my laughter, he gave a most amusing analysis of Hearst's character and ended by saying, "And now he goes about with his hands folded under his coat-tails, like Napoleon."

"Do you think he dreams of being nominated for President?"

"Dreams of it! He counts upon it. His editors are all trained to that purpose."

Aside from Davis and James L. Ford, I had never met any one who could tell me what Hearst looked like. Davis described him as a low-voiced, gentle autocrat whom nobody saw outside his office.

I never saw him, and to me he is a mythical being. That he has changed the make-up and the tone of the daily press of England as well as of America cannot be questioned. "Yellow journalism, whether one considers it good or bad, dates from his invasion of New York. I recall some one, perhaps James L. Ford, saying, 'Give

Willie Hearst five years and New York will have his millions and he will have the experience.' "

I quoted this to Davis, who replied, "Any one who knows William Randolph Hearst proclaims himself a fool by doubting his ability. He knows just how to reach our moron millions. He is their advocate and purveyor."

"And yet," said Borglum, "he never seems to control their votes. They read him, but ignore his leadership."

"That is true," said Davis reflectively.

[As I write this in 1931, Hearst is an old man living in almost inconceivable luxury on an enormous ranch in California. He owns and directs the policies of a chain of newspapers reaching from Boston to San Francisco. His income is fabulous, his influence world wide—and yet he is no nearer the White House than in 1901. His readers, like myself, regard him as an impersonal tendency, a journalistic magician of unaccountable origin. What will he leave behind when he dies? Will his chain of journals break and disintegrate?]

The MacDowell Memorial Concert came off while I was in town and was gratifyingly successful. A large audience was present in Carnegie Hall and applauded the program. I sat in a box with Mr. and Mrs. August Lewis, who found the program "very Celtic." They were (musically) very German! They were polite but critical. Edward's father and mother were in the audience, proud and pleased but very sad. All of Edward's students were in attendance and every face shone with pride in the music. Again the "Tragic Sonata" was played, this time as a requiem.

On April 2 Irving Bacheller and I took lunch

together at the club. "Remington was there with Willard Metcalfe and Alden Weir—Remington was on the 'water wagon' to-day and was, in consequence, a delightful companion. Afterward I attended a reception to Mrs. Humphry Ward at the National Arts Club, a mixed assembly but a jolly one—much jollier in fact than the guest of honor, who was very austere indeed. That this is partly due to the somberness of age is evident, but she has never been a joyous spirit."

"April 4. Emerson Hough came into the Players this afternoon looking pinched and pale. He and Rex Beach and Paul Armstrong dined together—a vigorous, successful group. They all have something to give, but they present it without literary distinction. Beach is a manly writer, but his books are forceful rather than fine. Some will say they are all the better for their lack of style, but to me such work is ephemeral—like most of our present-day fiction and drama."

At Mrs. Robinson Smith's, I met Kathryn Kidder and her husband, Louis Anspacher, also Charles Rann Kennedy and his wife, Edith Wynne Matthison, a group of bright people. Kathryn Kidder was especially amusing with her account of "Muldoon's Rest" and William's autocratic methods with millionaires and senators. Kennedy told several good stories. "He is very much in the public prints at this time by reason of his thought-provoking play, 'The Servant in the House.' Lorado Taft and I saw it together and were very deeply moved by it. It rose to the dignity of symbolism in the last act and Tyrone Power as the Man of Toil was superb. Walter Hampden was nobly simple in the part of Manson and read the lines beautifully. The piece is extraordinary in that it nowhere hints at romantic love. It is wholly unconventional and very strong and sane and helpful."

On Thursday, Taft was my guest at the Authors Club, where we found the usual collection of editors, critics, and journalists surrounding two or three well-known authors. Colonel Thomas Higginson came in late, a tall, gray wraith of a man, eighty-four years old. "He recognized me, but his handclasp was that of a dying man, chill and nerveless. He seemed a survivor from an heroic past. He 'waits for the bugle' and for him 'the night winds are cold.'"

The sonnet in which these lines occur was written years ago for a Grand Army reunion, and is one of the noblest sonnets I know. "We wait for the bugle, the night winds are cold" are the only lines that remain in my memory, but they still have the power to stir me.

"I told him how much the sonnet meant to me—the son of a veteran—and his face lighted into a smile of pleasure."

The Council of the National Institute of Arts and Letters met February 18 at four-thirty and transacted considerable business. Later, as Allan Robinson's guest, I heard the Mendelssohn Glee Club sing "The Crusaders" by MacDowell, a powerful and thrilling chorus which was repeated at the unanimous request of the audience. "I was particularly struck with the character of the auditors who were all genuinely American, of the best type. I didn't know there were so many of us left in this city of foreign-born population. It was a quietly intellectual and harmonious assembly."

The annual dinner of the Institute came on the 20th, with only twenty men present, a discouragingly small number indeed. Four obituary notices were read. Stedman, Aldrich, MacDowell, and St. Gaudens had gone, and the speaking was somber. At the request of the chairman I spoke on MacDowell. "Notwithstanding this official recognition of the death angel, we struggled to maintain a hopeful tone." My private comment reads: "This struggle to put literature and the arts into honorable position proves our persistent provinciality. As writers and artists we are still apologizing for our existence, in a world of farmers, mechanics, and tradesmen—many of them entirely alien to our blood."

"Riverside, March 13. Bacheller's royalties have built for him a new and spacious home in Riverside, a mansion of many rooms with a huge sitting room whose wide fireplace is a most beloved feature. There he and I sat last night singing songs and telling tales of our youth. At ten a little fountain, just beneath my window, sang me to sleep. I woke this morning to its sound. It is a never-ending poem. It reminds me of the day when Irving brought me over from Sound Beach to see this bare knoll and pointing at this spot said, 'Right here my pleasant mansion shall arise.' Now here it stands. He has created it as he creates his books, with tenderness and homely imagination. There is something quietly forceful in this slow-moving, absent-minded man of the north woods."

On my way back to Chicago I stopped at the Judahs in Indianapolis, and when Whitcomb Riley heard that I was in town he came to call on me—"a great concession on his part," Judah assured me, "for he doesn't get out much these days."

"I was saddened to find him a white and feeble old man. Mentally alert and humorous, he talked well on literary matters, confiding to me that he had an enormous admiration for Henry B. Fuller. This astonished me, so exactly opposite is his literary quality. Fuller, who was visiting the Judahs, came in shortly after and a very delightful dialogue resulted. Riley was inspired to his best expression, and Fuller was wittily concise. The Judahs and I had little to do but applaud."

CHAPTER THIRTY

CLIFF DWELLERS AND OTHERS

I

FULLER's attitude toward the Cliff Dwellers Club remained antagonistic. He refused all invitations to lunch or dine there. His perversity was almost comical and at last I ceased to mention its name in his presence, trusting his restless curiosity to bring him in at some later time. I never succeeded in defining the reasons for his stand. Some said it was due to my choice of name, others said, "It is due to poverty—or penuriousness. He will not pay dues in any club." Whatever his reasons he succeeded in staying out. So far as I know he never entered the door. I am sure he did, but I never saw him there.

I never knew his real opinion of me as a lecturer. He was in the audience when I spoke one afternoon to the Polytechnic Society on "The Indian's Point of View," and appeared rather more pained than usual. Knowing that he despised red Indians and that he was keenly critical of my English, I understood his suffering. He was like a skilled musician enduring a well-meaning amateur! He listened to every speaker with a bored expression, looking wearily downward or askance, acutely conscious of every bungled sentence. "He is quick to reward excellence, however. Some-

thing masterful as well as inexorable is in his small
head. He is too honest intellectually to allow affection
to soften his judgment. Relentless in his analysis of
motives he accepts no cant phrases of pity or piety."

My desk at this time was on the third floor of my
Greenwood Avenue house, in a small room with three
windows looking to the south. It was a sunny chamber,
but hard to keep clean by reason of the dust which
blew in from the neighboring roofs. It was not a
study; it was an office. Furthermore, being in the path
of fumes coming from the great oil refineries of Whit-
ing, I worked now and again in the smothering stink
of kerosene. Fortunately the wind seldom came from
that quarter, and so I went on as contentedly as I could,
carefully refraining from a comparison of my home
with those of my more prosperous fellow craftsmen.

Late in January I went to Madison to witness Donald
Robertson's production of my play. I had not been in
the town for ten or twelve years, and the new University Club was a very real improvement. At luncheon I
met William Ellery Leonard of the English Department,
a poet whose books had interested me, and a little later,
Herbert Quick joined us. My note reads, "Quick is a
big, farmerlike individual with a rough sense of humor,
talkative, kindly, and thoughtful. I have known him
for twenty years and like him, but his writing appears
rather footless to me. He is still trying to do an acceptable novel."

Robertson's company arrived in the midst of a storm,
a typical blizzard, in fact, and we drove to the theater,
at eight, through clouds of snow and a howling wind.
It was a sad opening, but Robertson, with true Thes-

pian buoyancy, said, "It's all in the game!" and composedly went about his dressing.

The house was only half filled, but the play was received with kindly applause. I was not deceived. "It has none of the elements of a popular success," I said to Robertson. "The real test will come in Chicago."

"I have no fear of it," he gallantly replied.

On my way back to Chicago I read Quick's latest story, "The Broken Lance," finding it a strong but inarticulate book, with a perfectly frank didactic appeal.

On the night of Robertson's presentation of my play at the Art Institute, I stood in the aisle at the back of the theater, not much excited by the event; in fact, I had made up my mind beforehand that the audience would not like the piece and that the critics would roast it to a cinder. It was not altogether foolish. It held the attention of the audience—held them very still and tense to the end, and some of my friends were much affected by it, but their interest proved nothing as to its acceptance by the general public.

As I left for New York early next morning I saw only two of the reviews, but they were quite enough. I had expected three critics to be critical and I granted the justice of their comment, but it seemed to me that they were not quite ready to admit certain merits which the play undoubtedly had. My own judgment reads thus: "This whole play-writing episode has been a foolish waste of time. I wonder that I allowed myself to be drawn into it."

II

"New York: At the National Institute dinner last night some thirty men assembled. The talk turned upon the design for the Lincoln Memorial in Washington, and all through the discussion I found myself in the minority. With several others I argued the inappropriateness of a Greek temple—however beautiful—as a memorial to an American who was as far from Athenian culture as a popular leader could possibly be. I said, 'To house a Kentucky rail-splitter in a marble palace seems to me acutely incongruous. I cannot define exactly what a Lincoln memorial should be, but I feel in Bacon's design a lack of originality. It is beautiful, but it is almost wholly derivative. It is not of our world. It has nothing to do with Lincoln or with the West. If we are to have an architecture of our own we must stop constructing in the image of ancient temples.' "

Naturally, my judgment went for nothing in the chorus of acclaim.

(I still hold to my opinion. I never pass this Greek temple without a sense of its incongruity as a monument to Lincoln.)

At a reception given by George P. Brett in his city home, I met Zona Gale for the second time. "She is a little, slender woman, fair and sweet and serious who has made a hit with her stories of 'Friendship Village,' " I wrote. "While not precisely true of Portage, her sketches are a charming blend of humor and sentiment. She knows her Mid-West villagers, but is not quite direct in her expression. Certain tricks of phrase (caught from O. Henry and other newspaper fictionists) mar her pages. Nevertheless, she is to be counted high in the list of American novelists. 'My home is in Portage!' she said to me. 'I am a neighbor of yours!' Brett thinks highly of her and is disposed to push her books."

One afternoon John Cosgrave and I went up to the Hispanic Museum to see Sorolla's exhibit of Spanish paintings and here is my impression of it: "This is the biggest and best individual show I have ever seen, jocund, powerful, full of sunlight.—I met Archer Huntington for the first time. He is a man of giant frame with serene and noble face, a millionaire to whom wealth has given immense cultural power. With all his endowment he remains singularly modest. As an enthusiastic student of Spanish literature and art he has built this museum and filled it with books and pictures to bring about a better knowledge of Spain. He is at once scholar, poet, and historian."

"February 14. Howells is in his new apartment on West Fifty-seventh Street, and greatly pleased with it. It is far finer than anything he has ever had, and when I bantered him on its splendor, he replied, 'It *is* more than I can afford; but I am luxuriating in it—while my conscience is cajoled.' "

III

"February 16. I am in Washington and it is glorious spring! As I wandered about in it, some part of my youthful rapture came back to me. Roosevelt's term is nearly at its end and this afternoon I called at the White House in order to see him for the last time as

President. The vestibule was muddy and but thinly populated by waiting visitors. The old king is passing just when he is at his highest powers.

"He came out into the waiting room looking small, compact, muscular, and still young. He has grown older, of course, but is still untouched by age. On catching sight of me he playfully shook his fist at me and called, 'You old trailer, come in! I want a word with you.'

"Our interview was very short, for it was Cabinet Day and the hour of meeting was at hand. That he sensed the impending change of attitude toward him was instantly evident. He spoke of his 'release' with a tone of regret—'of course I hate to leave.'

"I urged him to write a book and call it 'On Being President'; but he protested, 'I can't do it. I'm too much the man of action. I can't write now. I'm not sufficiently the anchorite.' I reminded him of the advice Howells gave at Brander Matthews' luncheon in '97. 'Howells said to you, "All you need to do is to talk, as you are talking now, to a stenographer," and I repeat his words. Dictate the story of your life here while it is all fresh in your mind. You can revise it later!' His eyes filmed with thought. 'You convince me. I may try it—but not now, not for a year or two.'

"As we stood thus a Western senator was ushered into the room—a politician who hated the President. Roosevelt courteously offered his hand, but his caller boorishly ignored it. Roosevelt, not in the least disturbed, went on with his statement, but I saw in that man's action another sign of revolt. 'The King is dead—long live the King!' What a superb ruler Theodore

Roosevelt has been, so young, so vital, so essentially the gentleman and the scholar."

My return to Chicago was coincident with a great dinner, given by members of the Art Institute, in honor of Lorado Taft. "It was a very successful affair. Something like one hundred and fifty of his friends assembled in Blackstone Hall to congratulate him on his selection to do the Columbus Memorial in Washington, a commission which marks a culminating point in his career. The audience, or rather the guests, included representative men from all the arts, mostly fellow members of the Cliff Dwellers.

"He has earned his success and deserves all these friends," I recorded. "He has won the support of Daniel Burnham and has the promise of future association with his firm's colossal plans. Deeply moved by the tributes paid him, Lorado modestly (too modestly) deprecated them. He is a man of power and has no reason for apology. So far as I know he has no enemies and no envious rivals. His aloofness from New York has the effect of disarming his competitors in the East."

The following night Mrs. Barnhart took my wife and me to Orchestra Hall to hear Paderewski play and here is my record of his performance:

"He is a grizzled, aging man. I had not seen him since he played at the White House eight years ago. He is older, but has lost nothing of his power. He was flawless, both in manner and performance. His calm, haughty, almost entirely subconscious mastery of the unwieldy instrument was superb. The box in which we sat was on the right-hand side and as he looked up from the keys his somber glance was lifted in our direction.

He suggested a tawny, self-centered, dreaming leopard. The look of him was almost as moving as his music. He appeared the great personality that he is, entirely satisfying to the eye as to the ear. No one disputes his supremacy in his art."

"March 2. On my way back to New York, I stopped off at Detroit. With Corey, a musician, and lover of MacDowell's music, I visited the Freer Gallery of Whistler pictures. Freer, a tall, red-bearded, kindly man, patiently showed us about, although he must consider it a tiresome task. It is an extremely valuable little museum—but I don't want it. It was all rather boresome, even the famous Peacock Room left me un-enthusiastic."

"March 22. Back in New York. I saw 'The English-man's Home,' the new play which is making so much talk in London. It was interesting and it has a definite message for the British, but is not vital to me or to any other American. No one really believes that there is any such danger from the Germans as this play prophesies. I can understand, however, why it is taken so much more seriously in England. It is reported that it has strongly influenced their War Department. As a picture of English country life the first act is mildly entertaining. The other acts are exciting only as imaginary events."

[This play became more interesting to me later, for its forecast of the methods of the German army as it invaded Belgium was quite accurate. The author showed a most amazing comprehension of the military system, and my most vivid memories of it concern the businesslike action of the young officers as

they entered that English country house, taking possession of it in the name of the Kaiser. The final scene
also remains—the Englishman standing alone in the
center of his great hall, while its walls crumbled and
flakes of burning cinders fell from the ceiling.]

March 27th was Safonoff's last night as conductor
of the Philharmonic Orchestra and all his friends
turned out in a great demonstration. The MacDowell
Club, having prepared a set of resolutions, delegated
me to present them, and Mrs. Loomis gave me a seat in
her box. As soon as the concert was over we all made
a rush for the green-room to congratulate the director,
the hero of the hour. The crush was disheartening, but
I finally located Safonoff, who was standing in the
throng, his face streaming with sweat, turning in hopeless bewilderment from side to side, meeting with hundreds of frantic admirers entirely unknown to him.

"At last I faced him with the resolutions. He did not
comprehend a word of my brief speech, but I forced
the papers into his hand and fled—hoping that they
might mean something to him later. It was a rather
depressing picture of American taste and feminine hys-
teria. Why all this excitement? He will be forgotten in
a year or two."

Having promised young Rouland, John Burroughs'
artist friend, that I would sit for a portrait, I started
in, although I had an inflamed eye. "His method as a
painter interests me. Holding his brush at arm's length,
and crouching like a man about to spring, he advances
upon his canvas. He is very handsome and boyish and
engaging."

"On the train returning to Chicago, I read 'The

Happy Average,' by Brand Whitlock, a delightful picture of the sane and wholesome life of a small town, one of the truest and best stories of that description I have ever read. I also read 'Holyland,' by Frensson, very large and fine but a bit formless."

Immediately after reaching my home I set to work on "The Son of a Psychic" and wrote some two thousand words upon it. This story was suggested by a remark made to me by a woman medium who said, "I don't want my son ridiculed as 'the son of a psychic.'" I was aided also by a note in the papers which stated that "John Kern, son of Dr. Paul Kern, the famous New York medium, has entered Yale University."

At the Cliff Dwellers, one day, Brand Whitlock lunched with me and we had an intimate talk. "He is a handsome fellow, tall and thin and dark. I found him likable, and my praise of his 'Happy Average' pleased him. He told me that he had come to Chicago from Ohio in his early years somewhat as the hero of 'The Happy Average' had done, and that he worked as a newspaper man in Chicago. Emerson Hough, Howard Shaw, Lorado Taft, and Frank Lloyd Wright sat at our table, a significant group, in which Mid-Western fiction, sculpture, and architecture were powerfully represented. True, Howard Shaw is something of a classicist, an Italian enthusiast, and Wright a student of Oriental architecture; but Hough, Whitlock, and I are all of Middle West soil.

"During the afternoon I saw Hart Conway's students in a performance of Synge's 'Playboy of the Western World,' a highly original, fresh, and poetic drama. So far as I know this is the first production of this play in America. I found it interesting at every moment, a series of humorous surprises. I was on the edge of my chair in delight of its musical diction and its keen ironic power. It has no parallel in Irish literature. I feel grateful to Conway for presenting it. His pupils acted it well and read it especially well. The younger students of the school formed a noble mob of Irish peasants. It was all in sharp contrast to the conventional Irish comedies in which the hero sings a pretty song while shoeing a horse. There were in these scenes no young men wearing fine white shirts and green velvet knee breeches, dancing with light-hearted girls to the tune of a piper. Here is the Ireland of to-day— drunken, poetic, ragged, humorous, and savage. It will not please the Irish, I fear, but it is a work of genius. I know nothing of the author, but he is a master. The compression of his lines and their vivid coloring delighted me.

"At the Little Room, George Barr McCutcheon announced that he, too, had surrendered. 'I am going to New York in the autumn.' So they all go—as I would do if I had not so many ties in the West. It is to combat this tendency on the part of the writers that I have organized the Cliff Dwellers. It will not keep our successful writers here, but it may delay their going for a year or two."

Mrs. Morris took us to see Geraldine Farrar in "Madame Butterfly." "It was a marvelous performance and to me almost intolerably pathetic. Woman gets the worst of sex experience the world over. Man the libertine, woman the victim. This opera, with its startling mixture of the modern in dress and the conventional in

operatic cadences, surprised me by its power to move
me. I wept in company with hundreds of others. Miss
Farrar was quite marvelous in the title rôle. She made
the Japanese girl the symbol of woman's immemorial
self-sacrifice."

My first dinner at the magnificent new University
Club heartened me, so big and tasteful were its reading
room and dining hall. "Chicago is to be congratulated
on this superb building. It marks an advance in the
city's life, just as the Cliff Dwellers indicates a growing
cosmopolitanism. These two enterprises are not only
contemporaneous, they are related, for Roche, one of
our members, was the architect of the building, and
Frederick Bartlett, another Cliff Dweller, its decorator."

Louise Closser Hale, who came as a guest to the Little
Room, told me that she had been a pupil in one of my
classes in Boston in 1889. "I did not recall her, but I
hope I concealed that fact from her. She has just made
a great hit in the part of Prossie in 'Candida,' a most
delightful characterization. She is a bright and humorous woman and a capital actress."

Leaving on an afternoon train for New York, I settled down to read Hobart Chatfield-Taylor's book,
"Fame's Pathway." "It is a real achievement. I feel a
genuine admiration for the imagination and skill and
scholarship manifested here. Hobart gives me a clearer
notion of Molière's early life, and the ways of strolling
player folk at that time, than I have elsewhere gained.
Though a man of wealth he is a hard student and a
careful workman. I will not say that this is an inspired
book, but I do find it rich and colorful, a book I can
unreservedly recommend."

It was glorious spring in the Susquehanna Valley next day, and for several hours I was content to look from the window and dream of the past. The old thrill (a little of it) came back to me as my gaze swept over the smooth green slopes of waving grain. At intervals I read Maurice Hewlett's "Stooping Lady," a strong book with a somber, almost unnecessarily tragic end. Robert Chambers' novel, "The Fighting Chance," irritated and saddened me. Its tone and its gawdy characters—so cheap, so sordid, and so insolently conscienceless in their living, seem un-American to me. "I hope he is false in this interpretation."

Bacheller met me at the club and took me to call on Dunlap (of Grosset & Dunlap) whom I described as "a nervous, dark, shrewd little man, whom I could not relate in any way to the enormous business in cheap books which his firm has built up. I cannot say which of the partners possesses the brains of the firm, but together they make a powerful firm. They have no rivals in the field. They distribute fifty-cent books to every corner drug store in America. They sell millions of reprint novels to people who refuse to pay the price of the regular editions. They supply a need which the regular publishers cannot—or will not—meet. They give the public what it wants."

As Irving Bacheller's guest at Riverside, I found the country in the midst of odorous, tantalizing, radiant spring. "Nothing could be fresher or sweeter than the surrounding country. The birds are singing, the apple trees are in blossom, and the grass is dazzlingly green. To my Western eyes it is as unreal as a picture, so arranged does it all appear." The worm in the bud of all this beautiful country life lies in "the servant problem." Can we find cooks willing to live the solitary life for our sakes?—That is the question! Why should they endure the country? They want the town, not groves of blossoming dogwood.

I was up early next morning to enjoy the bloom and the smell of the sea. The sun came out by nine and the land was so beautiful that the senses ached with it. Irving and I walked about for an hour or two, investigating his improvements; then wandered back into the woods where the ferns were upshooting, and the dogwood spreading in snowy sprays. The violets were thick among the leaves, and the herons were calling from the high chestnut trees. The shore was magical with the light of spring. "Such pictures! Such perfume! Such radiant commingling of sun and sheen cannot come again to me. This country with its winding lanes, its vine-covered stone walls, and pretty cottages is a poem whose loveliness makes our drab Mid-West plain a waste of plodding prose."

CHAPTER THIRTY-ONE

WYOMING AND THE CLIFF DWELLERS

I

AFTER so much time given to the study of "The Shadow World," with its dark chambers and inexplicable voices, I felt the need of a counterbalancing return to the world of sunshine, the world of the forest ranger. Out of my experiences in the Green River Mountains in 1907 I had won a story, and I felt moved to go again into these heights, approaching them this time from the East. On June 29, after a night spent in my Chicago home, I took the train for Lander, Wyoming, intending to enter the upper valley of the Wind River from that point.

"When I awoke we were nearing Chadron, a drab little cattle town on the plain. Changing to a local train I spent all day ambling across a lonely, desolate country, reaching Lander late at night. The thought of living in such a land as I have passed to-day is appalling to me now. Of what avail is civilization to the lonely wives and mothers in these shacks?"

Lander proved to be a town in the foothills, a village swarming with ranchers, land boomers, and cowboys. "They all go around without coats but cling to their vests for the very good reason that a vest provides pockets for watches, toothpicks, pencils, and pen-knives."

In walking about and talking with these citizens, I heard much of an outlaw band of Shoshone called the "sheep-eaters," who once lived high in the range, and of a "lost mine" they discovered. "This story can be verified at Fort Washakie," said one of my informants; and as the tale interested me, I took the stage for the fort one morning and reached it at noon after a fairly comfortable ride.

The Indian agency was the usual makeshift settlement of discouraged farmers and parasitic department incompetents. "Two wretched little people from the South, a man and his wife, who had been on the stage with me, reported to the agent as newly appointed 'farmers.' They were eager to tell the Shoshone just how to till this weird, arid soil on which the shrewdest white man could hardly make a living. What folly!"

The only hotel in the settlement was an unkempt little shack, and I ate my dinner in company with drunken half-breeds, weather-worn cowboys, tourists, and exiles—all waited upon by two worried, emaciated, weary women, cooking in the stifling heat of a kitchen swarming with flies. "Upon the toil of such women all our pioneer states have been built."

Hearing that a series of races between the ponies of the Shoshone and the horses of the cowboys was to be run on the flat below the town, I strolled down to the course. Scarcely had I taken my place in the crowd when a group of the riders called upon me to serve as a judge of the contest, a singular position for me to fill. I agreed, however, and served acceptably to both sides. In talking with one of my fellow umpires, an old-time scout and guide, I heard something more of the "lost mine" and the exiled band of "sheep-eaters" who had made their home for several years high in the hills. Out of these rather vague suggestions grew my story of "Pogosa," which later became a chapter in "They of the High Trails."

Two days later, disgusted with the dirt, flies, and human derelicts of Washakie, I returned to Lander, where the forest ranger met me, with plans for a trip into the high trails of his district. He was a plain-visaged, serious little man who owned a ranch some twelve miles distant. His "beat" was a stern mountain land many miles in extent, all high and wild and stormy—just the kind of country which appealed to me. With my own bed, saddle, and tarpaulin, I needed but a horse and this he agreed to furnish.

One morning I took the trail alone and rode steadily all day seeking the ranger's upper cabin. Reaching it at sunset I found in its locker all the raw materials for a meal and in half an hour had coffee and bacon on the table. I was just sitting down to eat when a stranger rode up and said, "The ranger sent me to keep you company."

"I have no need of help. I am quite happy," I replied. I had gotten back to the wilderness and was at home in it!

II

"September 16th, my birthday, I am again in New York getting the psychic articles into final shape. This is the close of my own articles, but *Everybody's* having issued a call for 'the best authenticated ghost story,' I have a mass of them to read and judge. Gutzon Borglum came in to the Players for dinner, full of the flying machines which the Wrights have been trying out. 'I am convinced that this is to be a natural and practicable future method of travel,' he said. 'The machines sail precisely like a bird. I am confident that men will soon use aëroplanes as we now use autos.' He gave me a better concept of this 'toy' of the Wrights than I had hitherto owned."

"Chicago. October 13. I went down town this afternoon and signed the contracts for the Cliff Dwellers' building, meeting Clarkson, Taft, Hutchinson, and Aldis. It is settled that we are to have a real club on the top of Orchestra Hall. My psychic book 'The Shadow World' is out and Hoynes has sent me some of the circulars concerning it.

"Charles R. Crane phoned me asking me to lunch with him at the South Shore Club. My wife could not go. The party consisted of Madame Nazimova, Mrs. Milward Adams, John T. McCutcheon, cartoonist of the *Tribune*, and myself. Nazimova, though tired and not disposed to talk, impressed me as a thoughtful and aspiring actress, not at all the shallow person she had been reported to be. Probably she is an egotist (most of us are) and I can imagine that she and her playwright are now repellent particles. The luncheon was not conversationally brilliant. McCutcheon hardly uttered a word and Crane was in one of his reticent moods. He spoke only to provide more food for his guests and to ask a question. Nazimova, plainly the Jewess, was a handsome type. No one seems to know whether she is married or not."

In dining with Mr. and Mrs. Hammond I met Professor William Lyon Phelps of Yale, finding him very agreeable and very much alive. We all listened to his lecture, which was most effective. Although speaking without manuscript, his judgments were keen and his diction graceful and direct. He and Richard Burton are without doubt two of our soundest, most effective literary lecturers. Both are humorous, scholarly, ready, and trenchant. Phelps is said to be unusually popular with the students at Yale, and Burton is equally successful in his work at the Minnesota State University.

"November 2. We went to the theater to see Zangwill's 'Melting Pot,' which is in effect a message to the American people and to the American Jews, a noble message, calculated to do good. It was not well done in all parts. In its best passages it was very high and fine."

"En route, November 17. The Mohawk Valley was a wintry region as I came through it to-day, with squalls of snow now and again. I worked at my letters and read 'Joseph Vance' by William de Morgan.

"Boston, November 18. While breakfasting at the Tavern Club, I met Arthur Pier, a young Pittsburgher, now a native of Boston, and Frank Benson, a big, fine man and a serious painter. I also visited my long-time friend, John Enneking, tall, bluff, bungling, but a faithful New England landscapist. The men at the Tavern Club did not awaken my enthusiasm. A good many of them were doctors. All appeared supremely satisfied with their conditions and Boston."

It seemed essential, in view of my work for the

MacDowell Club, that I should visit the MacDowell home in Peterboro, New Hampshire. "Taking an early train, I soon found myself in a snowy New England landscape—beautiful in color and warmed with association. The old homes, expressive of dignity and repose, were poems. The pines, exquisite, snow-covered, were like designs in a Japanese painting.

"November 19. It is midday. I am writing in Edward MacDowell's music room. I have built a fire on his hearth and if his spirit is able to return he is with me now. All about me are his books which speak of his wide interests—volumes on painting, philosophy, the novel, and poetry. I see Sidney Lanier's essays, Cellini's Life, and a volume of Machiavelli. Alternating with books on music, I find Thackeray's novels, the Blue Fairy Book, a guide to the Alps, a treatise on Darkest Africa, and stories by Stevenson and Mark Twain.

"This is the most unpretentious of homes with all the characteristics of a summer camping place. Outside lies a beautiful winter landscape with snow falling gently, while here, within, the fire bravely crackles. In spite of every evidence of MacDowell, the homestead does not seem like him. It is more in the nature of a fantastic summer camp. It does not express him to me."

New York was roaring along its muddy avenues under a brilliant sun as I called on Mrs. MacDowell. Though still on crutches, she was bearing up bravely. "I live only for the club and Edward's memory," she said, and her courage was a reproof to me. What had I to complain of?

At luncheon with Mrs. Grossman, Edwin Booth's

daughter, I learned that Frederick MacMonnies had been asked by the Players to do the statue of Booth which is to stand in the park opposite the club. Mac-Monnies, who was keen for the job, wished to see all of the Booth costumes and photographs, and Grossman invited me to go with him. We spent nearly two hours studying portraits and swords and jewels—all of high poetic interest to me, whatever they may have meant to MacMonnies. Later we all met at the club to discuss the site for the statue. MacMonnies insisted that it should be at the center of Gramercy Park and to this we all agreed. "It is the logical place for it. Also, I must choose the phase of Booth's life which most appeals to me," he added.

I was brought into this discussion not because of any official connection with the committee, but because Mrs. Grossman knew that I revered the memory of her father and was acutely concerned in having the memorial erected near the club which he had founded. As a member of the Players I had a voice, but not an authoritative voice, in the conferences. All my boyish admiration for the great tragedian was awakened by the objects which he had touched and the garments he had worn. "It seems but yesterday since I heard his voice."

"November 28. Leaving on the eight-thirty train for home, I finished reading 'Joseph Vance,' a long, loosely written but very human book, frankly old-fashioned in tone and quality.

"Chicago, November 29. On meeting my fellow Cliff Dwellers at our new rooms I began to plan the disposition of the furniture, much of which I had bought. The committee depends upon me to arrange the furnishings as well as to provide the program for the opening ceremony. Fortunately my afternoons are free and I rather enjoy such detail work. It rests me from my desk. If this club succeeds it will bring about a new era of artistic fellowship in this city. I am trying to direct our fire-lighting ceremony into unconventional and characteristic channels, using the art of the ancient American in one way or another as a basis for the program. Ralph Seymour is making some drawings of the Hopi as well as of the pictographs or 'glyphs' of the Aztecs; and Tom Stevens is helping on a pageant of primitives. The songs, poems, and pictures are all to have the color of aboriginal art, all in harmony with our name, the Cliff Dwellers."

For an out-of-town member I suggested Charles D. Stewart, whose "Partners in Providence" had helped shorten a tedious journey. "There is something so full and rich in the descriptive passages of this book that I marvel at the author's memory. I know nothing of him except that he is a resident of Milwaukee."

The board of the Players met and voted an official greeting to be read at the opening of the Cliff Dwellers; and I wrote asking the Tavern Club of Boston and the Bohemian Club of San Francisco to send similar greetings, and to appoint a delegate to represent them at our housewarming. "I want to have the Cliff Dwellers take its place among this brotherhood of clubs."

One night in New York I dined with Lawrence Gilman. "After dinner he played several of MacDowell's pieces for me. He is a fine young fellow. I have a very real affection for him. He is not only a very talented and thoughtful critic, he is a talented musician. He plays, and plays well. His small home is plainly that of the scholar and the poet. It seems a pity that one so fine and so true should be reading proof on a journal of not very high aims, but he has a wife and some babies and must work like a galley slave every day to provide for them. He has appealed very strongly to me from the first, not entirely because MacDowell loved and trusted him, but because he is so handsome, so serious, and so high-minded. His writing possesses a notable charm. His words have a glow of color, a music quite unusual in a critic, and yet, in spite of all his fine qualities, he does not appear to gain ground as rapidly as he ought to do. I wonder why. Perhaps being poor, he must write to earn his monthly rent."

A lecture date carried me to Muskogee, Oklahoma, on December 28. "This day was like exquisite late March or early April. Torrens and I rode over to Agency Hill and spent a couple of hours on its top. At night we all dined at his home. Emerson Hough was there and my brother Frank. The town is as much a boom town as ever and we all talked tirelessly of its future. I do skitter about over the landscape, but it is due either to my lectures or my publishing business or to father's claims upon me. My lecture here was a failure and I put down a vow never to do this again. I am getting too old to take on these poorly paid dates."

On the train I read Gilbert Parker's "Weavers" which helped to pass several weary hours. "Some parts of this book are fine and true but it is not all of a depth, however, and is rather conventional in its framework. He knows his official ground, that is evident."

III

January 6 was the date fixed for the housewarming
of our new Chicago club and I was busy all day and
most of the night putting the program through. "The
whole affair came off smoothly, some said 'brilliantly,'
and the club may consider itself launched on a long and
prosperous voyage. Otis Skinner, representing the Players Club, lighted the fire in the north chimney whilst
I read greetings from other organizations. The Tavern
Club sent a barrel of Atlantic driftwood and the Bohemian Club a great beam from the wreck of a Spanish
galleon. In my address in verse introducing the various
events of the evening I used these lines:

Far in the mountain west a spring once rose
    Whose sparkling waters held such charm,
That those who came to drink, though foes,
    Feared neither hand of man nor any spirit harm.
For Manitou, the mighty one, had laid
    Upon this desert fount, a potent spell—
Whoso shall drink in peace and unafraid,
    Shall of his deepest wounds at once be well.

And so it was—thus runs the ancient story—
    The dark Comanche and the vengeful Ute
Crept to these waters, maimed and gory,
    And humbly drank and waited, awed and mute,
Till they were healed: then, strange to see,
    These blood-stained chieftains of the desert sands
Reclining in peace, gaunt knee to knee,
    Extolled the sacred well with open grateful hands!

Warriors are we, but in another fashion,
    Rivals for wealth and happiness and fame,

Down in the city's deeps we meet in savage passion
  And play as best we may the selfish, sordid game.
But here, at peace, before these glowing embers,
  Meeting this ample bowl's hospitable design,
Man greets his fellow man, and only now remembers
  Art's magic bond of light, and beauty's bloodless shrine.

It was, at its best, but a small and rather tepid celebration. Few saw in it anything but the opening of another club, but to me it was—at the moment—a significant design in the unraveling web of Mid-West history.

CHAPTER THIRTY-TWO

A DUCAL RANCH

I

My readers will recall, I trust, that in an earlier chapter I chronicled a meeting with one of the "dukes" who were reported to be living in palaces on ranches near Sheridan, Wyoming, and that one of the "lords" (lord and duke being interchangeable in cowboy phrase) had kindly said, "Whenever you are in Sheridan, call me up and I'll come in and bring you out to my ranch." I carried this in mind, but it was not till August, 1909, that I found myself at the Sheridan Inn which is a point of departure for the Big Horn Mountains.

This trip is of especial value in my record, for it started me on my novel, "Cavanagh, Forest Ranger," and before I take my readers to visit "that bunch of lords," I would like to go over some of the ground which I covered in preparation for the writing of this story.

The train was late and I did not reach the inn till two o'clock in the morning. I caught the one o'clock stage for Buffalo that afternoon and enjoyed my second motor ride in the plains country, and a most suggestive experience it was, for on the way we passed an ancient, dusty, clattering coach, which I at once set down as

"The symbol of the old-time West which the automobile West is crowding into the weedy ditches of the past. The driver, as typical as his vehicle, turned upon us a look of malevolence and spat as if ejecting his rancor. At several points in the road we overhauled groups of cowboys whose ponies reared and shied in fear of the newfangled monster roaring by. The riders whooped with joy and raced us for a time, laughingly calling opprobrious epithets—feeling that they, too, were being dispossessed."

The town of Buffalo, a ratty little village built beside a rushing stream, was just beginning to feel the stir of new life. As the hotel was being remodeled, I was forced to take lodging in a shack beside the main restaurant. Leaving my camp bed and duffel bag in my room, I set out to find the ranger whom the supervisor had ordered down to meet me.

The postmaster told me that Mrs. Hettman was in town and I found her in a miserable cabin on the outskirts of the village, sitting in the midst of a cloud of flies calmly eating her supper—an astonishing picture. The building was hardly more than a hunter's lodge, and being without screens the flies were swarming round the woman's head like bees. She was of the Southern mountaineer type, thin, dark, and apparently in wretched health. Her speech, however, was vigorous, not to say virile, and while she announced her willingness to drive me up to the forest station, she was plainly not pleased at the prospect of spending the night in this house, and I could not blame her.

She met me at the corner of the street next morning driving a pair of broncos hitched to a light wagon and

I, throwing my outfit into the box behind, took a seat beside her. With the skill of a man she set her team to the mountain trail.

She had as outrider a weather-worn fellow by the name of Thomas, who confided to me later that he had been a cattle rustler "in the old days." He had the appearance of a mounted hobo, but may have been a desperate character—once. For five hours we plodded up the trail toward the High Country. Part of the time I rode in my own saddle on Thomas' horse and part of the time I sat beside the woman, who needed but little questioning to tell me all about the cattle war in which she had taken part. My record reads: "We reached the ranger's station at one. The ranger, Albert Hettman, is a blunt, powerful man of German birth. He has been a soldier in the German army but is loyal to America and the Forest Service. I respect him, but he is sullen and forbidding at times." He improved on acquaintance.

"After several rather somber explorations with Hettman I decided to move on. Mrs. Hettman took me back to Buffalo, and on the way talked freely of her girlhood, making some amazing yet unconscious revelations of her point of view. She said, 'Buffalo is not a tough town; I don't believe more than nine or ten men have ever been killed there.' She described how certain of her friends tied handkerchiefs about their left arms so that the rustlers would know them to be friends. It was all valuable testimony for a novelist." (To any one interested I will say that this region is the scene of several chapters of my novel, "Cavanagh.")

II

Another rushing ride in the auto stage brought me to the Sheridan Inn at eleven, and in the afternoon I went to the Fair Ground to see some races. This turned out to be a very profitable outing, for I not only met some of the officers of the post, but Malcolm Moncrieff, whose cowboy polo player had won such distinction at Colorado Springs. Moncrieff again invited me to come out to his ranch and this I promised to do, for I was curious to see this "nest of lords" of which I had heard so much. The cattlemen and foresters all spoke of it as a cluster of palaces in which fugitive dukes and earls lived in splendor; even the people of Sheridan spoke of them with awe.

On the following day, as I was about to visit the commander of the barracks, the clerk announced a phone call for me. Upon making contact a pleasant voice said, "This is Oliver Wallop, a brother-in-law to Malcolm Moncrieff. I am coming to town in the hope of taking you back with me."

"I shall be delighted," I said.

"Splendid! Expect me at three," he replied.

At three o'clock I had my bag ready and was standing in the lobby when a small, plainly-dressed man walked up to me. "Is this Mr. Garland?"

"It is, and you are——"

"Oliver Wallop. Where is your bag?"

I stooped to take it up, but he forestalled me. Seizing it with surprising vigor, he led the way out and down the walk.

Naturally I looked for his car, but no vehicle was in

sight except a low, rusty mountain wagon to which a fat and sleepy pair of bay horses were attached. At the gate I glanced up and down the road, still looking for the ducal automobile, but Wallop flung my valise into the back of the wagon and said, "Climb in, this is my team."

Amazed (and amused) I climbed over the wheel, and Wallop, taking up the reins, clicked at the drowsy old nags. They lifted their heads in a feeble demonstration of willingness, but did not stir from their tracks.

Wallop turned a comic glance at me. "I declare! I forgot to untie their hitching strap!"

This was a small thing, but highly instructive to me. A "lord" as forgetful as that—one who handled his visitor's grip and drove a fat and lazy pair of brood mares hitched to a "democrat wagon," could not be living in dazzling splendor. I began to doubt the cowboy reports of these representatives of the English nobility.

As we jogged along the twelve or fourteen miles of wandering road leading toward his ranch, he talked of Wyoming, cattle-raising, forestry, and a dozen other subjects. I warmed to him quickly. He was a gentleman and a reader of books—that was evident. He told of establishing a game sanctuary in the hills above his pasture, and this brought out the fact that he had served in the state legislature. Altogether he delighted as well as puzzled me.

At last he said, "There is my house."

It was not a palace, but it was a fairly large structure, not unlike a spacious suburban home. Its lower story was of logs, but it was not in the least like a

Western farmstead. It faced a magnificent mountain wall several thousand feet above the level meadows on which herds of cattle were feeding.

As we neared the garden, he turned to me with a comic light in his eyes and said, "Do you see that gardener watering the lawn? Watch him turn into a hostler."

As we drove up to the door this man laid down his hose and took charge of the team. Wallop said, "Peters, I want two saddles to-morrow morning. Mr. Garland and I will be riding into the hills."

"Very good, sir!" said Peters, and I heard in his voice the spirit of the respectful English servant. He was not a citizen of Wyoming.

No one met us in the hall and Wallop showed me up to my room, explaining that his wife was in the East. "I am without our regular staff," he added, "but I'll see that you are made comfortable."

It was like a tastefully decorated, suburban home, filled with books and pictures. I had the feeling of being suddenly transplanted to Lake Forest, and when I joined my host in his handsome library I found in it signs of interest in all that was going on in the literary and artistic world.

We sat talking for half an hour, and being very hungry I began to hope that he dined early. Seven o'clock came and passed, then half past seven, but as he was in the midst of delightful reminiscences of early days on the range, I concealed my restlessness. "I came here twenty-five years ago directly from England," he said, "and I've been here ever since."

At a quarter past eight the butler brought in two

cocktails and Wallop said, "At last! Now we shall dine."

The butler withdrew and a moment later opened the doors leading into the handsome dining room and it seemed to me that he resembled the gardener who had turned into the hostler. Wallop said, with a quizzical glance, "Don't mind if the courses of our dinner are a bit erratic. Our butler and waiter is also our cook. In fact, he is also my valet, hostler, and plumber."

"He must be invaluable."

"He is invaluable and incorrigible. Every six months I discharge him for insubordination or drunkenness or some infraction of good service, but he ignores my orders to leave. After a decent interval I find him brushing my boots or watering the roses."

Peters came back and calmly served the soup. We ate our soup and waited a long time, a very long time, for the meat and vegetables. Wallop explained, "If you could peer out into the kitchen you would find Peters in his shirt sleeves busy at the range. He will resume his waiter's jacket and bring in the next course presently."

It was an incredible situation, but Wallop carried it through with such humor, defining himself as the weak and long-suffering master of the house, bullied by a servant who would not be discharged, that I could hardly conceal my mirth as Peters deftly served the vegetables. It was all like a delightfully improbable English comedy.

After we returned to the library, Peters appeared with some most delectable coffee and then withdrew with an air of finality. Wallop then said, "He will now assume the rôle of scullion and wash up the dinner dishes."

Breakfast was cooked and served by Peters next morning, and then as hostler he brought the two saddle horses to the door, and Wallop and I rode away up into the hills that were as beautiful, with their grassy slopes and clumps of trees, as a vast park designed by a master architect, and as we ambled along the trails of this game sanctuary he talked—I made him talk—of his experiences in Wyoming and his changing psychology.

"Oh, yes," he said in answer to my question. "I go back now and again, but I soon grow homesick for Sunset Cañon. I am not only an American—I am a Wyoming citizen."

On our return to the house he showed me a photograph of his family home in England, a great mansion with a cluster of chimneys rising from a grove of oaks, and as I studied it I wondered how he could leave it for Wyoming. That he was the younger son of a fine old family was evident.

III

On the third day, as the time came to leave, I grew uneasy. I wished to catch the express going north—there was only one—and remembering the plodding feet of the old mares, I watched the clock. "Don't be uneasy," said Wallop, "I'll see that you get your train."

We had eaten our luncheon and were having a delightful chat on his porch and I fully expected Peters to bring the team to the door. Another hour passed and then I rose. "I hate to seem importunate, but I must try for the train. If you could send me down——"

"I'll take you down myself," he said, and put aside his pipe. "Will you wait here or go with me to the stables?"

Still more uneasy, and hoping to gain time, I replied, "I'll go with you."

Wondering why he had not ordered the team brought round, I walked out to the barn expecting to find the carriage waiting there. Nothing of the kind! The stable door was shut, the wagon in the shed, and neither man nor horse in sight. It was now within two hours of train time and the horses on the range!

Wallop explained "the men are all haying," and taking a bridle on his arm, said, "Will you go with me to rustle the nags—or will you wait here?"

Concealing my dismay, I said, "I'll wait here." Slowly he walked away toward the hills.

Three-quarters of an hour later he came jogging back, riding one horse and leading the other, unhurried and unworried. With eager hands I helped harness the horses and hitch them to the wagon, although he assured me that the three o'clock train was always several hours late.

Nothing that he said on our long ride in gave me the slightest hint of his being the son of a duke. It is true he had shown me a picture of his family home—but I parted from him at the station in the belief that he was only another "younger son" who had sought his fortune in the West.

(I visited his ranch twice some years later, the last time just before the outbreak of the World War, and even then I knew nothing very definite about his family history. Then in the midst of the War came the announcement that his brother, the Duke of Portsmouth, and his sons were dead and that Wallop was called upon to return and assume the title. The cowboys had been right, after all. He was in very truth a duke.

Immediately upon receiving this information I wrote him a letter in which I said "I am in doubt whether to congratulate or commiserate you. In assuming your place in the peerage you are taking on heavy responsibility at a most trying time."

In his reply he indicated that he realized clearly the quiet joys which he was surrendering when leaving his beautiful sun-set ranch.)

CHAPTER THIRTY-THREE

ALFRED EAST AND ENGLISH ART

I

"NEW YORK, January 22, 1910. I have just been to see Moody's new play, 'The Faith Healer,' which Henry Miller has recently put on. Moody is one of the few dramatists in America who write with a literary concept in mind. He is not slamming together the material for a 'show'! His acts are written, not carpentered. I was deeply moved by this piece, although Henry Miller's personality did not fit the title part. He is too old, too heavy, and not sufficiently spiritual. If the play fails, as I fear it may, it will be due, in my judgment, to the fact that Miller is unsuited to the part." (The play failed and is seldom mentioned now.)

At a supper in the home of the Lewisohn sisters, I met Ben Greet, a sad-voiced, attractive man. "I had never talked with him before and was puzzled by the wistful cadences of his voice. He appeared melancholy, almost dispirited. I wonder why."

My evening among the races of the East Side led me to a discussion of the task which confronts the rulers of New York in assimilating these immigrants—so divergent from the old-time American. "They are eager folk, these Jews, Poles, and Italians, avid for success, and in single-minded pursuit of the luxuries of life. Many

439

of them come from the dirt floors of peasant homes in Europe and it is not strange that some of their children drift into piracy in their haste to get rich. As I study them I realize that my books have no appeal to them. They are of another world."

"Washington, January 14. I met Irving Bacheller here to-day, and (at the request of his manager) presented him to his audience in one of the theaters. He is in high favor at this time, and so much better known than I, that my position as chairman was absurd. However, in my introduction I told some amusing incidents illustrating his absent-mindedness, saying (I recall), 'he has planted rubbers, umbrellas, and overcoats all the way across the continent. He forgets his valise but he never forgets to be kindly and generous and American.' "

Still busied with a series of novelettes, in which "Socrates Potter," a country lawyer, wisely humorous, is chief character, he devised an amusing opening for his lecture. As he rose to speak on this occasion, he impersonated a presiding officer, humorously introducing himself as "my friend, Soc Potter." He then took a seat and waited for himself as Socrates Potter to rise and respond. It was all very deftly done and amused the audience greatly, once the little play had clarified itself before them.

In calling on Franklin Lane, Secretary of the Interior, I discovered that he, too, had once been a "Henry George man," and that we had met as youngsters at the Reform Club in New York. There was something essentially literary about Lane, and we fell at once to discussing the sad lack of authors in Washington. He said: "This is a most benighted place so far as literature goes—a hollow place. I dine out every night, always with uninteresting women seated on both sides of me, ladies with nothing to say, and from whom there is no escape."

"It *is* strange," I agreed. "This is an ideal place for writers—quiet, clean, reposeful."

That night I dined with Winston Churchill, one of the few American writers living in the capital. I found him like his books, earnest, sincere, and noble of purpose, but lacking in grace of phrase. "He is never subtle, or precious in his use of words. He said, 'I have been too much the man of action to give careful attention to words.' He admitted also that he had no ear for music in phrase or nicety of epithet. Like Rex Beach and others of the journalistic school, he seeks the popular effect rather than distinction of method. I liked him and enjoyed his generous hospitality."

II

"Ray Stannard Baker and I went this afternoon to see 'Children of Earth,' a play by Alice Brown. It is in many ways a very original and powerful play—entirely New England, and well played."

Whenever and wherever Augustus Thomas and I met, we never failed to talk psychics, for he had been, at one time, advance man for a celebrated mind reader named Bishop who gave marvelous public performances, and this had led to his interest in telepathy. He had one of the quickest minds and one of the most eloquent tongues I knew. With him I had no need to speak my whole mind—he divined it. Although his way of life differed widely from mine, we met on the friendliest terms and I enjoyed his witty and fluent comment. It was his experience with the mind reader which led to his writing "The Witching Hour," one of his best plays—and his most successful, strange to say.

"Gus," as every one called him, was always applauded as an after-dinner orator. His beautiful voice, his handsome, smiling face gave his wise and witty words a special charm. He was equally popular as a political orator, I am sorry to add, for he made votes against my man. He was one of the originators of the Lambs' Club—which was the antithesis in many ways of the Players—and was its "shepherd." I lunched with him there once or twice, but its constant stream of "petitioners at the bar," its smoke, noise, and laughter, were disturbing to me. Without a particle of religious sentiment in the matter, I considered drinking at a bar a poor way to amuse oneself.

Another of our wits at the Players was Oliver Herford, whose sayings were more often quoted than that of any other member. His sister Beatrice was one of the best monologists on the platform at this time, and one afternoon Gertrude Hogan, a Wisconsin neighbor of mine, took me to hear her. I found her very clever and daintily amusing. "Her comic spirit and keen perception enable her to do what few people have the art to do. She makes the commonplace and familiar things delightful. She made me think of Howells' remark concerning the criticism of a novel, a review in which the writer had said, 'The book is commonplace.' To this Howells replied: 'Commonplace! that is precisely what most writers can't get into their confounded books!'

Miss Herford puts a halo of humor round the common-place New England people."

III

Soon after my return to Chicago Henry Fuller came in to see me. He looked the forlorn, tired little man he was as he sat against my firelight. "Why do you play the janitor and rent collector?" I demanded.

"There is nobody else to do it," he replied somberly.

Following this sad visitation I wrote this paragraph: "Fuller's censorious habit of mind begins to trouble me. One gets tired of a visitor who never has anything but words of complaint or censure. He has lived so long in restaurants that his table manners annoy me. He automatically polishes his coffee cup and wipes all the forks and knives on his napkin or on a corner of the tablecloth. He turns each piece of toast (looking for a possible fly) and peers into the milk or cream jug for a cockroach, all of which is funny for a time but comes to be an irritation at last—and yet he is the ablest, most distinctive, most intellectual of all our Western writers. He can be—and generally is—the most satisfactory of all my literary companions."

One of the most significant of our visitors at the Cliff Dwellers during the week was Alfred East, the president of the English Art Society, who gave a talk to the College Woman's Club, and afterward came to the Little Room for tea. He had already promised to speak for us, but asked me to name a subject. "I am full of indignation at the degenerate art of modern France and I am eager to bring about a better understanding of English art by Americans."

"That is precisely what I should like you to say to the artists here," I replied. "The plain truth is our artists are nearly all Paris-instructed and know nothing of modern English art. They say, 'There *is* no modern English art! We accept literary judgments from London, but our notions of painting and sculpture derive from Paris.' If you can broaden our knowledge of English art, you will prove a valiant missionary."

He gave a good, serious talk at the club along these lines, but the presence of a Frenchman, M. Erlart, kept the discussion politely counterpoised. It did not make quite the stir that I had anticipated. "Nevertheless, I felt more strongly than ever the value of our meeting place. Without it, Chicago would be an intolerable gray waste to me. I find a large part of my thinking is devoted to its advancement."

Walter Damrosch and Adolph Mucha, the Hungarian painter, were guests a few days later, and a lively discussion or symposium took place at the round table. The subject was the music drama. I started it by asking, "Is not opera a monstrous hybrid?" Several of the musicians agreed that it was, and argued that the symphony is a greater and more lasting musical form.

"The opera *is* absurd," Damrosch declared. "Especially when it deals with modern life." This surprised me. That I should complain of its unreality and its morbid sex themes was natural, but I hardly expected a celebrated composer to agree with me. He went on to make fun of the operas where people in modern dress proclaimed their love by howling it aloud in hotel lobbies. "Wagner's legendary themes were less illogical," he added. "One can imagine Brünnhilde singing on her mountain top."

Alfred East came to Clarkson's studio dinner and I recorded that he was "as easy as an old shoe, quite at home and happy. 'The art atmosphere here is not very different from the atmosphere of London,' he explained, 'I feel at home with those who write and sculpture and paint.' He was an admirable emissary, and did much to bring about a desire to know more of what was going on in English studios. 'Your artists know nothing, or next to nothing, of what we are doing. Their commerce is all with France.' "

Arthur Aldis and George Hamlin brought Kreisler, the violinist, to the club. "He is a big, dark, manly chap whom we all liked. He sat beside me and during the meal I asked permission to examine his left hand. On each of his fingers I found a highly developed cushion of cuticle with a deep groove made by the strings. They evidenced the years of labor which had gone to make him the master that he is. He impressed me as a strong, serene character of wide intellectual interests. He made a very favorable impression on us all."

CHAPTER THIRTY-FOUR

FOREST RANGERS AND ROOSEVELT

I

As ROOSEVELT was announced to speak at a conservation meeting in St. Paul and also at a luncheon to which I had been invited, I left my summer home on September 4, 1910, and spent the night at the Severance "farm," which had become almost baronial in its dignified spaciousness.

From St. Paul I had planned another vacation tour of Montana, but at the last moment I changed my mind and bought my ticket for Colorado. My desire to travel was alarmingly weak. For nearly twenty years I had been going to the Rocky Mountain wildernesses, but now, for some reason, I found myself reluctant. "My two little daughters had much to do with this, but there was something else at work. I asked myself, 'What are you going for? Not to escape the heat, for it is delightful in Wisconsin during September? Why go at all?'"

This may be taken (if any one cares to give thought to it) as the moment when I began to think of work more important than my fiction, although all of my stories had been based upon the actual life of the West. I was nearly fifty years of age and the writing of love stories seemed silly, as well as futile.

446

"On my way to Denver I read Patterson's 'Little Brother of the Rich,' a very good book, and Locke's 'The Beloved Vagabond,' a much better one in some ways. Youth and indignation are in Patterson's book, but Locke's has mellowness and literary charm. I also reread Howells' 'My Mark Twain,' the first half of which I found rarely beautiful, perfect in phrase and tender in feeling."

Reaching Denver on the night of the 9th I left next morning for the Arapahoe Forest, where I was to be the guest of Supervisor Cook, a soundly cultivated young fellow, and that night, as we sat round his fire, I found myself once more concerned with the problems and plans of the Forest Service and something fine came to me from them. For the time being I was the forester.

After lunch the following day I took the train and rode on down to Yampa, a strange, empty land not much changed since my visit in 1901.

At Yampa I hired a rig and rode to the forester's station, about six miles up the Yampa Cañon. Stevenson, the ranger, a tall fellow with a small head and candid eyes, made me at home in his neat new cabin, and his wife, a handsome and quick-spoken young woman, cooked an amazingly good dinner. At my request he packed an outfit on a horse and we rode for five hours up the trail. "We went into camp beside a small waterfall under a big fir. I cooked supper while absorbing the remote and beautiful scene. To the south a big peak looms and a stream is roaring from its covert. It is a quick, deep plunge into a familiar wilderness. For part of the way up here we rode through a forest of aspen with leaves like golden coins. I have never seen anything more beautiful."

For several days I worked with Stevenson, cutting out trails and rolling stones from rough places, going back to camp to cook our meals. The ranger, a big, resourceful man, was glad to have me do the cooking and I was glad to escape the care of the horses.

On September 16, Little Trapper's Lake: "This is my fiftieth birthday, and I have spent it all alone in camp, for Stevenson is away hunting our runaway horses. Having made many notes of the fishes, muskrats, squirrels, birds, gophers, and grouse, I am now rejoicing in the marvelous beauty of the lights across the lake."

"At nightfall rain began to fall, and putting everything under cover, I heaped the fire with wood and retired to the tent. The rain turned to snow, and the night became intensely dark. I am now a bit uneasy about Stevenson. How can he find his way in such blackness? Late at night the moon came out and by its aid he came into camp. While he dried out before the fire, I rose and got his supper.

"All this is typical of the mountains and has put me back into the mood of my thousand days of trailing. I have recovered something of my youthful confidence and skill. It has been a day of transforming memories. I am again the trailer, at home in the wood. 'This out of all will remain, I have touched the most primitive wildness again.' "

For two weeks I loitered amid these exquisite scenes, camping beside these glorious lakes, renewing my memories of saddle and tent and forest. I camped with woodsmen and engineers, putting aside all that the city meant,

I gave my close attention to the lay of the land, listening intently to those who spoke the language of the wilderness. Slowly a story formed in my mind, a short novel which my little Isabel named "The Forester's Daughter," and if my readers are inclined to read this book they will find in it much of the forest and something of the romantic life of that forest ranger.

On my return to Chicago I passed, without knowing it, close to William Vaughn Moody's deathbed in Colorado Springs. He had been taken there in hope of a cure. The news of his passing came to me on the day I reached my home and I at once suggested a joint memorial ceremony in which the University, the Little Room, and the Cliff Dwellers should pay tribute to him. I felt that American literature had suffered a great loss in his premature death, and that Chicago should express that sense of loss. "I called Manly, of the university, and asked him to join with us. He hesitated. 'Moody has withdrawn from most of his old friends,' he explained, 'and I fear you cannot count on Mrs. Moody's coöperation. Her attitude toward all of us who were Moody's associates has changed.'"

This took the edge from my zeal. I let the project drop.

"October 19. Clarkson is painting my portrait for the Cliff Dwellers, but I feel more and more unworthy of being painted. If I had realized how old and soggy I am I would not have begun these sittings. 'This is the way we all do,' I said to Fuller, 'wait till we are physically in decay—and then get ourselves painted and future generations judge us by our infirmities. Here I am, gray and wrinkled and lifeless, with little to live for except my children—blessed little women—and Clarkson is perpetuating my wrinkles and my gray hair. I should have been painted ten years ago, when I was still vigorous, brown-haired, and confident.'"

II

One afternoon Allen Pond telephoned that Jane Addams wanted me to dine with her at Hull-House to meet W. J. Locke, the English novelist; and after a visit to the Little Room, I ventured over to Halstead Street where I found a group of my friends. Locke turned out to be a tall, blond man of forty or more with a high, wrinkled, sensitive brow—a kind of "Septimus Felton" in his own way, a gentle and ugly man. We had a pleasant chat, although the room was noisy and conversation difficult.

Shortly after dinner, he said, "Miss Addams, I'm very sorry, but I have an appointment and must be leaving," and as I was about to speak a parting word he said, "Come with me, I need a guide." I consented, and no sooner were we safely out of the door than he confessed, "My appointment is at a music hall. I want to see an act which has been commended to me as something worth while."

"What would Jane Addams say if she knew this?"

"She will never know—I hope; but the dinner was a bit boring and noisy, now wasn't it?" I was forced to admit that it was not joyous.

We saw the sketch, which might have been invaluable to Locke, but left no impression on me. To this day I am mystified by his interest.

I think we must have discussed spiritualism, for that

night I dreamed that I had suddenly become a psychic able to emit an astral substance which took on the semblance of human forms. For the time, I was a celebrity and proudly gave remarkable exhibitions of my powers. I was a kind of wireless receiver, catching and restating fugitive words and phrases. "This is the second time in all my life that I have dreamed on this subject."

"October 29th was the day of our special luncheon to Campanini, the great conductor, and as president of the club, I sat beside our guest. We had no speeches, but Campanini talked interestingly to the men at my table. In his broken English and with dramatic gestures, he said, 'In Italy—lakes, mountains, many flowers, loafly climate—no mohney! In Milano, Napoli, Rome—music, art, grand building, mooch history—no mohney! —I stay here!'

"We all applauded his decision. His reasoning is sound."

III

"Des Moines, November 3. At six-thirty I was driven to the Country Club where I was the guest of honor of the city's literary folk, and a handsome dinner it was. Later they all gathered about the great fire in the sitting room while I read to them and talked of early days on the prairie, a program which they all seemed to enjoy. They made me feel like a Western landmark. Late at night I went to my bed, weary with a day of greeting and conversation, but feeling that I had been making literary history—in my small way."

At six o'clock the following day Roosevelt arrived and the city seethed with excitement. My own "show" shrank to a meager luncheon. He had come to address a convention of public-school teachers, and to meet the commercial club at dinner. As one of the guests I caught his eye. He called me to him. "What are you doing here?" he asked. I told him and added, "I have waited over a day to hear your address to the teachers."

"When are you going back to Chicago?"

"On the night train."

"So am I. There is an extra berth in my private car. Why not ride with me?"

With no attempt at concealing my pleasure, I accepted his offhand invitation.

His audience at the Coliseum that night was singularly impressive. I had never seen anything like it— two thousand women, all blonde, all Anglo-Saxon, and all tense with interest and admiration, awaited him. As I studied these auditors, I considered as never before the importance of the fact that American education is very largely in the hands of spinsters and that their pay is pitifully inadequate.

At the close of Roosevelt's speech, I hurried to my hotel and from thence to his car, where I found him, almost alone, deep sunk in one of the chairs of the small reception room. He admitted his weariness, but made instant inquiries concerning my wife and daughters and my literary plans. He was quietly cordial, and spoke of our long friendship and common interest in literary affairs. I liked him in this subdued, entirely human, mood. He seemed glad to chat in this intimate way, with no hint of politics or even economics. He spoke of our meeting in St. Paul and admitted that he had not recognized me. "The loss of your beard was a complete disguise." He spoke of the 1901 pageant in Colorado Springs and that led to an expression of our mutual love for the White River plateau.

It was one of the most satisfactory talks I had ever had with him and I was sorry when he said, "It is time to turn in," although I knew he was in need of rest.

I rose early the next morning and was out on the observation platform when he appeared. In the course of our conversation he said, "I'm tired of public meetings. I am going back to Sagamore Hill, and into retirement for a time. I want to rest. I don't want to see a soul."

I had never seen him in this mood before, but I understood it. He was sick of swarming, excited crowds, of blaring bands and fulsome orators. The campaign had sapped his vitality, but as I took his arm I found its power undiminished. It was solid as an oaken beam.

Speaking of some lines of his in a recent magazine article on Africa, a paragraph describing the song of victory by his black lion hunters, I said, "That paragraph is magnificent. It is in effect a prose poem."

His eyes lightened, his face softened. "I value your judgment," he said, very simply and gravely. "I am not a poet, but that song and that scene would have inspired a poet."

Inevitably he referred to President Taft and his policies, but he spoke in sadness rather than in anger. He was deeply hurt by the attitude of a man for whom he had done so much. He did not go into detail, but I could see that he considered Taft a disloyal friend.

CHAPTER THIRTY-FIVE

AMERICAN ARCHITECTS AND FRANCIS HACKETT

I

DURING all the years of my friendship with John Burroughs I had never obtained so much as a glimpse of his wife. He seldom referred to her and, when he did, it was with a tone of veiled antagonism as though his wishes and hers were habitually in opposition. He mentioned his son Julian occasionally but only casually. He was plainly not a doting husband or father. One of those who had met Mrs. Burroughs said, "She is the kind of woman who keeps her parlor darkened and follows her husband around with a cloth to wipe up his tracks on her clean kitchen floor. And I suspect John leaves plenty of tracks."

All these allusions to an unhappy marriage came to my mind when I learned that they were both in Chicago on their way to California. With some misgivings, I went at once to call on them and to urge that they come to dine with us. I didn't see her, but John agreed at once to come. He didn't explain how it happened that they were taking this excursion, but I suspected it to be a Christmas gift from some considerate friend.

Their North Side host, Mr. Bush, sent them down to our house in a handsome car, and as they came in, we thought them both delightfully New England. He was in a new suit of gray, and she had put on her very best black silk gown. We found her a prim and plain type but not at all an "impossible person." Uplifted by the excitement of a trip to California, and enjoying her freedom from household responsibility, she was plainly on her best behavior. She made a pleasing guest. They both remain in the memory of my daughters as ideal grandparents. Having weathered the storms of nearly sixty years of married life, they were now sailing an untroubled sea.

From luncheon with these fine Catskill characters we passed to a midnight supper which Mrs. Ira Nelson Morris was giving for the Chicago opera singers. All the principals of the company were there: Caroline White, Caruso, Sammarco, Bassi, Zappelli, Warnery, Guardobassi—the women all vividly painted, the men short and reeking with dramatic fervor. After supper, Caruso, at the urging of his associates, did a clever impersonation. After pulling a lock of hair down over his brow, he folded his arms and assumed a lofty look —the look of Napoleon—and in truth his resemblance to the great Corsican was amazing. Evidently this was one of his regular "stunts" and delighted his fellow singers as much as it did us. We all applauded him.

"At the club to day I again met Edward Sheldon, an extraordinarily handsome boy who has already won a high position in the dramatic world. He is a gifted youth. If he will work hard and not permit himself to be hurried or cheapened, he will go far. It is not strange that he should feel his success and that he should think his work a great deal better than it is, for he is perilously handsome and socially successful. His beauty will be his

ruin unless some stern inner principle sustains him."
[A few years later this beautiful boy was stricken with
arthritis and is reported to be only the bed-ridden
wraith of the man I had met and admired.]

At the Blackstone, February 9, 1911, I spoke for the
Architectural Club, an address which was something
more than the statement of a mood. It was a conviction
born of a study of the city's flimsy, crude, and ugly
buildings. Among other arguments I said: "The theory
that lines of Chicago business blocks should conform
to the lines of the plain is to my mind illogical. The
tendency of each new building is to soar—to rise above
its fellows, and this urge should be expressed in predomi-
nating perpendicular lines. Most of our great buildings
are merely piles of packing-boxes, without cohesion,
others are imitation Greek temples swollen to gigantic
proportions and I now take some satisfaction in watching the increase of New York's latest towering struc-
tures in which the perpendicular lines are nobly
stressed."

I ended by saying, "The genius of America has not
yet found adequate expression in your art or in mine.
Our pathfinders, our soldiers, our engineers have been
mighty conjurers, seldom disheartened and never appalled by the untrodden way. Unencumbered by tradition, by culture, they have worked at problems which
place them among the world's great men. None so
bold as we in digging tunnels, spanning rivers, sinking
mines—only in literature and in art are we timid and
boyish, keeping close to the beaten thoroughfare, imitative and apologetic or weakly subservient. By and by
the spirit of the trail-makers will enter the hearts of

our painters, our sculptors, our architects, and they, too, will be bold and free to match with the physical spread and splendor of our continent."

II

The literary editor of the *Chicago Post* at this time was a young Irishman named Francis Hackett, a fine, sensitive, scholarly boy quite as good looking as Edward Sheldon. He interested me keenly and I took an avuncular pleasure in his vivid and charming personality. His rosy cheeks, slight figure, and smiling lips made him seem younger than he really was, but he could not have been more than twenty-five or six.

Early in 1911 I made this note concerning him: "Francis Hackett was at the Little Room to-day, and we had a friendly talk. He is looking thin and worried. He told me that he had decided to leave the *Post* on which he has been for several years a vital figure. 'I am going up to Wisconsin to write a novel,' he smilingly declared. 'I want to write as good a story as your "Rose of Dutcher's Coolly." Anyhow, I am going to give a year to the attempt!'

"This is a perilous resolution, and, while I did not discourage him, I doubt his fictional ability. Fuller is equally skeptical. 'Francis is a brilliant essayist, not a fictionist,' he asserted, and to this I agreed."

He carried out his plan. On November 18, 1911, he wrote me from Madison, Wisconsin, reporting progress. "You are most kind about offering to look at my manuscript. I should be honored. I have started typewriting the first few chapters and the first time I go to Chicago I shall bring them with me."

In December he wrote again from Madison, and, while I ought not to include this letter, I am unable to resist its praise, for my "Rose" had suffered many hard knocks! Hackett's letter was a comfort to me.

"Thank you most kindly for sending me 'Rose of Dutcher's Coolly.' I suppose it was 1896 or 1897 when I read it first, and I was very curious to read it again, as an entirely different person. I read it slowly these last few days, and with such a keen interest. People seem to think that America is an open book and that an Irishman who has lived here for ten years or so is practically an American. But it isn't so. Now that I know a little about this country, the Americanism of your book is its chief pleasure to me. It opens for me the book of American youth, Wisconsin youth, of which I only see the bindings, the closed covers, in the young people I meet.

"The chapters that interpreted Rose up to the time she leaves the coolly are as fragrant as anything I have read. They have a wild-rose beauty, and I shall always be glad to think there was even this one flower in Wisconsin. By this I don't mean that even so lovely a character and so big a character cannot have her counterpart, but of course Rose is an unusual woman, in no sense a type. Her reality is all the more creditable for that reason. I feel that Wisconsin could have produced her, as Staffordshire could produce Hilda Lessways, although it took imagination to see it.

"The book seems to me impatient, the book of a poet rather than a novelist. It is far, far too short, too much at the gallop, too romantic. As I see it, a novelist has to do two things: he has to interpret and to substan-

tiate. Had there been two hundred pages more sub-
stantiating Rose I should have been rejoiced. It would
have taken a year more, perhaps, but that would have
given to America a woman of the Middle West who
was still Rose, but Rose not quintessential but emanat-
ing from the prose America that we all know."

That this brilliant young Irish journalist should join
Henry James in commending my only Wisconsin novel
is worth recording, even though the book is now almost forgotten. My supporters were few in those days,
and the reader who has persisted thus far will forgive
me, I trust, in quoting this charming letter.

[Here again I shall anticipate. After years of struggle as an editor in New York and London, young
Hackett found opportunity to concentrate on the
writing of a life of Henry VIII and after five years of
study and research, brought back to America one of
the most perceptive, colorful, and original books of the
year. I was prepared for a subtle and beautifully written volume, but I was not prepared for the author's
masterly use and arrangement of historical records. The
book was rich in texture and bold in concept. It became the success of the season and the royalties from
its sale lifted Hackett from a life of ill-paid drudgery
to the ownership of a castle in his native country. In this
well-earned security I rejoice. His answer to my letter
of congratulation was altogether charming and modest.
In it he made allusion to our association in Chicago and
of his attempt to write a novel. He quite frankly confessed to the poverty in which he had so long dwelt and
with the same candor expressed the joy he took in his
sudden release from care.]

III

On February 14, Sorolla, the great Spanish painter, was the feature of a luncheon at the Cliff Dwellers. Although he spoke no English, he appeared entirely at home with us. Ralph Clarkson our Spanish expert had him in charge, and after luncheon William French, director of the Art Institute, invited us all over to see the "show." It was a noble exhibition and the painter was himself a worthy accompaniment of it.

"I have never seen sun-lighted figures painted with equal zest and brilliancy. Sorolla loves the color of noon. He feels the mystery of midday. Sunny beaches, gay gardens, and vividly colored figures fill his canvases. Some say they are lacking in depth, in power, and solidity, but to me they are their own justification.

"At the Little Room afterwards I met Alice French who greeted me with the directness of a man, professing an abiding interest in all that I am doing. She is huge of body—huger than ever—but her handsome face is thinner. She is not unlike a successful lawyer in appearance, shrewd, humorous, and quite certain of her opinions. I like her, I have always liked her. She is not only a fine writer and a useful citizen, but a 'good fellow.' She is companionable, a literary comrade in a way few women achieve. In this respect she recalls Ruth McEnery Stuart, whose humor has much the same spontaneous expression. Both are pioneers in their lines."

"Octave Thanet," Miss French's pen name, is associated with the fiction of the Mid-West early in the eighties. I am not sure whether my stories preceded

hers or not. If they did they counted for little alongside her published volume. She was a writer for *Scribner's Magazine* in 1889, whilst I was a seedy youth writing for the *Arena* and knocking at the doors of weekly
papers. I heard of her demands with amazement (three
hundred dollars for a story of six thousand words—
fabulous!), at a time when I was glad to get thirty for
mine. There was an element of injustice (or so it
seemed to me at the time) that she, the daughter of
a wealthy manufacturer, should command such prices.
However, I had perception enough to grant that her
work was more popular than mine, and that she was
a skillful artist. I did not begrudge her the success she
had earned.

CHAPTER THIRTY-SIX

THE VILLAGE MAGAZINE

I

ONE afternoon at the club, I read in *Current Literature* a two-page article by the editor, my good friend Edward J. Wheeler, in which he announced the discovery of a new Western poet, one who was also illustrator, editor, and art evangelist. The name of this threefold genius was Nicholas Vachel Lindsay and the material on which the critic based his comment was a publication called *The Village Magazine*, which had come to him from Springfield, Illinois.

The editorials of *Current Literature* had great weight with me, but in this case I found immediate confirmation of the editor's judgment in the excerpts quoted from the publication before him. First of all, the preachment of this self-confessed art evangelist in Springfield was in harmony with what I had been proclaiming for several years, namely that it was the duty of the American artist and writer to use American material, but young Lindsay had gone beyond me in a passionate plea to the artist and author to remain in the place of their birth and lend the best of their brain and the skill of their hands to the task of making the home town beautiful.

The article quoted a paragraph by the young pub-

lisher in which he stated that he was sole editor, proprietor, and vendor of *The Village Magazine* and that
he would gladly mail a copy to any one who would
send him a dollar. In this admission I read an appeal.
Addressing him at Springfield, I enclosed two dollars
and asked him to send me two copies of his periodical.
Three days later, I received a very amusing letter dated
Springfield, Ill., March 7, 1911: "It was a great pleasure
to me to hear from you, and I am honored indeed that
you should inquire about my humble plans. It is a little
flustrating to admit that I have none in especial. 'Come,
eat the bread of Idleness, said Mister Moon to me.'

"What I produce, if I may say so, is not a definite
plan, but *yeast*—if it is anything. The other man, once
leavened, must produce the plan and do the work. In
short, brother Garland, I am an inert gentleman who
makes a loud noise.

"I have a hope that the villages will send for me
some day, as an Art Evangelist. In that case I will go
to them and conduct Ruskin Revivals, and distribute
the tracts of the Massachusetts Civic League."

This letter, which was signed Nicholas Vachel Lindsay, increased my wish to know this young man, and
when his magazine came I opened it with more interest than I had ever felt in any previous Mid-Western
publication. It was a large, square, paper-bound volume
filled with hand-made script which was almost illegible
by reason of its minute characters but as beautiful in its
way as a medieval manuscript, and the text, both prose
and verse, was illustrated by decorative pen drawings of
singular remoteness from anything in Springfield. Con-

sidered as a piece of book-making it was an amazing performance.

"In sheer audacity and original power, it has no Mid-West predecessor," I said to Fuller, with whom I shared all such discoveries. "The whole effect is at once medieval and modern, and slightly mad. His prose, however, has a solid content. He argues that the artist should not run away from his native town, selfishly seeking some colony of his kind, but remain in the home city or come back to the home city and help to civilize it. This magazine is born of that high enthusiasm, but the man himself is more than that; he is a poet of astonishing skill. His mastery of lyrical forms and his freedom from anything parochial in his expression are unaccountable. How could such work come out of Springfield?"

I then read to him one of the poems called "The Wizard in the Street" which was a defense of Poe. After describing him as a worn, pale, wandering faker confronting a jeering throng of citizens, halted for a moment on the pavement, he says:

> There stands the useless one
> Who builds a haunted palace in the sun.
> Good tailors, can you dress a doll for me
> With silks that whisper of the sounding sea?
> One moment, citizens! the weary tramp
> Unveileth Psyche with the agate lamp.
> Now which of you can spread a spotted cloak
> And raise an unaccounted incense smoke
> Until, within the twilight of the day
> Stands dark Ligea in her disarray,
> Witchcraft and desperate passion in her breath
> And battling will that conquers even death?

To get the full force of this poem as it came to me that day, one should read it as a whole and with a knowledge of the city in which it was written. To me, that day, it was a miracle. How could an unknown youth write with such penetration, such mastery of phrase? Almost any of us can write love poems or nature poems, but which of us can spread a spotted cloak and raise an unaccounted incense smoke?

"This poem alone justifies Wheeler's editorial," I went on to say, "but it does not stand alone. This astonishing magazine is filled with verses quaintly humorous, exquisitely musical, and at the same time esoteric in concept. His argument against stripping the mid-land of its artists and writers to build up New York's Bohemia can have no effect, but I honor him for making it."

In a second letter to the poet, I expressed my sympathy with his argument that men of talent should remain in their native towns and said, "I should like to have you address the Cliff Dwellers on that subject. They need it. I'll arrange a special luncheon for you and give you a chance to preach your art theories to an audience of writers, architects, musicians, and painters who are all secretly planning to join the New York colony. I shall be glad to have you stay at my house for the night."

His reply was jubilant: "This is my lucky day. Your invitation has arrived, also *Collier's Weekly* for March 18th. Read 'The Education of Aladdin,' page 36, if you are not already weary of my affairs. I suggest that Tuesday noon will be a good time for us to meet at the Cliff Dwellers Club. Unless you say otherwise, I will speak for you then, being careful to make it fifteen minutes only. Subject, 'The New Localism' or 'The Returned Art Student.' I was an art student, you know, in the Art Institute from 1900 to 1903 and recognition from that quarter is just like being able to please one's cousins and aunts. At that time I read Mr. Fuller's books and was able, I thought, to identify a good many of the characters in 'Under the Skylights.' It is like taking up a half-read poem after many years to have contact with Mr. Fuller, Mr. Garland, and the rest."

On the day appointed he appeared at the club, a quaint, rough-hewn, and highly individualized youth of twenty-six, with sandy hair, blue eyes, slanting brow, high cheek bones, and a freckled skin, much more rural in figure than I had expected to see, but his talk, though unpolished, was ready and forceful. He had ideas and did not hesitate to make them known.

He privately confessed his inability to find a place in the world. "My father and mother are not entirely sympathetic with my literary ambitions. They have a good home in Springfield and let me live with them, but when the neighbors ask 'What is Nick doing now?' they are not able to report favorably and are mortified. My tramping and especially my writing of verse, not to mention the time spent on *The Village Magazine,* has made me an object of compassion to my relatives and a ridiculous figure to my neighbors."

The substance of his address to the members was admirable, but his manner of speech was a bit ludicrous. Our dining room was small, and his voice, needlessly sonorous, caused some of his auditors to smile. Nevertheless he had a very real message, and his points were ably presented. He failed in grace rather than in logic. Several of the men came up to congratulate him and he had no sense of failure.

At my suggestion, Mr. French, director of the Art Institute, had arranged to have our orator address the students, and several of us went across the way to give him support. He redeemed himself. In the larger space of the hall his voice was less strident, and the fact that he had once been a student in the building enabled him to catch and hold the interest of the young artists. As a preacher he was fairly successful, but it was not till that night at my house, and in the presence of Taft and Fuller, that he fully justified Wheeler's editorial.

At my request he recited some of his poems, and when he had finished by saying his lines on Poe, I was convinced that the Mid-West had at last produced a genuine poet, one whose endowment was so largely subconscious that he himself had no adequate concept of its depth. He did not appear to know the value of his poem on Poe, which had in it something of the quality which Stephen Crane had possessed.

Some weeks after this I found myself in Springfield along with Augustus Thomas, Percy Mackaye, Milton Royle, Josephine Peabody, and Fola LaFollette who were on tour, speaking against state legislation excluding young children from the stage. Our party occupied a private car, and while it was lying on the side-track, young Nicholas Lindsay called and asked me to visit his home. "I want my father and mother to meet you." I consented to go with him, for I was curious to know the kind of family life from which he came.

The Lindsay house, a spacious old-fashioned mansion,

stood in an ample tree-shaded lot, and as we approached it, Nicholas said: "My father is a physician, an old-fashioned family doctor." Leading me into the parlor he gave me a seat and went to fetch his father and mother. Dr. Lindsay, a bearded man of sixty or thereabouts, met me coldly and remained absolutely silent. Whether this was due to reticence or dislike I could not tell. He did not utter a single sentence during my stay. Nicholas said little, his mother and I did all the talking.

As I studied Mrs. Lindsay, I perceived that her son had inherited from her his blond hair, his keen blue eyes, and his strongly modeled face. From her he had drawn his missionary zeal. As she told me that she had a daughter in China carrying out the purposes from which she herself had been prevented, I knew that while she undervalued her son's ability as a poet, she was proud of him as an orator.

That both of these able and conscientious citizens were troubled by their son's literary activities was plainly evident, and I set about instructing them. "I think I understand your anxiety about Nicholas," I began. "It does seem, at times, as if he were wasting his days, but let me assure you," here I became very positive, "any youth who can write such a poem as that which your son has written on Edgar Allan Poe is certain of recognition. I know of no other tribute to Poe of equal grace and power. It is impossible that a writer of such skill and judgment should remain unknown. It is not a question of quantity but of quality. Your son is a genius. Be patient with him a little longer. Give him time to find his place. Loan him money, if necessary. His *Village Magazine* has aroused the interest of Eastern editors and it will not be long before his work will be in demand."

Whether my words were of comfort to them or not, I could not determine, for they both listened in grim silence, but Nicholas was boyishly grateful. To him I was an almost providential ally. As we came away, he said, "You put my case just right. My people are constantly meeting just such comment. Our neighbors consider me a crank and a loafer. They can't see the use of a fellow sitting around drawing pictures and writing verses which no one will buy."

"Can you blame them?" I asked. "It takes a fellow crank like me to understand and value 'The Wizard in the Street.' To me you are a miracle. If I can't explain you how can your neighbors? All I can say is I couldn't write that poem at your age or any other age and I can't understand how you could. It is a thousand miles from Springfield. It is cosmopolitan in its technical skill as well as in its content."

In spite of all my praise, and my assurance of his ultimate success, he remained doubtful. "It isn't easy to believe myself a genius when my fellow citizens all consider me a 'nut,' " he said in effect.

Shortly after my return to Chicago, he sent me a bundle of sketches designed to make a volume which he called "A Handy Guide to Beggars." "It is, in fact, a record of my tramping trips through the South and East."

One of these stories had a delightful blend of ironic advice and mock warning, and I saw at once the possibilities of the theme.

"If you can carry throughout your volume that mixture of description, narrative, and droll information concerning the ways and means of begging, I will guarantee the success of your book," I said to him. "I'll do my best along those lines," he replied.

Some weeks later, he sent me the completed manuscript, but alas! the ironic note had faded out in the third chapter. The quality which I had hoped for was absent. The manuscript was ultimately printed, but only as a collection of descriptive sketches and received but casual mention.

The reader will perceive that my interest in Lindsay was due not merely to his originality and his skill as a versifier but to the fact that he was a glorified "village poet." He was a prophecy. To understand my enthusiasm, one should come at *The Village Magazine* as Wheeler and I did, after years of reading newspaper poems. Lindsay in some way, partly from his three years at the Chicago Art Institute and partly from his tramping in the East, had gained a comparative concept of the art of poesy. He spoke as a citizen of Springfield, but he wrote like a cosmopolite. Beneath all his localism he was a genius; that is to say, he was unaccountable.

[At a later date I find in my diary this revised estimate of Lindsay: "He has disappointed my expectations. Influenced by the free-verse advocates and possibly from necessity, he has gone off into bizarre posturings and experimentations. He still writes verses which are exquisitely lyrical and some which are delightfully humorous, but his wide fame has been won by 'The Congo' and other jazz chants which do not, in my opinion, represent his lasting qualities. I would not give 'The Wizard in the Street' for a volume of these platform show pieces."]

II

Almost immediately after this visit to Springfield (April 27, 1911) I became involved in the organization of the Chicago Theater Society of which Donald Robertson and his company of actors were the forerunners. Mrs. Harold McCormick having agreed to aid in the financing of these players, a group of the laymen Cliff Dwellers joined their subscriptions to hers, and asked me to help organize a company and to act as secretary. I should not have accepted this position, but I did. I saw in it a chance for diversion. Already the president and superintendent of a club, I now became the secretary of a theatrical organization.

The theory underlying this theater movement was this: "The commercial manager will give no consideration to plays of supreme literary merit unless he sees a money success in them, therefore, in order that the small public, which is eager to support plays of high character, may have its share of production, each city needs and should have an endowed theater where the box office will not be the final test of a production."

Fuller, who had been on the play jury one year, was skeptical of the whole project. "The plays I read were mostly amateur fumblings," he said bluntly. "To read them was a waste of time," and after a study of the stacks of manuscripts in Schubert's files, I came to Fuller's point of view. None of these unacted plays and few of those produced were *written*, as Shaw and Barrie wrote plays. They were almost all *carpentered*, knocked together, pieced out, wholly without quality, and the ones we selected and earnestly presented failed to interest our own subscribers, and so at last the project failed of support and is now forgotten, except as a curious wave of dramatic history.

For a year or two Lorado Taft had been working on a gigantic statue of Black Hawk, a monument with which to mark the spot from which the defeated red chieftain once looked down upon the ruined village of his people. It was a colossal figure nearly fifty feet in height and built of concrete. Taft was one of the first sculptors to employ this material. As it grew to a finish the plans for its dedication took shape. The date was fixed for July 1, with Colonel Frank Lowden as presiding officer. Dr. Charles A. Eastman, the Sioux, and Miss Cornelius, a daughter of the Oneidas, were invited to represent the red man; while Edgar Bancroft, Elia Peattie, and I were to speak for the white race. My diary account of it reads:

"Eastman was in full Sioux costume, and Miss Cornelius wore a beaded pouch hanging from the girdle of her handsome white gown. Colonel Lowden presided and Bancroft gave a carefully prepared address. Mrs. Peattie's poem was pretty but not strictly apropos. Eastman's speech was admirable—but too long. Miss Cornelius was incisive and musical. Sixty feet above us, the brooding Black Hawk loomed with folded arms, in silhouette against the sunset sky like a shadow of the past. As I read my poem, I was genuinely moved by the scene. I quote the final stanza to indicate my argument:

And so, freed from all hate, all dread
Of him—here on the land he fought to save,
We meet in tribute to the many dead
Whose ashes mingle in one common grave.
To him who died in exile—red man still—
A victim to our greed, with broken heart,
We raise upon his sentinel hill
This towering symbol of remorseful art.

III

In August, 1911, I again rode with the Colorado forest rangers, putting aside for the month my literary enterprises. One of these foresters, a youngish man, with the glance of an eagle, a slender, fearless mountaineer, living a lonely life in the Arapahoe Mountains, proved a most valuable host. Though hardly half the age of the Indian trader Hubbell, of Ganado, he was quite as experienced in border life and a capital storyteller. As we cut trail and camped together he talked of his wanderings in New Mexico and Arizona, and of his employments in the High Country.

His life had been one of hardship and danger, but he had tasted the joys of the trail. From him I derived some of the incidents in the life of "Tall Ed Kelly," who figures in several of my short stories. Kelly is not Acord, but some of his experiences were drawn from Acord's history. He had been cowboy, miner, trailer, hunter, town marshal, and deputy sheriff. He had been assaulted and nearly killed several times, but had escaped without a scar.

My note reads thus: "He neither chews, smokes, nor swears. He never drinks whiskey and is a sparing eater. Although slender and rather delicate in physique, he is

an epitome of the Mountain West. His experience as
marshal at Pogosa Springs is an amazing story. He told
it to me quite freely, reliving it in the telling. I could
see that the menacing glare of his eyes had aided him
in making arrests, for it came into evidence as he re-
lived those perilous moments of his service. I can imagine a band of criminals developing a chill when he
turned the blaze of his resolute eyes upon them. His
quality grew upon me as he told of long days on the
deserts of New Mexico and Arizona, with only a burro
as transportation. I said, 'You may see some of these
adventures in print some day.' He smiled as if in ac-
quiescence, certain, I believe, that I would not do him
an injustice."

I never saw him again, but he remains a fine type
of the man who takes chances. He was only forty, but
he had accepted more opportunities for injury or death
than any man I knew except my father, who took a
grim pleasure in recounting how many times he risked
his life on the Wisconsin river in the early days of
rafting. My book of stories wherein "Tall Ed" figured
was never completed, but even now I have moments of
regret that I did not carry out my design. In truth
Kelly was less a portrait of Acord than of a miner I met
in British Columbia, a slab-sided, wind-bit, smiling
wanderer whom we called Montana. His real name I
never learned.

When I think of the stories which Acord quietly
related while sitting beside the fireplace, I experience
something of the awe I feel as I see a riveter at work
on an iron beam six hundred feet above the pavement.
Something large ran beneath Acord's heroic zeal for

law and order. He was at once public servant and invincible trailer.

A few days after leaving him I stood on "the ledge" at the Cliff Dwellers, looking down upon Grant Park, watching men in heavier-than-air flying machines rise from the ground so unexpectedly, so miraculously that I did not for a moment realize what was taking place. Here was another kind of daredevil taking chances in a new way. Seven of these birdlike machines were in the air at once. *"The air is conquered.* In half an hour I accepted these great steel dragonflies as a part of the world's advance."

My father, an old Wisconsin pioneer, who had found his way to La Crosse in 1850 by stage, by canal boat, and by ox-team came down to see these air-borne pioneers ride their brazen eagles above the clouds. Frank Logan, Charles Hutchinson, and other of my fellow members of the Cliff Dwellers took a genuine interest in him. They brought a table out upon the narrow balcony and placed a chair upon it so that he could sit at ease and watch the airmen at their play. His eighty years spanned the gulf between the sickle and the tractor-drawn reaper, and now here he sat to watch men ride a thousand pound metal bird above the clouds. He was so deeply moved that he could not speak. This seemed the end of the world he knew, and a troubled vision of the world to follow filled him with awe. To me afterward he said, "I am ready to go. Life is getting too swift and complicated for me."

CHAPTER THIRTY-SEVEN

VISITING CELEBRITIES

I

EARLY in January of 1912, Chicago entered upon another literary flurry of which Lady Gregory and the Dublin Company of Players were jointly the cause. Immediately after the announcement that this famous dramatist was on her way to Chicago as patron as well as courier of the company, reception rooms and studios buzzed with interest. Here again was something to talk about. Invitations showered upon the visitor and reporters waylaid her at every door.

My first meeting with her was at a dinner given in her honor by Mrs. Harold McCormick, also a patron of the drama, and I found her a handsome, middle-aged woman of pleasing manners. I had very little conversation with her at the dinner, but one night at the opera I sat beside her in a box, and discussed with her the value of local-color literature and the service of a community stage.

She was interesting, but like all specialists, including myself, was bound to an idea, and talked too much about it. She had read my "Main-Travelled Roads" and said of the characters in the book, "They are as native to the prairies as our plays are to the sod of Ireland. Why haven't you dramatized them? Your Chicago theater society should be producing pieces of that sort instead of spending its time and money on classical French comedy."

Thanking her for her suggestion, I confessed that our theater society had not been able to interest an audience in *any* production, classical or otherwise. No important or striking play had come out of our competition and the accepted ones had all failed. "Our generous patrons are disheartened and the entire venture has dwindled to a forlorn neglect. A play based on my stories would only deepen the gloom. What we need is a farce, and we are all too dispirited to write a comedy."

My comment reads: "I like Lady Gregory and I like her plays, 'The Rising of the Moon,' 'Spreading the News,' and 'The Workhouse Ward.' They are not great literature, but they have the spirit of old Ireland in them. As to the players, I find them lacking on the pantomime side of their art. While they read their lines almost flawlessly with musical sincerity, their action remains negative. At all vital points of the action, they fail of satisfactory achievement. They brought out all the humor and much of the poetry of 'The Playboy,' but in certain respects they were distinctly less effective than Hart Conway's pupils have been. They all use the same cadence and the same tempo and they succeed in giving the lines their full value as literature, a quality which compensates for their shortcomings as actors. At the same hour, while this crowded house is applauding these outsiders, our Chicago Theater Society is giving an almost perfect performance of 'The Thunderbolt' to a handful of depressed and listless auditors."

As I look back on this situation now, I do not wonder at the success of the Dublin players and the failure of our Donald Robertson Company. First of all the Irish plays were humorous, redolent of the soil, and essentially poetic, whereas our productions, though skillfully presented, were drab and dry. The Irish players were a free-flowering group with a touch of mystic significance here and there. They had something remote and charming in their voices. I went night after night to see them, rejoicing in the deep-running stream of Celtic poetry which they brought to our prosaic town.

Hearing that Gilbert Parker was in town at one of the South Side hotels, I went down to call upon him. Since our last meeting he had become a distinguished figure in England both as novelist and as member of Parliament, and I wondered a little as to what my reception would be. It was reported that he had been high in favor with King Edward and I knew his novels had a wide sale. The hotel at which he was a guest was the finest in the city. He had every reason for self-satisfaction.

It happened that I came upon him just as he was asking for the key to his room. I recognized him instantly, although, like myself, he had grown heavier and grayer. He greeted me with unaffected friendliness and in a few moments we were talking as if our last meeting had been six days instead of six years before. He had read my psychical books and spoke of them with enthusiasm. "I like all your work," he said, "because it has a sociologic significance. It isn't just amusing fiction—but let's not stand here. I must be moving, for I am leaving on the five o'clock train.

Come up to my room and we'll talk while I pack my bags."

On the way up I pondered his words. He spoke as if he had but one room—and also as if he had no valet, and this I soon discovered was the fact. Seating me in his one extra chair, he threw off his coat and set to work packing his valises very much as I would have done in similar case. There was nothing English in his manner, speech, or action. He was of the New World, self-helping, frank, and humorous. "I am still able to wait on myself, you see. I haven't forgotten my early training in Canada and Australia."

As he folded shirts and coats he talked of his experiences in Parliament and of the king's friendship. "He valued me, I think, because I could definitely tell him something of his colonies. I realized England's dependence upon Canada and Australia—and I knew the United States, important information which the ordinary member of Parliament could not furnish. It was for these reasons that the king favored me."

From this he passed to an account of his recent trip to California and of his visit to Utah. "I was enormously impressed with Salt Lake City," he said. "I would like to live there. I found its climate invigorating. California is finer than the Riviera—in some ways. I hope to spend many winters there."

He was disposed to recall our early meetings and our mutual friends in Boston, but time did not permit much of that. We parted in a glow of renewed friendship, and I went away thinking of our first meeting in the office of the *Arena Magazine,* in 1890, or thereabouts. He dressed at that time like an Episcopal clergyman, but was a handsome figure of a man, tall, black-bearded, and bright-eyed. I felt his power, but thought him a bit formal, not to say oratorical, in his talk. He set the stage for his anecdotes, but I rather liked this attention to detail. He will come again into this chronicle.

I said something in praise of the Irish players to Fuller, who had just returned from a visit to New York—the first in eight years—but he was more inclined to talk of his trip, presenting a gay and cheerful picture of "the great metrolopus," as he called it. I said, "I am obliged to report that the Irish players have drawn all our patrons away. Apparently nothing we do, neither Molière, Pinero, nor native play, will bring an audience to our theater. I am done. That I have wasted my time in promoting this venture is evident."

Fuller was not sympathetic. "Why should people come to Robertson's performances when they can see better plays done at the regular theaters? As for plays, if a man has a really good play he is certain to find a place for it on the commercial stage. I discovered this while reading manuscripts in last year's contest. All the plays which came to my hand were amateurish in style or lacking in interest—pieces which no shrewd manager would consider. Of course there is a chance—a remote chance—of making a find, but that is not a justification for your company. You'd better return to your Middle Border muttons."

"You're right! I'm going to resign," I replied. Shortly after this I dropped out of the management and bent all my energies to my writing, which I had almost wholly neglected.

Hamilton Wright Mabie, who came to lunch with me at the club, talked National Institute matters for a time and then spoke of the award of the poetry medal to James Whitcomb Riley. "I hope you approve."

"I am frankly for it, not because Riley is old and ill and needs money, but because he has earned the honor by contributing something new and characteristic to our verse."

As Mabie signed our register I was shocked to see how slowly and feebly he used the pen. I observed also that his eyes were dull and his face congested. "The man is dying on his feet!" I said to myself.

He was a most genial guest, however, and told many stories of Roosevelt, whom he had seen almost daily in the editorial offices of the *Outlook*. "There is no fake about Roosevelt's knowledge," he declared. "His memory is prodigious. He can meet any man—any specialist on his own ground. His luncheons in New York are quite as notable as those he used to hold in the White House. He is still our chief citizen, no doubt of that. He holds court in our office. Everybody goes to see him."

After Mabie left I wrote of him as follows: "Mabie's case is one of distinction for cultural and not creative powers. He is a wise editor and a polished speaker. He is an agreeable but conventional essayist and a delightful dinner companion, but his election to the Institute and later to the Academy was based on these personal qualities and not on the books he has written. He frankly disclaims any great literary distinction, and his friends are forced into long explanations of the honors they have voted upon him. He did much to advance the Institute, almost as much as Robert Underwood Johnson, whose interest in matters literary never flagged."

One day some one brought Kubelik, the latest acclaimed violinist, to the club and I had a half-hour talk with him. He was "all the rage" at this time and I was interested in him as a character. I examined his hands just as I had studied those of Paderewski and Kreisler. The tips of the fingers on his left hand, exactly like Kreisler's, were flattened and capped with pads of hardened cuticle, protective thimbles somewhat like the metal guards a harpist wears, and across each of them ran a deep, permanent groove caused by pressing the strings. This amazing adaptation bore witness to the long hours, the years of practice.

He good-naturedly submitted to my inspection and countered by expressing admiration for my hands— and again I tried to explain that I had gained my huge paws by heavy labor on a pioneer farm, but I suspect he found it difficult to believe my tale although he, himself, was reported to be the son of a market gardener. This I could believe, for he was an awkward figure on the platform, bent and timid, but he could make his violin whistle and chirp and wail! He is forgotten now, but in those days he was a king. The women mobbed him at every performance, and it was said that he was almost dazed by his success.

Our next distinguished club guest was Arnold Bennett, whose triumphant approach had been prepared by Bert L. Taylor in his "Colyum," and feeling it my duty as presiding officer of the Cliff Dwellers, I called on the Englishman at his hotel. I found him in bed, sadly used up by his long ride from New York City, and resting in preparation for the big reception which the Art Institute had arranged in his honor.

This party was called "entertaining our distinguished guest," but in reality it was a way of putting him on show for the benefit of a lot of bored citizens. It was an afternoon of torment for him.

My record reads: "He is a tall, pale, dark-eyed young man with a black mustache partly concealing an ugly set of teeth. His glance is pleasant and his speaking voice, though high-keyed, is musical. His accent is almost Bostonian in quality—plainly he is neither Oxford bred nor London born."

He came to the reception and for two hours stood beside Charles Hutchinson, president of the Art Institute, confronting an endless line of people of whom he had no knowledge and in whom he had no interest —remaining cordial, humorous, and alert throughout the ordeal. Some of his remarks were very amusing and showed that he was entirely master of the situation. After the lines broke up and he was led through the galleries, groups of insatiate admirers gathered about him. Gusts of laughter followed his witty retorts, some of which stung. In truth, it was all a publicity stunt engineered by his publishers, but no matter, we were amused.

At four the next day, Hutchinson and I, as a reception committee, met our distinguishd visitor and his publisher and took them to another reception at the home of Harry Pratt Judson, president of the university. Bennett submitted gracefully, but was not at ease.

On the way out I said, "I find in the speech of your characters expressions which we of the Mid-West regard as native to New England."

To this he replied, "That is natural, for I am writing of a region from which Massachusetts drew many of its settlers."

He pretended to an interest in Chicago, and I think he was genuinely amazed by its rise in seventy years from a frontier trading post to one of the most populous cities of the world. His high-pitched voice was strikingly at variance with his composed glance as he delivered himself on the subject of American railways and the cities he had seen. He regarded me as a fellow craftsman and readily promised to lunch with me next day at the Cliff Dwellers and meet the members.

He arrived at our door in happy mood and as he glanced around the little dining room he said, "This is something like home!" and in truth it was a little like the Savage Club in London.

In attendance this luncheon broke all our records, for the newspapers had made Bennett a colossal figure and all the Cliff Dwellers came, whether they knew and liked his books or not, eager to see and hear him. He declined to address the meeting, however, but those who sat near him were amused by the frankness of his criticisms. He did not pretend to like our ugly city; the best he could do was to marvel at it, and I understood his point of view.

After luncheon Jensen, one of our artist members, proposed to take our guest on a circuit of our boulevards and as I rode with him past sixty miles of flimsy, detestable buildings and other miles of cluttered, vacant lots, I wished we had taken some better method of entertainment. The one thing beautiful in our three hours' drive was the West Side Greenhouse, which Jensen had designed and built. Realizing how dreadful all this ugliness was to Bennett, I kept the talk on his books and on English acquaintances. He remained genial and self-contained through it all, but I could see that the drab town wearied and depressed him. It was worse than his "Five Towns" because there was more of it.

When I spoke of the marvelous insight he had shown in delineating the two main characters in "The Old Wives' Tale," and the skill with which he had characterized them from their girlhood to their decrepit years, he quietly replied, "That was easy—they were my relations." He went on to explain that the "Five Towns" of his novels were actual cities in central England—an England utterly apart from Surrey or Sussex. "Your New England ancestors came from that region and many of the expressions which I find in your work and in the stories of Miss Wilkins are survivals of common usage in my country."

He found himself genuinely interested in Lorado Taft's studio and the school of young sculptors at work there, but he was weary, and with a knowledge of how he felt (judging from my own somewhat similar experiences in Western towns) I helped him to escape and to return to his hotel. The strain of being genial was wearing him down. He was ready to faint with fatigue—and his Chicago visit would have been unpleasantly futile had it not been for its value as advertising. I hope his publisher sustained him with reports of augmented royalties.

II

Meanwhile I had revised my Amerind manuscript, "The Silent Eaters," and Fuller had read it. "It is one of the best things you have ever done," he said, and this encouraged me to send it to Harper's. As a brief epic of the Sitting Bull, it had been in my desk for ten years. From time to time I had taken it out to rewrite some part of it. "I believe it to be—as Fuller says it is— one of my best pieces of writing. It has no popular appeal, however. My thought in writing it was to present the Sitting Bull from the standpoint of an educated young Sioux who regarded his chief as a young Italian of a certain period looked upon Garibaldi. What sort of figure would any patriot be if his deeds were presented only by his enemies?"

In 1897, and again in 1900, I had visited the Standing Rock Agency to obtain the basic facts, so far as I could learn them, in the life of this famous red man. I had dug into the records on file at Fort Yates and also those at the agency, copying all references to him. In addition, I had sought out his friends and relatives, especially the warriors who were with him in all his campaigns, and out of this information I had built my story. "That it is a piece of special pleading, I admit, but I contend that the red man is entitled to his side of the argument," I said to Fuller. "Sitting Bull was a Sioux. He believed in being a Sioux—in that sense he was 'irreconcilable.' "

"The 'Silent Eaters' were the men with whom he met and counseled—a society which ate without song, whose members became his bodyguard."

This manuscript, which was published finally as part of a volume of my short stories concerning the American Indian, has never had the wide reading which I—the doting author—feel it should have won. Few of my friends know anything of it. Some day I intend to republish it in a small volume and send it out as a present to all my associates.

On April 19, the papers brought to us the story of the *Titanic* which had struck an iceberg on the way to New York and had sunk with all on board: "This is a dreadful disaster and yet there is something grand as well as appalling in the fact—if it is a fact—that somewhere in the profound deeps of those icy northern waters, this ship with all its thirteen hundred bodies is swinging to and fro at some unimaginable depth, there to drift for centuries in the chill of those soundless deeps."

III

This silly literary flurry over Bennett, so characteristic of Chicago life, came as one of a long procession of similar enthusiasms, and we all knew that it would be succeeded next week or next month by another flutter over some other author or singer. Any one whose personality provided something to talk about was joyously entertained, and Chicago was not alone in these fictitious fervors. New York usually set the pace, by greeting the Old World visitor at the gangway. Buffalo, Cleveland, and St. Louis merely echoed the acclaim and passed it on to smaller, more remote towns, all to the advantage of the alien author and his agent.

There was nothing in these invasions to complain

about. On the contrary, we were grateful. Bored with one another, we of the midland towns welcomed these entertainers. While they filled their purses we buzzed and bustled. If our local stars were momentarily obscured, we said they will shine after the visiting luminary has departed.

"Despite all our protestations to the contrary, we are aspiring provincials, and the more kindly of our visiting celebrities consider us heroic souls on whom they are glad to confer momentary pleasure and a lasting inspiration."

Fuller saw all this. "We are and must continue to be 'the New World,' the world of young, aspiring arts," he said after all the social flutterings over Bennett had subsided. "However, if we are entertained, no one is the worse for our hypocritical enthusiasms. I wonder if London has similar ripples of excitement when a writer from the Continent comes to town."

"Oh, yes, London can be stirred, but it is a bigger puddle and not so easy to set in motion. Visiting royalty can do it, however."

Fuller went on: "There is one fact which one or two of our visiting authors have learned, to their humiliation. These flurries cannot be repeated by the same man. A celebrity making a second round finds the front pages devoted to some other man. The first visit is news, the second social gossip, the third is likely to be—silence! You who lecture at small prices all the year round can pretend to consolation when you see English authors reaping a fortune in a few weeks, and express it by saying, 'Oh, well! we'll be here when they are gone.'

"And so we are, but our over-seas rivals carry our harvest with them.

"The truth is we live in the traditions of a province. Our people are so recently from England, Germany, Italy, and other Old World countries that they unconsciously concede the superiority of the European author or British orator—and the worst of it is, these celebrities usually *are* superior."

CHAPTER THIRTY-EIGHT

SONS OF THE MIDDLE BORDER

I

SOME twelve years before this date, in the spring of 1898, just before leaving for my gold-seeking trip over the long trail through British Columbia, and while I still had a desk in the Congressional Library, I began to dictate a manuscript which was to be, when completed, an account of the pioneer life of my family in Wisconsin and Iowa. "I may not return from this Alaskan trip," I said to Howells, "and if I don't this will serve as a rough chronicle of my career." I called this manuscript "Grant McLane" and held the narrative to the third person, throughout. Within a week the manuscript had grown to a bulky volume.

I put this chronicle away in my desk and for more than ten years it lay there, almost forgotten, until late in 1911, for some cause not quite clear to me, I dug it up and began to ponder the question of making it a homely history of the pioneer life my people had shared on the prairie border. I perceived that it must be something more than an autobiography. "It must deal minutely with the Garlands and McClintocks and the families who moved with them into Wisconsin in 1850, and from Wisconsin into Iowa in 1869." The actual date of my decision to revise this chronicle is fixed by the following entry in my diary:

"Monday, October 23, 1911. I have settled down to rewriting my autobiography and I am reliving with joy those colorful days on the Iowa prairie. Fuller came in last night, and when I told him what I had been doing he became alertly interested. 'Go ahead!' he exclaimed. 'This is a natural phase in your literary career. Such a history will bring you back to your own people and your native soil. It is likely to be more valuable than any fiction you could write.' "

As I went on with this writing, I found something singularly remote in my mother's brothers, dark-eyed, gigantic Scotchmen, whose youthful world was bordered by forests and made bright by rivers. By shutting the door on my present, I could reënter their far mystical valley and recapture something of the joy with which as a child I listened to their tales. Once more I heard the songs my mother and her sisters used to sing to the accompaniment of the dulcimer in Grandmother McClintock's little rag-carpeted parlor. Each morning I reëntered that dim region to relive my youthful adorations, and the deeper I penetrated into my past, the less inclined I was to fictionize my present. "It is a dangerous 'bout face," I admitted. "Not yet fifty-two, I am taking on the attitude of a dreaming old man, but if I am to do this work well I must do it now."

No one outside my family but Fuller knew precisely what I was writing, and with no definite plan for the publication of this manuscript I kept at its revision. "I intend to record the homely facts of a vanished era, to write a story which certain readers of my own age, as well as those of my father's generation, will recognize as a truthful picture of life in a simpler, more unhurried age."

It may be that I was influenced by a failing of my vitality. As my confidence in the future weakened I found it easier to sit and dream of the past than to create fictitious characters in my present environment. I did not put this feeling into words, but I worked in accordance with a premonition that I had no time to lose.

As president of the Cliff Dwellers I still gave my afternoons to the task of building up a club spirit. To this end I levied upon all passing celebrities, no matter what my private opinion of them might be. Certain of my committee were "scouts" under orders to spy out and bring to my attention all passing notables, an arrangement which proved a source of entertainment to us all.

Theoretically, from the lofty standpoint of Thoreau and Whitman, I should have been entirely content with my lot in Chicago. "As head of a club, secretary of a theater society, and the owner of a comfortable home, what more can you ask?"

Notwithstanding all these interests, I was not content. I felt as thousands of other Mid-Western residents felt, that I was missing something which could only be caught in New York or London. Acknowledging the clutch of that centralizing force, I suffered a hunger (imaginary to be sure) which filled me with a sense of futility. I was sick of the narrow round, the noise and the dirt of my life in Woodlawn, for I must again repeat Fuller's caustic comment, "This is not a city, it is only a town. Nine hundred and ninety-nine thousand of its millions are wholly negligible as civilizing factors. As writers the best of us are second or third raters, or worse."

Weak as it may seem, I had begun to lose confidence in my ability to make a living in the Mid-West. It was all very well to say, "You are established in the region to which you belong," but I didn't belong. In a literary sense the island of Manhattan was my home —not precisely a heavenly home, but my literary source of supply. While there I took on confidence. In a few editorial rooms I was still in demand, and certain publishers valued me. In these facts I found comfort. At the Cliff Dwellers I was rated as steward and general manager, at the Players I met those who considered me a man of letters, and after all recognition is an aid to composition.

Fuller said, "Go. Why stay here? I stay because I can't get away. I have no expectation of seeing satisfactory improvement in this town during my lifetime. It can't improve without killing off a lot of its cheap and criminal citizens."

In making my confession of unrest I am willing to concede that my failure was due to my shortcomings. Had I been a man of wider sympathies, or larger ability, I would have found the city inspiring, but I more and more resented its journalistic trend, its second-rate literary and art criticism, and its insistence on bigness rather than fineness. I had so far overtaken Fuller's pessimistic position as to say, "I have reached the end of my term as a literary exile."

"New York—December 9th. While in the Harper office at Franklin Square looking at a set of my books which they had handsomely bound in red, I saw Howells come in. He had just landed after a tour of Spain. Glowing with memories of his joyous experiences, he outlined his plans and said, 'I have agreed to write an introduction to a uniform edition of your books.' This pleased me greatly. He is the one man who knows my work from the beginning."

That night I saw the Irish players do "The Playboy of the Western World" while certain Irishmen of the city raged, and on the following night I was a speaking guest at the Dramatists' Society. I sat beside Mrs. Fiske and during the evening met a dozen or more of our play writers of the moment. On the third night of my stay my friends took me to see a little Scotch play, called "Bunty Pulls the String," a delightful character comedy, and on the fourth I gave a dinner to Grace and Ernest Seton, Mary and William Carman Roberts, and Juliet Wilbor Tompkins. At the Roberts' home, I met Robert Henri (a big, singular character —a portrait painter with a mad theory about colors), Yeats, the father of the poet, and several of the Irish players. On my fifth day I lunched with Howells, and two days later John Burroughs came to dine with me.

In this list of my activities lies the answer to the question, "Why do you prefer New York to Chicago?"

Howells was amused by the description I gave of Chicago's whoop-hurrah reception to Arnold Bennett. "I like Bennett's books quite as much as you do, but I wonder if he merits such a 'Katouse'—as our New England people would call it."

"I don't think he does, but to say so would seem like outspoken envy, so I'm not saying it—publicly."

On my return I lectured at Ann Arbor, which I discovered to be a typical Mid-West town, comfortable, secure, and democratic, but the college buildings were entirely lacking in the grace which comes from a comparative knowledge of architecture and decoration. My honest impression is here set down, "Its halls are old and ugly, its classrooms primitive, and its fraternity houses, for the most part, barrack-like. I was amazed at its back-country quality. The girls I saw were all soberly dressed, and the boys were closely akin to my schoolmates in Iowa. The university impresses me as a plodding school with few workers of distinction in literature or research. It appears far less progressive than the University of Wisconsin. Two of the classes I visited were studying the Bible. Just why or in what connection, I did not learn. I met some fine young people, however. After all, the pupils make the college, not its buildings."

II

The final page of my 1911 diary is a confession of failure and distrust: "This has been a futile and rather disheartening year. I have done many things, but nothing which now seems important except the revision of my Middle Border chronicle. All my club duties and Chicago theater transactions have been time-killers, diversions, and have added nothing to my reputation. My distaste of the Chicago climate has deepened for the reason that its harsh winds constantly threaten the health of my children. The grime and the blowing refuse of the streets disgust me. Woodlawn is so depressingly drab and ugly and dirty!"

Notwithstanding my ceaseless activity I was in bad health, which accounts, perhaps, for my mood of depression, a mood which I carried into the new year dispite the influence of my wife and daughters. My discouragement extended to the Cliff Dwellers, which had not proved the distinctive meeting place I had visioned. "Few men entertain there. The same little groups come every day to lunch. It is a struggle to maintain anything literary in Chicago. I am playing a losing game by staying on, but Hutchinson and other friends assure me of my value to the city. I need such assurance!"

I spent the spring and early summer in West Salem, but my depression persisted. I saw my native valley in terms of prose while musing on the poetry of its past.

"June 10. I am rereading Nathaniel Hawthorne and contrasting the literary atmosphere of his home with mine. How little I have to work with. Compared with his Concord, West Salem is utterly prosaic. It has no history. The only moss I have is a patch on my woodshed. My family portraits are enlarged photographs. My 'manse' is less than fifty years old and without a particle of original or acquired grace. Standing close to a concrete walk on the village street, its yard is open to every passing dog, and yet, were I a genius, I could make it interesting to the world.

"Now and again, as I talk with Fuller, I gain literary perspective on my life and my valley, but only for a moment. That the fault is in me I acknowledge, but I am too old and too harassed with the problem of making a living to remedy the defect. The sense of my own failure deepens my admiration for Zona Gale, who is steadily reporting her village in terms of tender and humorous fiction. She moves among her characters in smiling aloofness—but she sees them and sympathizes with them."

My little daughters were now coming to the age when I could read some of my chapters to them; and as I watched their delight in every phase of my boyhood and pioneer life, I said, "I shall train them to report their impressions of their home valley. They shall make this old house illustrious. To them it is beautiful and poetic. As they grow out of it and above it they will look back upon it with tender eyes. After all, poetry is in the poet and not in the landscape."

It had been my custom, for many years, to go to my desk at seven every morning and to work until eleven or twelve. Theoretically nothing was allowed to interfere with these hours, but actually my work at the club and for the Theater Society had distracted me far beyond the hours actually given to my duties at my office downtown. A sense of my responsibility ran through all the hours in my study. Correspondents demanded and obtained my interest, and then, in the midst of my other distractions, came the war between Roosevelt and the Old Guard Republicans, a struggle which involved me in the Progressive campaign. I attended both conventions and offered my services to the Progressives, an offer which I could ill-afford to fulfill.

I shall not go into any detailed description of the two great conventions which met in Chicago, but there is one story I cannot afford to leave out. In the most turbulent hour of the convention, when the papers were denouncing Roosevelt for coming to the city, and some of them were openly saying, "The man is insane," I went to the hotel in which he had established headquarters. I had some notion of sending my name in, but when I saw the dense, excited, milling throng which filled the corridors before his door, I turned away and went back to the club. It was, to me, an exhibition of crowd insanity and I had a distinct fear that the man whose tremendous fighting quality had led to strife would be touched by the folly and fury of the hour.

It happened that an old friend of Roosevelt was lunching with me, and as he smilingly unfolded his napkin he said, "Well, I've seen Teddy!"

"Have you? I haven't. I gave it up when I saw the crowd pressing against his door. How did you find him?"

My friend laughed. "I can answer that by describing our conversation. After bucking that close-packed mob in the hall, I reached his inner door. The guard, who knew me, took my name in and I was told to enter. The secretary let me into the reception room, and then, a few moments later, into the chief's private room. The moment I stepped through the door, I stepped into a dead calm, the quiet center of the storm. Roosevelt looked up, smiled, rose, and shook hands. 'I'm glad to see you. There is a question concerning the structure of the hangbird's nest which I'd like you to clear up. You set forth in your bird-lore article—' He was off! The political storm was nonexistent. Not one word did he utter concerning his mission to Chicago. For fifteen minutes he discussed hangbirds and their habits, absolutely regardless of the frenetic crowds filling the hotel and clamoring to see him."

III

The dedication of the Harper Memorial Library, which took place on June 11, was a rich and colorful ceremony although to my thinking it should have been more distinguished, involving literary figures of the faculty. It was almost local in its effect. "The most notable number on the program was a poem read by Edwin Lewis, a member of the faculty. When the moment came for his reading, Professor Lewis rose, removed his cap, and spoke his lines with admirable art. It was as fine a recitation as I have ever heard on any platform. The poem was scholarly rather than inspired, but his delivery of it was quite perfect. The trees, the sky, the brilliant color of the academic robes all united to make this poem the finest literary event of the day. And yet I could not avoid contrasting it with similar scenes at Harvard."

I discussed it with Fuller. "Small and Lewis were admirable, but how far will their names carry outside the city?" I asked.

"Not very far—but why should they? After all, it is a Chicago event."

"But that is my criticism of it; it should have been much more than a Chicago event. When Lowell or Emerson appeared at Harvard the nation was concerned."

There was in this ceremony the same failure of vision of which I complained in the opening of the Cliff

Dwellers. To me such events were figures in a vast, unrolling, historical web. This dedication should have symbolized a centralization, a fusing of all the university's literary interests. I had often discussed with Dr. Harper its esthetic shortcomings, and I knew how ambitious he was to have its creative men honored. He was not a man of letters, but he knew the value of writers like William Vaughn Moody in building up poetic and fictional traditions. To me the whole institution was pitifully bare of such associations, but this program should have gathered up and recorded all that it had of literary tradition, linking it for all time with this beautiful home for its books. "Admirable as an academic function, the ceremony was not inspiring. Dignified and stately, it failed of being significant."

"West Salem, August 9. Last night the Dudleys, one of the last of my father's pioneer neighbors, came to dinner and an attractive lot they are. They are carrying forward something of the poetry, the youthful beauty, and the romance which farm life in this valley once possessed. The youngest son has just come back from college to take up the management of the farm. One daughter is a freshman at Beloit, another the director of a Woman's Christian Association in Kansas City, and a third is a missionary in China. George, a banker, is my neighbor. When they are all at home the walls of their fine farmhouse (a mile or two out of town) echo with jocund voices and the tones of violin, 'cello, and piano. There is in the life of this the third generation of a pioneer family something suggestive of English country life. The young folk will scatter in September, but at present they are an almost ideal example of family loyalty and filial love. How seldom do we see anything even approaching social stability in these new lands where change is swifter than the seasons. The wilderness allures, the city calls, and family pride and unity are lost. None of us have time to take root."

During the summer I succeeded in writing a story of Wyoming, a novelette which I intended to include in "They of the High Trails," a companion volume to "Main-Travelled Roads," but mainly I kept my grip on "Sons of the Middle Border," holding, besottedly, to the belief that it was important enough to warrant continued effort. Each time it was rejected by an editor I set to work on its revision.

"Philadelphia, December 7. Here I am again in the friendly and invigorating atmosphere of the Bok home. Edward's serious and able talk is helpful. He loves his work. He lives for his magazine—that's what makes him what he is. His earnestness, his singleness of purpose, his never-resting energy are inspiring to me. After a long period of intense physical labor with carpenters and plumbers rebuilding my West Salem home, I feel like writing again. Edward's beautiful house and his keenly intelligent and lovely wife, together with their expressed love for the Garlands, are making my stay delightful and have given me renewed desire to do at least one more book.

"He does not value my 'Sons of the Middle Border,' but I do not lay that up against him. He sees all manuscripts in terms of his magazine, and rightly, for it is precisely this devotion which has made him one of the most successful editors of his time."

On the following day, one of the sub-editors of the Curtis Publishing Company took me through the new and magnificent plant, a tour which reduced me to a still lower deep of humility. "I ate luncheon with a group of the editors of both the *Post* and the *Journal* in their own special room, and their lively, up-to-the-minute talk put me in my place as a respected relic of a bygone period.

" 'We are out for circulation,' they frankly declared. 'We are hot after the stuff which the people—our people—want. "Literatoor" cuts no ice with us. We are not publishing for the few but for the million.' They were respectful to me, kindly in truth, but they made me feel my diminishing importance in their world. I came away intimidated and a bit disgusted with their candid commercialism."

CHAPTER THIRTY-NINE

TWO NOTABLE DINNERS

I

AMONG my fellow members at the Players was Vivian Burnett, son of Frances Hodgson Burnett, and one afternoon he said to me, "Would you like to sit in my mother's box at the theater and see 'The Yellow Jacket'?"

"Will your mother be in the box?"

"She will and she would like to have a chat with you."

As a matter of fact I had seen "The Yellow Jacket," but I had never met Mrs. Burnett, for whose work I had a very high respect.

I had read "That Lass o' Lowrie's" more than twenty years before and I had followed her pretty constantly during all the intervening years. Her son Vivian, a small, sensitive young man (who had lost most of the curling hair which his mother had made famous in her story), lunched regularly at the Players, and we had often talked of his distinguished mother.

Her American home was on Long Island, but she spent much time in England and her international books like "Tembaron" especially interested me. We had a common interest also in psychic phenomena, and while a box at the theater did not promise the best opportunity for a discussion of such matters, it would at least enable me to express my high regard for her work and to gain a clearer notion of her personality.

I found her "a rather heavy, blonde woman a little beyond middle age, with a genial but impassive expression, markedly English in voice and speech. She is a gracious and able character, growing old like a fine man, handsome, dignified, serene."

She appeared pleased by my selection of "Tembaron" as one of her best international novels, and spoke of the enormous popularity of "Little Lord Fauntleroy" with affection but with full realization of its lesser value. We had no opportunity to do more than exchange a word or two on her "Secret Garden," but between the acts we did touch hastily on spiritualism. I carried away, however, a very pleasing impression of her and promised to call on her at her home.

Once afterward I met her at some public reception, but we never renewed our discussion of the occult. "Diverse as they are in some ways, she, Margaret Deland, and Gertrude Atherton are associated in my mind as admirable types of modern women. Substantially of the same generation, they are all able novelists. I will not say which is the ablest. They all deserve the high honors they have won."

II

At the National Institute dinner, the question of a Western meeting came up and was debated at length. Some of the men felt that as our charter was national in scope we were in danger of being criticized, for the reason that we had only New York citizens as directors, and also for the reason that all our sessions were held in the East. With this timidity I had no patience.

"No one will doubt the national scope of our organization as he reads the list of our members and the states from which they come," I argued. "Taft of Illinois, Page of Virginia, Allen and Fox from Kentucky, Cable of Louisiana, Riley and Johnson from Indiana, Howells from Ohio—nearly every state in the Union is represented. As for the officers, they must of necessity be residents of New York—no organization can carry on with directors so scattered that they cannot count upon a quorum. I should like to see a meeting in Chicago, of course, and if it is decided upon, I will do all I can to make it a success, but I do not consider it necessary."

The outcome of this speech was a motion on the part of Brander Matthews to hold the next meeting in Chicago and to make me chairman of a committee of arrangements. Nearly fifty men were present and voting—one of the largest meetings we had ever held —and a surprising number were in favor of going to Chicago. In all such discussions, however, I still considered myself one of the younger and less authoritative men and when my elders made me their representative in the West I was intimidated. My youthfulness, however, was merely by way of contrast, for I was approaching fifty-three!

Just before leaving for Chicago I sat in at a dinner of "The Highbrow Political Contributors" who had given their services to the Progressive campaign in favor of Roosevelt, an extremely able and vital group. The women were Edna Ferber, Inez Haynes Gilmore, and a Miss Smith whom I did not know. Will Irwin, George W. Perkins, Frank Munsey, and many others whom I cannot at the moment name were present and spoke. Roosevelt called me to a seat beside him and we had a great deal of talk. He was not only in the pink of condition, but seemingly undisturbed by his defeat. Of the wound he had received in Milwaukee he made no mention. Although the most famous man in the world at this time, he was "just one of us." Even if none of us could forget for an instant his overshadowing reputation, he fitted quietly into the design of the dinner.

My recollection is that Perkins presided, but my notes simply say, "The speeches were all good—except mine—Roosevelt's was notably short, direct, modest, and sincere. Perkins' introductions were capital."

Roosevelt and I had a great deal of talk concerning the literary value of his experiences in the White House, for when he jokingly said, "I am permanently out of politics," I said, "Good! Now you can write the book which Howells and I have long been urging upon you."

"By George, I'll do it!" he replied in his boyish way. "I'll begin it immediately, dictating in the way Howells suggested."

I told him what Mark Twain had said about the diary he was writing: "It can't be published while I'm alive, it can't be published while the people I write about are alive; but when it *is* published there'll be a noble squirming in their graves."

This amused him, but his smile passed as he replied, "I'm afraid old Mark was taking it out of some of his subjects—I have no desire to get even with anybody, but I do feel that my chronicle should be candid."

"Don't give us too much of the political, the official —write it the way you talk to your friends."

"That's not so easy as it sounds, especially when you consider the distractions I suffer. Being out of politics is not precisely retirement for me," he added, and his voice rose in that peculiar falsetto which preceded all his humorous phrases, "I shall still experience, for some time, repercussions of this political uproar. However, I shall set to work at once—tell Howells that, it may interest him."

As he looked round the table, he said, "I am proud of this volunteer committee."

"I am going to move that we make it a permanent organization—a kind of informal club of your friends to carry on the Progressive campaign."

This pleased him. "I'd like you to suggest that. There's fine potentiality in such a group."

When I was called upon to speak I had a neat literary design in mind. I intended to say something like this: "Some of you may have wondered at the almost uniform success of our illustrious leader who was for nearly eight years the ruler of this nation, but I am in possession of the secret. The truth is I am responsible for his advancement. When I knew him first along about 1895, he was Commissioner of Police in New York City, a rising young man, holding a position of trust and authority so important that he might well have been wholly satisfied, and when he was offered the position of Assistant Secretary of the Navy I felt it my duty to advise against his acceptance of it. 'It

is but a superior clerk's chair,' I wrote. 'Not to be compared with your present position.' He thanked me for
my interest, but—accepted the appointment.

"In 1898 the war with Spain came on and when he
said, 'I am about to accept a lieutenant colonel's commission in Colonel Leonard Wood's Rough Riders,' I
argued against that. 'You are a shining figure in Washington and in line of promotion, you can't afford to
resign even to become a brigadier general.' Again he
moved in opposition to my advice. He entered the war
a lieutenant colonel, and came out the Governor of
New York. His fame was now so great that the big
politicians decided to put the snuffers over him—they
offered him the vice presidency. Again with several
hundred thousand of his friends, I wrote to say, 'Don't
let them shelve you. Stay where you are.' Again he
thanked me for my advice—and forgot it! He became
President by way of Providence in 1901 and again—
on his own merits—three years later. Thus you will see
that by consistently disregarding my advice, he achieved
the most powerful official position in the world. When
I advised the right-hand trail he took the left.

"Now mark what happened! The moment my mind
and his ran parallel, his defeat was assured. So long as
I advised against his course, so long as I voted for
another man the other man failed and Roosevelt moved
triumphantly onward and upward, but with my support, he fell. As I claim the credit for his early success,
so now I take on myself the stain of his defeat."

Of course, I failed to carry out this humorous design.
It was a fine idea and Mark Twain would have made
an unforgettable speech on its lines, but I bungled it.

However, Roosevelt was enough of the writer to perceive at the beginning my ironic intent and smiled encouragingly. As I glanced down at him, he said now and again, "That's true, he did," in confirmation of my claims, so that while it came off lamely it was not entirely without effect.

I cannot be sure whether it was at this meeting or a later one that he mentioned his wish to explore the upper waters of the Amazon; but it must have been at this time. "I am as fit for the wilderness as ever," he declared, and so indeed he seemed to be.

III

The institute's formal letter designating me chairman of the committee of arrangements did not reach me till after my return to Chicago, but when it did, I decided to make the Cliff Dwellers the center of my campaign. I wrote at once to the presidents of all the literary and educational institutions in the city asking them to meet with me to form a reception committee which should unite the esthetic forces of Chicago. My suggestion, familiar to these men, was unanimously adopted. They met and pledged sufficient money to entertain all members of the National Institute from the time they left New York until they returned to their homes. "There is nothing small in Western hospitality," I wrote to Brander Matthews. "The bigger and more important you can make this invasion, the more generous the fund for entertainment will be. We grant that we are on the border of the esthetic world and we value the coming of such a distinguished group of authors and artists." As I wrote these letters I had a clear sense of the historical significance of this meeting. It marked another stage of Western culture.

Notwithstanding the distinction of this committee work, my year ended in shadow. "I have not felt so helpless and so unproductive in many years. No doubt this is the beginning of my supersedence by younger men. Next year my failure will be more marked. I have this comfort, however, I have laid up a small fund against dull times and I am rich in friends."

CHAPTER FORTY

CHICAGO ENTERTAINS THE ARTS

I

ONE afternoon, as I was leaving the Players, I met John Phillips of the *American Magazine*, who asked, "Is Charles R. Crane in town?" "I don't think so. I haven't seen him lately. He is probably in Samarcand, or Cairo or Timbuctoo."

This led to an interchange of our experiences with Crane, and in the midst of it a third man, some friend of Phillips, remarked with an amused tone, "You fellows make Crane out to be a most remarkable character."

"He is," I replied. "He is the world Vidocq. He knows more people and more places than any other man—except Roosevelt. I have a mind to write a character sketch of him."

"Why don't you?" said Phillips. "I'll be glad to print it."

Crane was still living in Chicago on a South Side avenue in a large brownstone house filled with Russian paintings, embroidery, and sculpture. Somewhat as Archer Huntington had achieved a youthful enthusiasm for Spain, so Crane as a boy had acquired a knowledge of Russian life and art. He knew Russia from Moscow to Samarcand. As a traveler he never seemed hurried, but he covered the earth with the network of his trails. With the air of a dreamer he flitted from palace to palace in Egypt, and was escorted from sheik to sheik in Arabia. He knew the head men of all the Balkan states and was a valued patron of art in Prague. I wrote of him, "His type is new in American life—especially new in Mid-Western life. He declines to be enslaved by business or time or space. I may be wrong about my relationship to him, but I never think of him as a business man. He is a fellow intellectual, a lover of books and pictures—not the pictures or books that I like—but works of art nevertheless. In matters of social welfare he is a valued friend of Jane Addams in Chicago and Lillian Wald in New York, and it is reported that he is supporting many special schools in the Balkans. In all these matters he may be taken as a divergent member of my generation—just as Fuller is, only Fuller's patrimony is small and his sphere of activity sternly limited. He is less widely traveled than Crane, but he, too, is a cosmopolitan."

One night, as my wife and I were sitting in the manager's box at the opera in Chicago, Madame Dippel spoke of Crane's sudden appearance at her country place in Poland the summer before. "His face was burned into strips," she said, "for he had ridden on horseback from the Sea of Marmora all the way up through the Balkans, over six hundred miles. He had been visiting some of the schools he had established there, and also he had been studying the monasteries of the Bosphorus, for what purpose I cannot imagine. He knows more about the Balkan situation than any other man of my acquaintance."

II

Some one, I have forgotten who, told me that Douglass Center, a colored organization of the South Side, would like to have me address them, and a few days later I heard from the committee who asked me to speak on the conservation of our forests (a singular choice on their part) and this I did one Sunday afternoon.

My record reads: "It was all poignantly pathetic to me—that threadbare little clubhouse filled with a patient, thoughtful, dark-faced audience. A realization that these Americans, who are not Americans, are struggling toward something, lifting their eyes to some vague upland, desiring some achievement, some victory over fate, made my address a futile gesture. 'They are so poor, so outlawed, so forgotten,' I said afterward to my wife."

(This was twenty years ago. That small band was, in fact, the advance line of a devastating army. Since then the region where Fuller, Hutchinson, and Crane lived has become a scene of desolation. Many of those South Side mansions, once the homes of my friends, are now tenements, swarming with blacks, while others stand vacant, half destroyed by hoodlums. Whole blocks have been torn down. Commerce, approaching from the north, and these blacks from the south have blighted this region as if a pestilence and an earthquake had conjoined. Furthermore, these Africans, with the soil of Southern plantations still on their shoes, have votes. They influence elections. They are not to be blamed—they are what we have made them; nevertheless, they are a menace to South Side Chicago.)

That I sent it out again is evident from this record: "West Salem, July 9. At the request of Sterling Yard, the new editor of the *Century Magazine*, I sent my 'Middle Border' to his office. His letter to me was like the fall of a mountain landmark, for although it bore the familiar *Century* heading, it carried neither the signature of Gilder nor of Johnson. The spirit of the present has invaded even the inner office of this famous periodical. The new management is in the scramble for wider circulation. Yard will probably reduce the price, 'ginger up' the reading matter, and the manager will raise his advertising rates. It is no doubt a sign of old age in me, but I hate to see these changes—although, to be candid, I seldom read the *Century*. It has printed nothing of mine for years and is not really a part of my life."

As it turned out Yard returned my MS. with kindly words of praise. "We recognize its truth to a time and place but we cannot use it," he wrote.

The mountain West still allured me, although the discomforts of travel had grown into a deterrent. I had no keen desire to leave my home in the valley, hot and commonplace as it was; but I did.

"Red Lodge, Montana. September 4. Getting in touch with the forest ranger yesterday morning, I rode out to his station and slept last night in his 'big room' with a glorious mountain stream singing my slumber song. Riding up here alone, in the dark, brought up thronging memories of a hundred similar journeys."

For two weeks I rode amid the splendors of the Sawtooth Range, the Absaroka Forest, and the region just north of Yellowstone Park. With my light, yet perfectly adequate, sleeping bag and kit, I was at home anywhere and in any weather. The foresters passed me on from camp to camp and seemed glad to show me the noblest views and the loveliest streams, all of which made Wisconsin seem very far down and wholly commonplace; but my experiences did not awaken in me, this time, the desire to fictionize Montana. It was only a healing vacation; it did not call for fiction. My fifty-third birthday was spent in the Bitter Root Mountains watching the men fight a fire on a slippery hillside, a desperate struggle; and the next day I rode on to the Jocko Lakes.

"Nothing wilder or more primitive of suggestion can now be found in Montana. This region is filled with elk and deer and bears. The rangers tell many stories of encounters with grizzlies. The tall berry bushes along the trail were bent down and twisted, in evidence that the bears had recently been feeding there. I spent one night in a newly built, unfinished cabin and recovered something of the thrill my father experienced when building his new home in Green's Coolly. There was magic in the smell of the pine shavings and in the whisper of the wind at the windows."

Notwithstanding the many beautiful scenes I had enjoyed, and the fine personalities I had met in the forest service, I find in my record a mood of distaste, almost disgust. "The people have changed for the worse —or I have come to them in a less idealistic mood. The settlements are no longer picturesque—they are pitifully squalid. The present phase of development is cheap, flimsy, and ugly. At fifty-three a man does not

from my personal knowledge of you) that it was autobiography and not fiction, and the little subterfuge
was therefore very transparent. To others it might not
be so."

This letter from one of my ablest and most friendly
critics profoundly affected me. I decided to call the
manuscript "Sons of the Middle Border" and to do
away with the personal pronoun. "This will make it
impersonal and its historical content will be emphasized," I wrote to Wheeler. Another editorial friend
suggested that I could avoid the charge of egotism by
calling it "A Prairie Family," and giving it the tone
of historical fiction. This I was willing to do, but as
he would not buy it under any title, I continued to call
it "Sons of the Middle Border."

I was especially chagrined when my good friend
Bok again rejected it. "It is good work, Garland, but
it is not for me. I cannot see it in my magazine." His
tone of regret especially disheartened me.

As chairman of the reception committee for the
Chicago meeting of the National Institute of Arts and
Letters I reported that I had united the esthetic leaders
of the city in a general entertainment committee and
that some of my fellow Cliff Dwellers had chartered
a special club car "for the use of New York members
with all hotel expenses paid."

The directors of the Institute expressed astonishment
as well as pleasure. "We should all go," they urged.
"Nothing but unavoidable engagements should keep
any of us away"—and yet, running through it all, was
a tone of condescension, of kindly effort. "No one is
eager to go, but as it will cost us nothing and will

please a Western public, it is our duty." Only the officers who considered such a meeting helpful to the
Institute announced their willingness to come. So the
Cliff Dwellers would have felt about a visit to a town
on the plain.

On November 12 the special car left New York, and
its approach was jocosely described by our Chicago
newspaper men as "An invasion of Eastern poets, philosophers, and novelists." None of these wits rose to
the humorous level of Eugene Field, who in his day
described an imaginary street parade of literati in
honor of Edmund Clarence Stedman, but they put the
city in possession of the salient facts of this "westward march of culture." Ralph Clarkson, Hobart
Chatfield-Taylor, and I were but an inconspicuous
committee of reception as we paced the station platform
to greet our visitors and direct them to their hotels.
Privately, I confessed to a disappointment. The group,
while satisfactory as to personnel, was smaller than I
had hoped for.

Chicago was a long way off and at the last moment
some of the most desired men had declined to come, but
I could not reproach them for this action.

The dinner in Blackstone Hall that night, however,
was beautifully ordered, the speaking good, and the
guests appreciative. Charles Hutchinson, president of
the Art Institute, made a genial toastmaster, and Professor William M. Sloane and Brander Matthews
replied in witty and graceful phrase. The audience was
pleased and the Eastern men impressed. When we came
out at eleven o'clock Michigan Avenue was at its best.
"It looks like a city," I said to William Gillette, who

had been my dinner companion. "It does indeed," he heartily agreed.

On the following night Hobart Chatfield-Taylor entertained the Institute members at his club. Forty-four were present, which was a gratifying number considering that nearly all were residents of New York, Philadelphia, and Boston. Brander Matthews, as head of the Institute, presided and carried through the official business of an annual meeting, including elections. He made a ready chairman, but his levity in presenting important resolutions and candidates disturbed me greatly and in a blunt speech I urged deliberation. "Every name should be fully discussed," I declared. "This organization is too important, too selective, to have its members voted upon *en bloc* as suggested by Chairman Matthews. I am aware that it will detract from our entertainment, but no candidate desires his name passed upon hurriedly and without individual judgment. Membership in this organization is an honor and should not be handed out in packages. I beg the chairman to reconsider his suggestion and permit us to vote on each name separately."

Matthews was so much impressed with my protest and the applause which followed it that he frankly said, "Garland's arguments are sound. I was only trying to save time. He is right, the good of the Institute must be considered. From this time forward we will follow his plan and vote on each name separately."

This was more important than appears on the surface, for it registered a complete change of attitude on the part of those members who had smiled at the idea of a selective esthetic organization and who had hitherto said, "What does it matter how we select our members?"

At our public session at the Art Institute next day, Augustus Thomas was given the gold medal of the Institute and his speech of acceptance was both humorous and eloquent. Among other things he said: "I shall at once inform my aged mother of this honor and I suspect she will say, 'Why have you waited so long?'" It was a charming glimpse of the loyal son whom city life had failed to alienate.

William Gillette was equally happy in the presentation of a paper which had for its theme, "On the speaking of lines the first time," or some such title. It was an exposition of his theory of naturalism in reading. "You should read your lines as if thinking them out for the first time," he argued.

At one point in his address he hesitated, shuffled his pages, and gave other signs of feeling his way through his paper. His blunders worried some of us till we discovered that they were all a bit of subtle acting on his part—then we all laughed. This (apparently) added to his embarrassment. He stopped and looked at us reproachfully, then as if by some great good fortune found his lost page and went on. "It was a delightful lesson in naturalistic platform reading. He and Thomas are past masters in such demonstrations."

A luncheon ended what all our visitors declared to be the most successful session the Institute had ever had. "All due to your Cliff Dwellers," said Professor Sloane and Robert Underwood Johnson, who had carried on most of the preparatory work in the East.

It will not do to say that this meeting of the

National Institute of Arts and Letters made any profound change in Chicago's intellectual life, but it has significance as pointing out once again the fact that in the eyes of the Eastern men the Cliff Dwellers were esthetic pioneers, digging stumps, draining marshes, and planting morning-glory vines around the cabin door. They respected us, but felt sorry for us. We were doing a noble, necessary, but rather unpleasant job. They shook hands, shouted "good luck!" and hurried into their Pullman cars with perfectly evident relief, glad that their lives were cast in a region where the esthetic grubbing and draining had long since been done. They returned to their studios and studies glowing with satisfaction in a missionary act conscientiously carried out, while we watched them go with a deepened sense of the building and the cultivation which our city demanded.

CHAPTER FORTY-ONE

GRAY DAYS AT FIFTY-THREE

I

Notwithstanding the increased honor which my fellow members of the National Institute of Arts and Letters declared I had earned by the management of the Chicago meeting, my fifty-fourth year began with darkening skies and chill winds. My autobiographic manuscript upon which I had toiled so long had again been declined, and in addition to this discouragement I was suffering some form of malnutrition which had the effect of confining me to my study for a larger part of the time than was wholesome. My only escape from this depression was by way of a return to boyhood and to my youth in Boston.

That this was my actual mood will appear in a reading of the following lines dated Jan. 2nd, 1913: "This was a bad day for me. I went to the club but was too ill to remain. On my return to the house I found little Constance suffering from some throat infection. She was in high fever and I was worried. I did no writing whatever." Three days later I added: "I was able to do a little revision to-day and that helped to raise the cloud which has been hanging over me for several weeks." I mention these facts in order that the reader who has followed me thus far may know the conditions of my life after twenty-five years of authorship. I take no credit for my persistency as a writer—I was incapable of anything else.

In the midst of this period of depression, Irving Bacheller came to town on a lecturing tour, ruddy, genial, and prosperous. I did not envy him his success; I rejoiced in it. "Everything that he does is nobly intentioned, and whatever its faults his writing is individual in tone. The fact that my own stories are no longer in demand and that I live meanly does not lessen his interest in me. His door is always open to me—as mine is to him." On this visit he spent the night with us, much to the delight of my little daughters, and listened to my story of discouragement sympathetically. "Come on to New York," he urged. "Bring the manuscript. Somebody will buy it. Come right out to Riverside. 'Thrushwood' is waiting for you."

Notwithstanding his confident assertion I fell back into my despondent mood as this entry proves: "The Mexican revolution is in full drive at this time and all the magazine editors are bored with peace and the history of normal human life. They are filling their columns with stories of raids along our Texas border, and have no time or space for quiet reminiscences of pioneering in Wisconsin. Their judgments are kindly but firm. 'Our readers want action, romance, warfare,' they write."

Nevertheless I bore Bacheller's advice in mind and when, early in January, I was called upon to fulfill a lecture engagement at the University Club in Pittsburgh, I decided to go on from there to New York in a last desperate attempt at selling my Middle Border chronicle, and to this end I again revised it with utmost care. "It is probably due to the feebleness of age," I confessed to Fuller, "but the fact is I have not succeeded in putting my story into satisfactory form, and yet some of it has been revised ten times."

"Take a rest from it, and remember, after all, you are writing it for your father's generation, not for the critics."

With no confidence in my mission I set out on January 16 for the East, carrying with me several short stories as well as the Middle Border chronicle.

"Pittsburgh, January 17. Midnight. My lecture, delivered in the dining room of the club, was a failure. It started late and being worried about catching the train on which I had reservations—I was hurried and ineffective. At the close of my talk I leaped into a taxi and rushed for the station, which I reached a minute after the gate closed. I am writing this in my room at the University Club to which I returned for the night with a feeling that my whole trip is doomed to failure. I was strongly minded, while at the station, to give up my trip to New York. I thought of taking the train back to Chicago, but my trunk was already on its way to the East. With no expectation of selling any of my manuscripts I shall go on to-morrow morning and have another talk with Duneka."

This was one of the darkest moments of my life. My lecture had failed, my stories were unsalable, and I had no other way of making a living. I saw no light ahead. My sleep that night was troubled, and when at nine the following morning I took the train for New York I humbly entered the day coach. "Here is where I belong," I grimly acknowledged. "Here among the workers."

After a tedious all-day ride, I reached New York and a room in a small hotel on Thirty-fourth Street. This was January 18. "What am I doing here?" I asked myself. "Why spend time and money on a venture which is certain to end in disappointment? All the newspapers and magazines are filled with stories of adventure, and all the talk is of war with Mexico. Nothing that I can offer has any value at this time."

Feeling smaller, weaker, and less worthy of consideration than at any time since my first days in Boston nearly thirty years before, I went to bed. Sleep came at last and when I rose next morning I was in better spirits. A condition which a hearty breakfast and a noble cup of coffee sustained. Going down to my publishers, in Franklin Square, I told the story of my revised manuscript to Wells and Duneka, hoping that they would say, "Let us see it. Perhaps we can use a part of it in the magazine."

Nothing of the kind happened. Duneka said, "We are willing to publish the book, but Wells can't see a serial in it." That he was not specially eager to print this book was evident. Notwithstanding his success with "Hesper" and "The Captain of the Gray Horse Troop," he was only mildly interested in my autobiographic manuscript.

"Why don't you go up to Collier's and see Mark Sullivan?" he finally said. "He is looking for American serials, I am told, and might be interested in this story of yours."

Thanking him for the suggestion, I went away

recognizing with some bitterness that he had lost interest in me. "In this he is justified, for none of my recent books have been profitable to Harper's or to me. It hurts me to think of myself as a squeezed orange—but that is what I am."

Collier's Weekly, one of the popular successes of the day, had for its editor Mark Sullivan, a fellow member of the Players. We had met pleasantly now and again, but I had never taken him into account when sending out my manuscripts. I considered *Collier's* too much the newspaper for any work of mine, and when I entered the barrack-like building in which it was edited and printed, my distrust was augmented. The floors vibrated with the speed of multiple presses, and messengers, clerks, artists, and editors skittered to and fro in breathless haste. I was dismayed. "What am I doing in this roaring, bustling, up-to-the-minute commercial caravansary? My slow-moving, reminiscent story of the Middle Border is wholly and ludicrously out of step with this periodical. 'What is the use?' I asked myself. 'Why bother Sullivan with my dull manuscript?' "

However, as my name had gone in to him, I could not run away and so I waited in the outer office, gloomily impatient to see him and have it over with.

The boy came back to say, "Mr. Sullivan will see you."

There was unexpected serenity in Sullivan's office, and serenity in his friendly blue eyes. "How are you, Garland? Come in and sit down," he said, and then abruptly yet genially, as one who sensed the situation and was disposed to come at the heart of my business, he said very quietly, "What is on your mind?"

With his clear glance expressing a kindly interest, he

listened in reflective silence while I told him of my Middle Border chronicle, and confessed to the years of labor I had spent upon it. I emphasized the narrative pioneer side of it but frankly owned that it dealt largely with my own career. At the close of my statement he said, "You come at a favoring psychological moment. I am in search of the kind of story you can give me. I want something American, something homely. It is true, as you say, our magazine is crammed with Mexican war stuff, but I want something to offset it. Your manuscript sounds good to me. Where is it?"

"At my hotel."

"Get it down to me to-day. I'm going West but I'll have it read at once. Come with me." Leading me to the desk of a small, blond young man, he said, "Sissons, you know Hamlin Garland?" and then as we shook hands, he went on: "I want you to read a manuscript which Mr. Garland has with him—read anything he brings to us, but I am especially interested in his Western chronicle. I want an immediate report on it. I am going out of town or I would read it myself."

On the strength of this editorial command, I returned to my hotel, and brought the manuscript down to Sissons. That night I recorded my experience and added with Scotch caution "I am almost hoping for a sale."

II

At luncheon next day Stewart Edward White, brown, sinewy, and laconic, ate with me. He was just back from Africa, laden with trophies and rich manuscript records of his adventures. Although not a loquacious talker, he gave me a clearer notion of the big-game country than I had derived from any other of the returned hunters—excepting Roosevelt. At the same time I doubted the wisdom of his lingering along this divergent trail. "After all you are a novelist of Western America," I argued.

"Africa was only a vacation," he replied. "I'll go back to the West as soon as I get this hunting material off my chest."

I liked White and I liked his books. He was vigorously, wholesomely native in all he did. A lover of the open air, the forests, and the mountains, he never permitted the psychology of the city to enter his fictional scene. As hunter, trailer, horseman, he was a master. We held many interests in common.

Irving Bacheller, who came into the club later, said, "I need another of our old-fashioned songfests and so do you. Come along."

He didn't know how much the promise of that fireplace meant to me although I told him I was awaiting a verdict on my Middle Border manuscript. He had not read it, but he had gained a fairly accurate concept of its importance to me and did his best to encourage me. "We're both in eclipse just now, but this war cloud will soon lift," he remarked. "Put your trust in Sullivan and he will pull you through."

Setting aside my troubles, I went out to Thrushwood. Again we discussed plans for future work and he read me some of his latest comment which I found delightfully humorous. "The story is nearly ready for the printing and the publishers are hounding me for copy," he said.

"Don't let them hurry you; that is your danger," I repeated.

On my return to the city the following day I lunched with the Authors League, and dined at the club amidst a swarm of assistant editors, rapid-fire novelists, popular dramatists, and war correspondents. On going to my room at the Arts I set down this note which indicates my critical mood: "As I meet the men who are the chief purveyors in present-day book and magazine markets, I am more and more impressed with the ephemeral character of their output. They are for the most part opportunists; their talk is concerned almost wholly with the question of pay. Seldom do I hear a word concerning the nobility of the writers' craft. Thirty years ago, when I began to write, rewards were small and authorship less of a trade.

"Something has gone out of American literary society. It may be the blindness of old age, but I cannot see in the writers I meet at the club the analogues of Lowell, Howells, James, and Emerson. It is not merely that they are less cultured, they occupy a totally different attitude toward authorship. I have no wish to be unjust to them and it may be that my impression of them is wrong—I hope it is.

"Another and still more disturbing change is in process. New York is becoming each year more European, more antagonistic to what certain of its writers call 'New England Puritanism.' Month by month these critics, contemptuous of 'the American tradition,' join in celebrating the novelists and dramatists who sound the sexual note most insistently. A claque for the pornographic has developed. It is becoming fashionable to sneer at marriage, chastity, home life, and the church, and to bring into the dining room the phases and jokes of the roadhouse. Certain so-called philosophers openly advocate the morals of the barnyard in their essays on 'freedom' and their attacks on 'the puritanic ideal.' Others, however, have achieved a success by the cheap and easy device of putting into print the stories and phrases of the saloon and the brothel. This is the most disturbing phase of the whole situation. Young writers, perceiving that the pornographic experts are the highest paid men and women in the field of authorship, are led to write their confessions and voice their defiances."

(I am now copying this comment nearly twenty years later, in the midst of an almost universal era of cynicism, obscenity, and destructive criticism. For more than fifteen years writers of a certain type have glorified the female libertine. As panderers they have prospered, for the publishers of books and magazines have welcomed them, shifting the blame to the public. "If the people want that kind of thing, we'll give it to them," they have said, and in this there lies a bitter truth. Women buy their books and support their plays.

Happily a reaction appears to have set in. Some of the most remarkable successes of the 1930 season were achieved by books and plays of imagination and idealistic quality. In the midst of a public which enriches the panderer and the bootlegger, another and vaster public exists, one which rewards the fine novelist and the decent dramatist.

It is well that in 1913 I had only a vague premonition of this destructive decade or I would have been still more hopeless of the future.)

III

On Tuesday morning, with very little expectation of anything definite concerning my manuscript, I went down to Sullivan's office. He was away, but Sissons astounded me by saying, "We like your Middle Border. We see in it five and possibly six large installments. Sullivan is reading the manuscript now and will report on it, definitely, in a few days. Meanwhile, let us see any fiction you may have with you."

From this highly encouraging interview I went at once to see Yard, of the *Century,* to whom I had sent a story of my dramatic friendship with James A. Herne. Yard, too, was helpful. He not only accepted this article, but handed me a check for three hundred dollars. My skies were brightening!

On the following Sunday night, January 25, I called on Brander Matthews as I had done so many times before, finding him among his books, and surrounded by his friends. "He and Howells are the only ones of the Old Guard left. Gilder, Stedman, Warner, Clemens —all are gone."

On Thursday I shared the Poetry Society dinner as the guest of William and Mary Roberts. Among those present I saw Ella Wheeler Wilcox, Richard Le Gallienne, May Riley Smith, Edwin Markham, and Irving Bacheller. "One of the speakers was William Marion Reedy of St. Louis, a large man, gross of face and figure, who spoke in the manner of a political orator, florid and resounding. He made a very poor impression on me, although he was greeted by the poets as a 'patron,' and his paper, *The Mirror,* was referred to as 'the first to print the work of Edgar Lee Masters," as if that were its chief distinction. Miss Jessie Rittenhouse, secretary of the society, spoke ably and briefly. So did Irving Bacheller. Edward Wheeler, as chairman, was entirely admirable. The society is prospering under his leadership, aided by Miss Rittenhouse.

"As I looked about the room filled with men and women in evening dress, I was obliged to revise my notions of our versifiers, for these handsome and happy residents of Grub Street were not distinguishable from ordinary millionaires. Only Ella Wheeler Wilcox and Richard Le Gallienne conformed in any degree to the popular conception of poets. Markham, like myself, had been tamed down and was almost completely disguised by a more or less conventional dinner jacket. From all accounts, poetry is looking up. Publishers are reported to be kindly disposed toward it.

"In his introduction, Wheeler said: 'The success of Edna Millay, Vachel Lindsay, and Edwin Markham has started a bull market for poetry,' and with a laugh in his voice he added, 'and truly it does seem that for the poet "with a punch" a new day has dawned. Longfellow and Tennyson are about to become second-raters—at least when measured by the royalty returns of our day, and it is freely predicted that our poets—some of them—will outsell novelists like Bacheller and Churchill.' Then with his customary humor, he concluded, 'but this is only the natural optimism of an after-dinner orator.' "

It happened that the Authors Society met the following night, and as I compared the sober garb and quiet talk of its guests with the shining figures of the verse writers' dinner, I was inclined to agree with Wheeler's prediction. Around the table were gathered the familiar elderly figures of Holt, the publisher, Drake, art editor of the *Century,* J. Wells Champney, Duffield Osborne, and others whom I always met there and nowhere else, and of whose work I knew little. "It may be that these editors and professors are more useful and more to be honored than fictionists or versifiers," I wrote. "I am only contrasting the fire and fury of the Poetry Society discussion with this subdued meeting in the dining room which the munificence of Andrew Carnegie has endowed. I felt like a young man in the midst of these octogenarians. It would have been a dull evening for me had not my old friend, Edgar Chamberlin of Boston, happened in."

In my mail the next morning I found a letter from Sissons saying, "Mr. Sullivan has wired us. He says 'I am thrilled with the truth and beauty of Garland's chronicle.' We will use six installments of it at once."

It would be difficult for me to exaggerate the relief, the confidence which this message from the busy editor of a roaring, rushing commercial magazine brought to me. To have my homely chronicle of pioneer life approved in a time of war news and growing sensualism was almost miraculous good fortune.

In justification of my despairing outlook, I must again record the fact that this manuscript upon which I had been working for nearly three years had been declined by six editors, all of them my friends, and that I had lost my interest in fictional subjects. Bearing all this in mind the reader will share in some degree, I hope, the joyous relief I experienced when (on the 3rd of February) Mark Sullivan commissioned me to put into form for immediate publication six installments of my "Sons of the Middle Border." My account of it reads thus, "I am to receive for these six installments twenty-five hundred dollars in cash. Sullivan has also accepted one of my novelettes in which 'Tall Ed Kelly' figures. I am returning to Chicago four thousand dollars richer than when I left home a month ago.

"Sullivan said to me, 'You have done a thoroughly good job in this chronicle. My boyhood was spent in a little town near Philadelphia, but I know the Mid-West well enough to feel that you have captured the spirit of it. I regard this as a most important serial. I am forced to print a great many stories to please my readers, I shall print this to please myself,'" and listening to his quiet voice and looking into his pleasant blue eyes, I recovered confidence in my future, and to my wife I wrote: "We owe a debt of gratitude to Mark Sullivan which we can never repay. He has given me a chance to 'come back,' as they say of a temporarily defeated prize-fighter."

CONCLUDING WORD

Under the title "A Son of the Middle Border" this narrative as an autobiographic story of family, was published by Macmillan's, and in my diary for 1917 I find this entry—"Onteora Park, The Catskills, Aug., 1917. At my gate this morning I found the Sunday *Times*, and in the book review, covering the whole front page, was an article on my book by William Dean Howells. This recognition by the *Times* is a most unexpected honor, and to have my old and revered friend and fellow craftsman writing in such praise of my chronicle is overwhelming."

The success of esteem which this narrative won led me to write and publish in 1921 "A Daughter of the Middle Border," a direct sequel to "A Son of the Middle Border" and in 1924 a preface to these two volumes which I called "Trail Makers of the Middle Border." Then to round the circle I wrote "Back Trailers" which dealt with those of us who, as sons of pioneers in the West, took the back trail of our grandsires and became trail makers in another fashion.

These four books form one continuous history of a group of migrating families from 1840 to 1925. In "Roadside Meetings" and "Companions on the Trail" the material is purely personal and literary. I make this recapitulation at this point in order that this volume shall be entirely self-explanatory.

At this point I end the second volume of my literary chronicle not for lack of material, for I have seventeen volumes of diaries yet unused, but in order that I may close (as I began) on a note of cheer. As "Roadside Meetings" covered fifteen years of my early life as an author, so "Companions on the Trail" includes the years lying between 1899 and 1914, my middle years. If my readers continue to find my wanderings and my comments of sufficient interest, I shall offer, at some future time, another volume of somewhat similar character, recording the literary events of my later years. With this plan in mind I close with the old-fashioned announcement:

Continued in our next.